This book comprises selections from the works of Canadian short-story writers from Thomas Haliburton to Ray Smith. It covers a period of some 150 years and reveals clearly that during that time significant changes occurred in the short story in Canada in terms both of kinds and techniques. Generally speaking, however, these changes fit within a pattern of fairly clearly defined periods and modes of sensibility, and it is these I write of here, leaving specific comments on the individual authors to the notes at the back of the book.

FROM THE INTRODUCTION

ALEC LUCAS holds a B.A. and an M.A. degree from Queens' University, Kingston, Ontario, and an M.A. and a Ph.D. from Harvard. For many years he has been a professor of English at McGill University, Montreal. A former editor of the Bulletin of the Humanities Association of Canada, Dr. Lucas has long been associated with the study of Canadian literature and has spoken and written extensively on the subject.

Great Canadian Short Stories

Selected and with
an Introduction and Notes by
Alec Lucas

<u>A Dell Book</u>

DELL DISTRIBUTING
A Division of Doubleday Canada Limited
105 Bond Street
Toronto, Ontario
M5B 1Y3

ISBN 0-440-95754-0

Printed and bound in Canada by Gagne Printing
Cover design by David Shaw
Reprinted by arrangement with Laurel Leaf Library, Dell Publishing Co. Inc.

ACKNOWLEDGMENTS

"Notes Beyond a History" by Clark Blaise. First published in *Shenandoah*. From *New Canadian Writing 1968*, Clarke Irwin and Company Ltd., Toronto. Used by permission of the author and Clarke Irwin.

"One Spring Night" by Morley Callaghan. Copyright 1934, 1961 by Morley Callaghan. Originally appeared in the *New Yorker*. Reprinted by permission of Harold Matson Co., Inc., New York.

"Acceptance of Their Ways" by Mavis Gallant. Copyright 1963 by Mavis Gallant. Originally appeared in the *New Yorker*. Reprinted from *My Heart is Broken* by Mavis Gallant with the permission of the author and the author's agent, Georges Borchardt, New York.

"A Trip for Mrs. Taylor" by Hugh Garner. From *The Yellow Sweater and Other Stories*, copyright Hugh Garner 1952, 1963, 1969. Published with the kind permission of the author.

"The Hard-Headed Collector" by Dave Godfrey. Copyright 1967 by Dave Godfrey. From *Death Goes Better with Coca Cola*, House of Anansi, Toronto, 1967. Used by permission of House of Anansi and the author.

"Snow" by Frederick Philip Grove. First published in *Queen's Quarterly*, 1932. Reprinted by permission of A. Leonard Grove and Mrs. Catherine Grove.

"The House on the Esplanade" by Anne Hebert. Reprinted from *Le Torrent*, Les Editions HMH, Montreal, copyright 1963. Used by permission of the publisher.

"Three Halves of a House" by Hugh Hood. Reprinted from *Flying a Red Kite* by Hugh Hood, Ryerson Press, Toronto. Reprinted by permission of the Ryerson Press.

"A Gourdful of Glory" by Margaret Laurence. Copyright 1960 by Margaret Laurence. Reprinted from *The Tomorrow Tamer* by Margaret Laurence by permission of Macmillan Publishers, London.

"Unemployed" by Irving Layton. From *The Swinging Flesh* by Irving Layton reprinted by permission of The Canadian Publishers, McClelland and Stewart Limited, Toronto.

"The Speculations of Jefferson Thorpe" by Stephen Leacock. From *Sunshine Sketches of a Little Town* by Stephen Leacock. Used by permission of The Canadian Publishers, McClelland and Stewart Limited, Toronto.

"Under the Volcano" by Malcolm Lowry. Copyright 1947 by Malcolm Lowry. Reprinted by permission of Harold Matson Co., Inc., New York.

"Requiem for Bibul" by Jack Ludwig. Copyright 1960 by Jack Ludwig. First published in the *Atlantic Monthly*. Used by permission of the William Morris Agency, New York.

To Emma and Bertie

Contents

Great
Canadian
Short Stories

Introduction

This book comprises selections from the works of Canadian short-story writers from Thomas Haliburton to Ray Smith. It covers a period of some 150 years and reveals clearly that during that time significant changes occurred in the short story in Canada, in terms both of kinds and techniques. Generally speaking, however, these changes fit within a pattern of fairly clearly defined periods and modes of sensibility, and it is these I write of here, leaving specific comments on the individual authors to the notes at the back of the book.

Until about 1870 the short story was largely a tale, a character sketch, an anecdote. It was sometimes humorous, but in general (and especially as it appeared in the Montreal *Literary Garland*, 1838–1851, the first journal of its kind in the country, and in its immediate successors) it was a melodramatic narrative of romantic love. During the next fifty or sixty years the story in French remained largely a *récit* or took the form of belles-lettres writing, concerned for the most part with legends and the lives of *voyageurs, forestiers,* and *bûcherons.* For the English it grew steadily more formal, centering on plot and "heroic" action, on love, local color, and often the long ago and the far away, either as frontier or foreign land. Besides, it had roles to play in the period from Confederation (1867) to the First Great War that it no longer has. It helped to fill newspapers and magazines and concomitantly the cultural gaps that movies, radio, and TV now almost completely fill. It was not the vehicle for the author's self-expression or individual vision, but largely a method of entertaining, a way of satisfying the taste of the everyday person, for despite its characteristic emotionalism and frequent sensationalism, the early short story was essentially dramatic and objective. If, however, on one level it was to entertain, on another it was to teach moral values, a trait that in the whirligig of fashion has become one of the most criticized of all its qualities. Yet in terms of the time and setting of many of the stories (a sparsely settled pioneer world where life was difficult and necessarily almost communal) much of the moral idealism may well have had a functional and humanistic basis. Within this broad framework, D. C. Scott admirably demonstrates an ability to keep a balance between the traditional requirements: the fanciful and emotional on the one hand and high seriousness on the other. Although these traits marked the story generally, humor still kept some place in it, but, as demonstrated in Thomson's "The Privilege of the Limits," humor, too, had changed, for unlike Haliburton's, it now contained little satire. A late nineteenth-century development, the animal story, as originated by Seton and Roberts, in a sense runs counter to the trend of the time in the stress it put on the (alleged) authenticity of its facts. Yet in a broader sense it was often simply a typical story of "thrilling adventure," except that heroic beasts and birds replaced human protagonists. Roberts at his best, however, could make art of natural history in the sketch or in the animal biography, for he knew something of both art and nature.

During the period from 1920 to 1940, a marked shift in sensibility occurred. The stories remained rural in their setting for the most part, but the romantic hero, the picturesque, and the pseudohistorical gave way to the everyday person in an everyday world, if "lonely" and "bleak" do not vitiate the meaning of "everyday." Indeed in the aftermath of war and during the Depression years the everyday for many was lonely and bleak. The short stories simply reflected the social conditions of an unhappy period. Their protagonists appeared in a context that denied them power, confronted as they were with overwhelming economic or natural forces. Their authors studied the individual in terms of environment, not of idealism, and were largely pessimistic *vis-à-vis* the earlier writers, who almost invariably made virtue triumphant. In addition, characters became the center of interest in a way far different from those in a highly articulated plot. Yet, if the perspective of the writer may have changed, the story was often obviously moral, and frequently indignantly so, as its author questioned the justice of a capitalist system in which poverty ground down the poor or as he searched for meaning in a world where God (if He existed) seemed powerless against the forces of a senseless, if not malevolent, nature.

Since the Second Great War, the Canadian short story, in common with the short story generally, has altered course again. In both French and English the writers have turned to the urban much more readily. Many, becoming more subjective, reveal (often through a narrator) their own feelings and thoughts directly, in the manner of lyric poetry, or indirectly, again in the manner of poetry, through a drama centered on allusion, symbol, and implication. The action is internal and psychological, whether the writer is a Gabrielle Roy reminiscing over childhood or a Mavis Gallant observing life in a *pension*. The modern author has completed the step taken in the twenties and thirties and has subordinated overt plot to a covert resolution of tension. The unity of action or of character yields to a more subtle unity of idea, attitude, or feeling that frequently produces what one critic calls "illuminated realism." As an art form the story may have become much more sophisticated, but it is nonetheless formal even if its pattern is far less obvious than it was in the stories produced during the late nineteenth and early twentieth century.

The short story in Canada has had its ups and downs. For seventy-five years it flourished, if less than luxuriantly, in newspapers and magazines, and in the 1930s and 1940s, CBC broadcasts gave it a fillip. Almost all contemporary writers and literary historians, however, lament the present paucity of Canadian outlets for stories, and the list is small —*The Fiddlehead, The Canadian Forum, Prism International, The Tamarack Review, Chatelaine, Saturday Night, Queen's Quarterly,* and one or two other magazines and university journals, to name the bulk of the periodicals that now accept short stories. Recently, too, the *Literary History of Canada* (1965) suggested dolorously that the short story had run its course. Yet within the last few years almost every author of note has issued a collection of his work, not to mention the several French and English anthologies that have also appeared during the same period —John Drainie's, Norman Levine's, Adrien Thério's, Armin Arnold's *(Kanadische Erzahler der Gegenwart)*, and Rimanelli's and Roberto's, in addition to Robert Weaver's three Oxford anthologies, and three recent editions of a collection edited first in 1947 by Desmond Pacey.

The stories here come from single-author collections, anthologies, and periodicals. I made my selections with no particular theme or thesis in mind. Nor did I think one kind of sensibility superior to another. If I have selected few stories from the nineteenth century, it is not because they were "romantic," but because I thought them bad "romantic" stories. Sir Walter Scott's heroes are not indigenous to Canada. As transplants their vital force does not flow from native perception and emotional response. I made no attempt to choose according to regions or periods; yet there are included stories from or about each of them. In addition, the selection suggests, if it does not prove, that humor in Canadian short stories has been almost as generally pervasive as the theme of loneliness.

As regards the French stories, limitations of space and other unforeseen difficulties have been responsible for their small number. They appear in translations rather than the original French, since the book was essentially planned as an anthology of stories in English.

Two further comments: Since I did not wish to become involved in the question "When is a Canadian author not a Canadian, and what is his identity?" I have simply included the work I liked of any writer who was either born in or immigrated to Canada and who lived or has lived in the country for some time, even if he were a transient like Lowry or Moore (who is a naturalized Canadian), an *émigré* like Gallant or Richler, or an immigrant like Blaise or Metcalf. My second comment concerns a related topic—internationalism in Canadian fiction. The modern "internationalist" Canadian is not the first Canadian writer to interest himself in some country other than his own, even though he may express himself and focus his attention differently. Nor does such an interest and practice automatically mean that Canadian writing "is maturing" or proving itself in the world at large. Internationalism is more than selling elsewhere, more than topicality, more than the use of a foreign setting. It can as easily rest on writing about Canada, so long as the writing reveals something of what lies behind and above the immediate time and place. Canadians have successfully gone and may well continue to go outside their borders for subjects, but many of the stories included here prove, I think, that they need not necessarily do so to become true internationalists.

ALEC LUCAS

An excerpt from

HOW MANY FINS
HAS A COD?

Thomas Chandler Haliburton

"Clear the road there! Make way for the gentleman!"

We had been anxiously expected all the afternoon, and the command was instantly obeyed, and a passage opened for us by the people falling back on either side of the street. As we passed through, my friend checked his horse into a slow walk, and led me with an air of triumph, such as a jockey displays in bringing out his favorite on the course. Robins was an important man that day. He had succeeded in his mission. He had got his champion, and would be ready for fight in the morning. It was reasonable, therefore, he thought, to indulge the public with a glimpse at this man. He nodded familiarly to some, winked slyly to others, saluted people at a distance aloud, and shook hands patronizingly with those that were nearest. He would occasionally lag behind a moment, and say, in an under but very audible tone:

"Precious clever fellow that! Sees it all—says we are all right—sure to win it! I wouldn't be in those fellows the plaintiffs' skins tomorrow for a trifle! He is a powerful man, that!" and so forth.

The first opportunity that occurred, I endeavored to put a stop to this trumpeting.

"For Heaven's sake," I said, "my good friend, do not talk such nonsense; if you do, you will ruin me! I am at all times a diffident man, but if you raise such expectations, I shall assuredly break down from the very fear of not fulfilling them. I know too well the doubtful issue of trials ever to say that a man is certain of winning. Pray do not talk of me in this manner."

"You are sure, sir?" he asked. "What, a man who has just landed from his travels in Europe, and arrived, after

a journey of one hundred miles, from the last sitting of
the Supreme Court, not to know more than anyone else!
Fudge, sir! I congratulate you, you have gained the cause!
And besides, sir, do you think that if William Robins says
he has got the right man (and he wouldn't say so if he
didn't think so), that isn't enough? Why, sir, your leather
breeches and top boots are enough to do the business!
Nobody ever saw such things here before, and a man in
buckskin must know more than a man in homespun. But
here is Mrs. Brown's inn; let us dismount. I have procured
a private sitting room for you, which on court days, militia
trainings, and times of town meetings or elections is not
very easy, I assure you. Come, walk in, and make yourself
comfortable."

We had scarcely entered into our snuggery, which was
evidently the landlady's own apartment, when the door
was softly opened a few inches, and a beseeching voice was
heard, saying:

"Billy, is that him? If it is, tell him it's me, will you?
That's a good soul!"

"Come in—come in, old Blowhard!" said Robins; and
seizing the stranger by the hand, he led him up and intro-
duced him to me.

"Lawyer, this is Captain John Barkins!—Captain Barkins, this is Lawyer Sandford! He is our client, lawyer, and
I must say one thing for him, he has but two faults, but
they are enough to ruin any man in this province; he is an
honest man, and speaks the truth. I will leave you together now, and go and order your dinner for you."

John Barkins was a tall, corpulent, amphibious-looking
man who seemed as if he would be equally at home in
either element, land or water. He held in his hand what he
called a nor'-wester, a large, broadbrimmed, glazed hat
with a peak projecting behind to shed the water from off
his club queue, which was nearly as thick as a hawser.
He wore a long, narrow-tailed, short-waisted blue coat
with large, white-plated buttons that resembled Spanish
dollars, a red waistcoat, a spotted bandanna silk handkerchief tied loosely about his throat, and a pair of volumi-
nous corduroy trousers of the color of brown soap, over
which were drawn a pair of fishermen's boots that reached
nearly to his knees. His waistcoat and his trousers were
apparently not upon very intimate terms, for though they

traveled together, the latter were taught to feel their subjection, but when they lagged too far behind, they were brought to their place by a jerk of impatience that threatened their very existence. He had a thick, matted head of black hair and a pair of whiskers that disdained the effeminacy of either scissors or razor, and reveled in all the exuberant and wild profusion of nature. His countenance was much weather-beaten from constant exposure .to the vicissitudes of heat and cold, but was open, good-natured, and manly. Such was my client. He advanced and shook me cordially by the hand.

"Glad to see you, sir," he said. "You are welcome to Plymouth. My name is John Barkins; I dare say you have often heard of me, for everybody knows me about these parts. Anyone will tell you what sort of a man John Barkins is. That's me—that's my name, do you see? I am a persecuted man, lawyer; but I ain't altogether quite run down yet, neither. I have a case in court; I dare say Mr. Robins has told you of it. He is a very clever man is old Billy, and as smart a chap of his age as you will see anywhere a'most. I suppose you have often heard of him before, for everybody knows William Robins in these parts. It's the most important case, sir, ever tried in this county. If I lose it, Plymouth is done. There's an end to the fisheries, and a great many of us are agoing to sell off and quit the country."

I will not detail his cause to you in his own words because it will fatigue you, as it wearied me in hearing it. It possessed no public interest whatever, though it was of some importance to himself as regarded the result. It appeared that he had fitted out a large vessel for the Labrador fishery and taken with him a very full crew, who were to share in the profits or loss of the adventure. The agreement, which was a verbal one, was that on the completion of the voyage the cargo should be sold, and the net proceeds be distributed in equal portions, one half to appertain to the captain and vessel, and the other half to the crew, and to be equally divided among them. The undertaking was a disastrous one, and on their return the seamen repudiated the bargain, and sued him for wages. It was, therefore, a very simple affair, being a mere question of fact as to the partnership, and that depending wholly on the evidence. Having ascertained these particulars, and inquired into the nature of the proof by which his defense was to be supported, and given him his instructions, I requested him to call upon me again in the morning before Court, and bowed to him in a manner too significant to be misunderstood. He, however, still lingered in the room, and turning his hat round and round several times, examining the rim very carefully, as if at a loss to discover the front from the back part of it, he looked up at last and said:

"Lawyer, I have a favor to ask of you."

"What is it?" I inquired.

"There is a man," he replied, "coming agin me tomorrow as a witness, of the name of Lillum. He thinks himself a great judge of the fisheries, and he does know a considerable some, I must say; but, d—— him! I caught fish afore he was born, and know more about fishing than all the Lillums of Plymouth put together. Will you just ask him one question?"

"Yes, fifty if you like."

"Well, I only want you to try him with one, and that will choke him. Ask him if he knows how many fins a cod has, at a word."

"What has that got to do with the cause?" I said, with unfeigned astonishment.

"Everything, sir," he answered, "everything in the world. If he is to come to give his opinion on other men's business, the best way is to see if he knows his own. Tarnation, man! He don't know a cod fish when he sees it; if he does, he can tell you how many fins it has, at a word. It is a great catch that. I have won a great many half-pints of brandy on it. I never knew a feller that could answer that question yet, right off the reel."

He then explained to me that in the enumeration, one small fin was always omitted by those who had not previously made a minute examination.

"Now, sir," said he, "if he can't cipher out that question (and I'll go a hogshead of rum on it he can't), turn him right out of the box and tell him to go a voyage with old John Barkins—that's me; my name is John Barkins—and he will larn him his trade. Will you ask him that question, lawyer?"

"Certainly," I said, "if you wish it."

"You will gain the day then, sir," he continued, much

elated. "You will gain the day then, as sure as fate. Good-bye, lawyer!"

When he had nearly reached the foot of the staircase, I heard him returning, and opening the door, he looked in and said:

"You won't forget, will you?—my name is John Barkins. Ask anybody about here, and they will tell you who I am, for everybody knows John Barkins in these parts. The other man's name is Lillum—a very decent, 'sponsible-looking man, too; but he don't know everything. Take him up all short. 'How many fins has a cod, at a word?' says you. If you can lay him on the broad of his back with that question, I don't care a farthing if I lose the case. It's a great satisfaction to nonplush a knowin' one that way. You know the question?"

"Yes, yes," I replied impatiently. "I know all about it."

"You do, do you, sir?" said he, shutting the door behind him and advancing toward me, looking me steadily in the face. "You do, do you? Then, how many fins has a cod, at a word?"

I answered as he had instructed me.

"Gad, sir," he said, "it's a pity your father hadn't made a fisherman of you, for you know more about a cod now than any man in Plymouth but one, old John Barkins—that's me. My name is John Barkins. Everybody knows me in these parts. Bait your hook with that question, and you'll catch old Lillum, I know. As soon as he has it in his gills, drag him right out of the water. Give him no time to play—in with him, and whap him on the deck; hit him hard over the head—it will make him open his mouth, and your hook is ready for another catch."

"Good night, Mr. Barkins," I replied. "Call on me in the morning. I am fatigued now."

"Good night, sir," he answered. "You won't forget?"

Dinner was now announced, and my friend Mr. Robins and myself sat down to it with an excellent appetite. Having done ample justice to the good cheer of Mrs. Brown, and finished our wine, we drew up to the fire, which at that season of the year was most acceptable in the morning and evening, and smoked our cigars. Robins had so many good stories, and told them so uncommonly well, that it was late before we retired to rest. Instead of being shown into the bedroom I had temporarily occupied for changing my dress before dinner, I was ushered into a long, low room, fitted up on either side with berths, with a locker running round the base, and in all respects, except the skylight, resembling a cabin. Strange as it appeared, it was in keeping with the place (a fishing port), its population, and the habits of the people.

Mrs. Brown, the landlady, was the widow of a seafaring man who had, no doubt, fitted up the chamber in this manner with a view to economize room, and thus accommodate as many passengers (as he would designate his guests) as possible in this sailor's home. A lamp hung suspended from the ceiling and appeared to be supplied and trimmed for the night so as to afford easy access and egress at all hours. It was almost impossible not to imagine oneself at sea, on board a crowded coasting packet. Retreat was impossible, and therefore I made up my mind at once to submit to this whimsical arrangement for the night, and having undressed myself, was about to climb into a vacant berth near the door, when someone opposite called out:

"Lawyer, is that you?"

It was my old tormentor, the skipper. Upon ascertaining who it was, he immediately got out of bed and crossed over to where I was standing. He had nothing on but a red nightcap and a short, loose, checked shirt, wide open at the throat and breast. He looked like a huge bear walking upon his hind legs, he was so hairy and shaggy. Seizing me by the shoulders, he clasped me tightly round the neck, and whispered:

"How many fins has a cod, at a word? That's the question. You won't forget, will you?"

"No," I said, "I not only will not forget it tomorrow, but I shall recollect you and your advice as long as I live. Now let me get some rest, or I shall be unable to plead your cause for you, as I am excessively fatigued and very drowsy."

"Certainly, certainly," he said. "Turn in, but don't forget the catch."

It was some time before the hard bed, the fatigues of the journey, and the novelty of the scene permitted me to compose myself for sleep; and just as I was dropping off into a slumber, I heard the same unwelcome sounds:

"Lawyer, lawyer, are you asleep?"

I affected not to hear him, and after another ineffectual attempt on his part to rouse me, he desisted; but I
heard him mutter to himself:

"Plague take the sarpent! He'll forget it and lose all. A
feller that falls asleep at the helm ain't fit to be trusted
no how."

I was not doomed, however, to obtain repose upon
such easy terms. The skipper's murmurs had scarcely
died away when a French fisherman from St. Mary's Bay
entered the room, and stumbling over my saddlebags,
which he anathematized in bad French, bad English, and
in a language compounded of both, and embellished with
a few words of Indian origin, he called out loudly:

"Célestine, are you here?"

This interrogatory was responded to by another from
the upper end of the room:

"Is that you, Baptiste? Which way is the wind?"

"Nor'-nor'-west."

"Then I must sail for Halifax tomorrow."

While Baptiste was undressing, an operation which was
soon performed (with the exception of the time lost in
pulling off an obstinate and most intractable pair of boots),
the following absurd conversation took place. Upon hearing the word Halifac (as he called it), Baptiste expressed
great horror of the place and especially the red devils (the
soldiers) with which it was infested. He said the last time
he was there, as he was passing the King's Wharf to go
to his vessel late at night, the sentinel called out to him,
"Who come dare?" to which impertinent question he gave
no answer. The red villain, he said, repeated the challenge louder than before, but as he knew it was none of
his business, he did not condescend to reply. The soldier
then demanded in a voice of thunder, for the third time,
"Who come dare?" "to which," to use his own words, "I
answer him, 'What the devil is that to you?' and ran off
so fast as my legs would carry me, and faster too; but the
villain knew the way better nor me, and just stuck his
bagonut right into my thigh, ever so far as one inch. Oh!"
said Baptiste (who had become excited by the recollection of the insult, and began to jump about the floor,
making a most villainous clatter with the half-drawn boot),
"Oh! I was very mad, you may depend. I could have mur-

dered him, I was so vexed. Oh! I was so d—— mad, I ran straight off to the vessel without stopping, and—jumped right into bed."

Célestine expressed great indignation at such an unprovoked and cowardly assault, and advised him if ever he caught that soldier again alone and unarmed and had his two grown-up sons, Lewis and Dominique, with him, to give him a sound drubbing, and then weigh anchor and sail right out of the harbor. He congratulated himself, however, that if the soldier had run the point of his bayonet into his friend, he had lately avenged it by making a merchant there feel the point of a joke that was equally sharp, and penetrated deeper. He had purchased goods, he said, of a trader at Halifax upon this express promise:

"If you will trust me this spring, I will pay you last fall. The merchant," he observed, "thought I was talking bad English, but it is very good English; and when last fall comes again, I will keep my word and pay him, but not till then. Don't he hope he may get his money the day before yesterday?"

Baptiste screamed with delight at this joke, which, he said, he would tell his wife Félicité, and his two daughters, Angélique and Blondine, as soon as he returned home. Having succeeded at last in escaping from his tenacious boot, he turned in, and as soon as his head touched the pillow, was sound asleep.

In the morning when I awoke, the first objects that met my eye were the bandanna handkerchief, the red waistcoat and blue coat, while a good-natured face watched over me with all the solicitude of a parent for the first moments of wakefulness.

"Lawyer, are you awake?" said Barkins. "This is the great day—the greatest day Plymouth ever saw! We shall know now whether we are to carry on the fisheries or give them up to the Yankees. Everything depends upon that question. For Heaven's sake, don't forget it!—How many fins has a cod, at a word? It is very late now. It is eight o'clock, and the Courts meet at ten, and the town is full. All the folks from Chebogue, and Jegoggin, and Salmon River, and Beaver River, and Eel Brook, and Polly Crossby's Hole, and the Gut and the Devil's Island, and Ragged Island, and far and near are come. It's a great day and a great catch. I never lost a bet on it yet. You may win many a half-pint of brandy on it, if you won't forget it."

"Do go away and let me dress myself!" I said petulantly. "I won't forget you."

"Well, I'll go below," he replied, "if you wish it, but call for me when you want me. My name is John Barkins; ask anyone for me, for every man knows John Barkins in these parts. But, dear me," he continued, "I forgot!" and taking an enormous key out of his pocket, he opened a sea-chest, from which he drew a large glass decanter, highly gilt, and a rummer of corresponding dimensions with a golden edge. Taking the bottle in one hand and the glass in the other, he drew the small round gilt stopper with his mouth, and pouring out about half a pint of the liquid, he said, "Here, lawyer, take a drop of bitters this morning, just to warm the stomach and clear your throat. It's excellent! It is old Jamaiky and sarsy-parilly, and will do your heart good. It's an antifogmatic, and will make you as hungry as a shark and as lively as a thrasher!"

I shook my head in silence and despair, for I saw he was a man there was no escaping from.

"You won't, eh?"

"No, thank you, I never take anything of the kind in the morning."

"Where the deuce was you broughten up," he asked, with distended eyes, "that you haven't lost the taste of your mother's milk yet? You are worse than an Isle of Sable colt, and them wild, ontamed devils suckle for two years! Well, if you won't, I will, then; so here goes," and holding back his head, the potion vanished in an instant, and he returned the bottle and the glass to their respective places. As he went slowly and sulkily downstairs, he muttered, "Hang him! He's only a fresh-water fish that, after all; and they ain't even fit for bait, for they have neither substance nor flavor!"

After breakfast, Mr. Robins conducted me to the court-house, which was filled almost to suffocation. The panel was immediately called, and the jury placed in the box. Previous to their being sworn, I inquired of Barkins whether any of them were related to the plaintiffs, or had been known to express an opinion adverse to his interests; for if such was the case, it was the time to challenge them. To my astonishment, he immediately rose and told the judges he challenged the whole jury, the bench of magistrates, and every man in the house—a defiance that was accompanied by a menacing outstretched arm and clenched fist. A shout of laughter that nearly shook the walls of the building followed this violent outbreak. Nothing daunted by their ridicule, however, he returned to the charge and said:

"I repeat it; I challenge the whole of you, if you dare!"

Here the Court interposed, and asked him what he meant by such indecent behavior.

"Meant!" he said. "I mean what I say. The strange lawyer here tells me now is my time to challenge, and I claim my right; I do challenge any of all of you! Pick out any man present you please, take the smartest chap you've got, put us both on board the same vessel, and I challenge him to catch, spit, clean, salt, and stow away as many fish in a day as I can—cod, polluck, shad, or mackerel, I don't care which, for it's all the same to me—and I'll go a hogshead of rum on it I beat him! Will any man take up the challenge?" and he turned slowly round and examined the whole crowd. "You won't, won't you? I guess not; you know a trick worth two of that, I reckon! There, lawyer, there is my challenge; now go on with the cause!"

As soon as order was restored the jury were sworn, and the plaintiffs' counsel opened his case and called his witnesses, the last of whom was Mr. Lillum.

"That's him!" said Barkins, putting both arms round my neck and nearly choking me as he whispered, "Ask him how many fins a cod has, at a word?" I now stood up to cross-examine him, when I was again in the skipper's clutches. "Don't forget! the question is. . . ."

"If you do not sit down immediately, sir," I said in a loud and authoritative voice (for the scene had become ludicrous), "and leave me to conduct the cause my own way, I shall retire from the Court!"

He sat down, and groaning audibly, put both hands before his face and muttered:

"There is no dependence on a man that sleeps at the helm!"

I commenced, however, in the way my poor client desired, for I saw plainly that he was more anxious of what he called stumping old Lillum and nonplushing him than about the result of his trial, although he was firmly convinced that the one depended on the other.

"How many years have you been engaged in the Labrador fishery, sir?"

"Twenty-five."

"You are, of course, perfectly conversant with the cod fishery?"

"Perfectly. I know as much, if not more, about it than any man in Plymouth."

Here Barkins pulled my coat, and most beseechingly said:

"Ask him. . . ."

"Be quiet, sir, and do not interrupt me!" was the consolatory reply he received.

"Of course, then, after such long experience, sir, you know a cod fish when you see it?"

"I should think so!"

"That will not do, sir. Will you swear that you do?"

"I do not come here to be made a fool of!"

"Nor I either, sir; I require you to answer yes or no. Will you undertake to swear that you know a cod fish when you see it?"

"I will, sir."

Here Barkins rose and struck the table with his fist a blow that nearly split it, and turning to me said:

"Ask him. . . ."

"Silence, sir!" I again vociferated. "Let there be no mistake," I continued. "I will repeat the question. Do you undertake to swear that you know a cod fish when you see it?"

"I do, sir, as well as I know my own name when I see it."

"Then, sir, how many fins has a cod, at a word?"

Here the blow was given, not on the deal slab of the table, but on my back, with such force as to throw me forward on my two hands.

"Ay, floor him!" said Barkins. "Let him answer that question! The lawyer has you there! How many fins has a cod, at a word, you old sculpin?"

"I can answer you that without hesitation."

"How many, then?"

"Let me see—three on the back, and two on the belly, that's five; two on the nape, that's seven; and two on the shoulder, that's nine. Nine, sir!"

"Missed it, by gosh!" said Barkins. "Didn't I tell you so? I knew he couldn't answer it. And yet that fellow has the impudence to call himself a fisherman!"

Here I requested the Court to interfere and compel my unfortunate and excited client to be silent.

"Is there not a small fin besides?" I asked. "Between the under jaw and the throat?"

"I believe there is."

"You believe! Then, sir, it seems you are in doubt, and that you do not know a cod fish when you see it. You may go; I will not ask you another question. Go, sir! But let me advise you to be more careful in your answers for the future."

There was a universal shout of laughter in the Court, and Barkins availed himself of the momentary noise to slip his hand under the table and grip me by the thigh, so as nearly to sever the flesh from the bone.

"Bless your soul, my stout fresh-water fish!" he said. "You have gained the case after all! Didn't I tell you he couldn't answer that question? It's a great great catch, isn't it?"

The plaintiffs had wholly failed in their proof. Instead of contenting themselves with showing the voyage and their services, from which the law would have presumed an assumpsit to pay wages according to the ordinary course of business, and leaving the defendant to prove that the agreement was a special one, they attempted to prove too much by establishing a negative, and, in doing so, made out a sufficient defense for Barkins. Knowing how much depended upon the last address to the jury, when the judge was incompetent to direct or control their decision, I closed on the plaintiffs' case and called no witnesses. The jury were informed by the judge that having now heard the case on the part of the plantiffs and also on the part of the defendant, it was their duty to make up their minds and find a verdict for one or the other. After this very able, intelligible, and impartial charge, the jury were conducted to their room, and the greater part of the audience adjourned to the neighboring tavern for refreshment. The judges then put on their hats, for the air of the hall felt cold after the withdrawal of so many persons, and the president asked me to go and take a seat on the bench with them.

"That was a very happy thought of yours, sir," he remarked, "about the fins. I don't think another lawyer in the province but yourself knows how many fins a cod has. A man who has traveled as much as you have has a great advantage. If you had never been in England, you never would have learned that, for you never would have crossed the banks of Newfoundland and seen the great fishery there. But this is dull work; let us retreat into the adjoining room and have a smoke until the jury returns. They will soon be back, and I think I may venture to say you are sure of a verdict. You displayed great skill in that matter of the fins."

Just as we were about retiring, our attention was arrested by a great noise, occasioned by a constable endeavoring to remove a turbulent and drunken fellow from the Court. The judge promptly interfered, fined him five shillings for his contemptuous conduct, and directed the prothonotary to lay it out in purchasing a bottle of wine wherewith to drink the health of the Stranger Lawyer. Having settled this little matter to his satisfaction, he led the way to the anteroom, where pipes were provided, and the officer soon appeared with the wine and some glasses. Filling a tumbler, the prothonotary apologized for not being able to remain with us, and drank respectfully to the health of the Court.

"Stop, sir!" said the judge. "Stop, sir! Your conduct is unpardonable! I consider your behavior a great contempt in helping yourself first. I fine you five shillings for your indecent haste, and request you to pay it immediately in the shape of a bottle of brandy; for that wine," of which he took a tumblerful by way of tasting, "is not fit for a gentleman to drink."

"A very forward fellow that prothonotary!" said the legal dignitary as the officer withdrew.

"Instead of being contented with being the clerk of the Court, he wants to be the master of it, and I find it necessary to keep him in his place. Only think of his confounded impudence in presuming to help himself first! He would drink the millpond dry if it was wine, and then complain it didn't hold enough! For my own part, I am obliged to be very abstemious now, as I am subject to the gout. I never exceed two bottles of late years, and I rectify the acidity of the wine by taking a glass of clear brandy (which I call the naked truth) between every two of Madeira. Ah, here is the brandy, lawyer! Your very good health, sir—pray help yourself; and, Mr. Prothonotary, here's better manners to you in future. *Seniores priores,* sir, that's the rule."

Here the constable knocked at the door, and announced that the jury were in attendance.

"Don't rise, Mr. Sandford," said the judge. "Let them wait. Haste is not dignified. Help yourself, sir; this is very good brandy. I always like to let them appear to wait upon me, instead of their thinking I wait upon them. What with the prothonotary treading on my toes and the jury on my heels, I have enough to do to preserve the dignity of the Court, I assure you. But *Tempus præterlabetur est,* as we used to say at Cambridge, Massachusetts; that is, John Adams, senior, and our class, for I was contemporary with that talented and distinguished—ahem—stingy rebel! Help yourself, sir. Come, I won't leave any of this *aqua vitæ* for that thirsty prothonotary. There, sir," he said, smacking his lips with evident delight, "there is the *finis* and his *fine.* Now let us go into Court. But give me your arm, sir, for I think I feel a slight twinge of that abominable gout. A dreadful penalty that, that Nature assesses on gentility. But not so fast, if you please, sir! True dignity delights in *otium,* or leisure; but abhors *negotium,* or hurry. Haste is the attribute of a prothonotary, who writes, talks, and drinks as fast as he can, but is very unbecoming the gravity and majesty of the law. The gait of a judge should be slow, stately, and solemn. But here we are, let us take our respective seats."

As soon as we made our appearance, the tumultuous wave of the crowd rushed into the courthouse, and surging backward and forward, gradually settled down to a level and tranquil surface. The panel was then called over, and the verdict read aloud. It was for the defendant.

Barkins was not so much elated as I had expected. He appeared to have been prepared for any event. He had had his gratification already. "Old Lillum was floored," the "knowing one had been nonplushed," and he was satisfied. He had a duty to perform, however, which he did with great pleasure and, I have no doubt, with great liberality. The jury were to be "treated," for it was the custom of those days for the winning party to testify his gratitude by copious libations of brandy and rum. As soon as the verdict was recorded, he placed himself at their head, and led the way to the tavern with as much gravity and order as if he was conducting a guard of honor. As soon as they were all in the street, he turned about, and walking backward so as to face them, and at the same time not to interrupt their progress to that mansion of bliss, he said:

"A pretty fellow that Lillum, ain't he? To swear he knew what a cod was, and yet couldn't tell how many fins it had, at a word! Who would have thought that milksop of a lawyer would have done so well? He actually scared me when I first saw him; for a feller that smokes cigars instead of a pipe, drinks red ink (part wine) instead of old Jamaiky, and has a pair of hands as white as the belly of a flat fish, ain't worth his pap, in a general way. Howsumdever, it don't do to hang a feller for his looks, after all, that's a fact; for that crittur is like a singed cat, better nor he seems. But, come, let's liquor!"

I did not see him again till the evening, when he came to congratulate me upon having done the handsomest thing, he said, as everybody allowed, that ever was done in Plymouth—shown the greatest fisherman in it (in his own conceit) that he didn't know a cod fish when he saw it.

"It was a great catch that, lawyer," he continued, and he raised me up in his arms and walked round the room with me as if he were carrying a baby. "Don't forget it— How many fins has a cod, at a word? Yaw never need to want a half-pint of brandy while you have that fact to bet upon!"

The next day I left Plymouth very early in the morning. When I descended to the door, I found both Robins and Barkins there, and received a hearty and cordial farewell from both of them. The latter entreated me, if ever I came that way again, to favor him with a visit, as he had some capital Jamaica forty years old and would be glad to instruct me in the habits of fish and fisherman.

"I will show you," he said, "how to make a shoal of mackerel follow your vessel like a pack of dogs. I can tell you how to make them rise from the bottom of the sea in thousands, when common folks can't tell there is one there, and then how to feed and coax them away to the very spot you want to take them. I will show you how to spear shad, and how to strike the fattest salmon that ever was so that it will keep to go to the East Indies; and I'll larn you how to smoke herrings without dryin' them hard, and tell you the wood and the vegetables that give them the highest flavor; and even them cussed, dry, good-for-nothing all-wives, I'll teach you how to cure them so you will say they are the most delicious fish you ever tasted in all your life. I will, upon my soul! And now, before you go, I want you to do me a good turn, lawyer. Just take this little silver flask, my friend, to remember old John Barkins by when he is dead and gone, and when people in these parts shall say when you inquire after him that they don't know such a man as old John Barkins no more. It is a beautiful article. I found it in the pocket of a captain of a Spanish privateer that boarded my vessel, and that I hit over the head with a handspike so hard that he never knew what hurt him. It will just suit you, for it only holds a thimbleful and was made apurpose for fresh-water fish, like Spaniards and lawyers. Good-bye! God bless you, sir! A fair wind and a short passage to you!"

I had hardly left the door before I heard my name shouted after me.

"Mr. Sandford! Lawyer! Lawyer. . . ."

It was old Barkins. I anticipated his object; I knew it was his old theme:

"Lawyer, don't forget the catch—How many fins has a cod, at a word?"

THE PRIVILEGE
OF THE LIMITS

Edward William Thomson

"Yes, indeed, my grandfather wass once in jail," said old Mrs. McTavish of the county of Glengarry, in Ontario, Canada, "but that wass for debt, and he wass a ferry honest man whateffer, and he would not broke his promise—no, not for all the money in Canada. If you will listen to me, I will tell chust exactly the true story about that debt, to show you what an honest man my grandfather wass.

"One time Tougal Stewart, him that wass the poy's grandfather that keeps the same store in Cornwall to this day, sold a plow to my grandfather, and my grandfather said he would pay half the plow in October, and the other half whateffer time he felt able to pay the money. Yes, indeed, that was the very promise my grandfather gave.

"So he was at Tougal Stewart's store on the first of October early in the morning before the shutters wass taken off, and he paid half chust exactly to keep his word. Then the crop wass ferry bad next year, and the year after that one of his horses wass killed by lightning, and the next year his brother, that wass not rich and had a big family, died, and do you think wass my grandfather to let the family be disgraced without a big funeral? No, indeed. So my grandfather paid for the funeral, and there wass at it plenty of meat and drink for everybody, as wass the right Hielan' custom those days; and after the funeral my grandfather did not feel chust exactly able to pay the other half for the plow that year either.

"So, then, Tougal Stewart met my grandfather in Cornwall next day after the funeral, and asked him if he had some money to spare.

"'Wass you in need of help, Mr. Stewart?' says my grandfather kindly. 'For if it's in any want you are,

Tougal,' says my grandfather, 'I will sell the coat off my back, if there is no other way to lend you a loan'; for that wass always the way of my grandfather with all his friends, and a bigger-hearted man there never wass in all Glengarry, or in Stormont, or in Dundas, moreofer.

" 'In want!' says Tougal, 'in want, Mr. McTavish!' says he, very high. 'Would you wish to insult a gentleman, and him of the name of Stewart, that's the name of princes of the world?' he said, so he did.

"Seeing Tougal had his temper up, my grandfather spoke softly, being a quiet, peaceable man, and in wonder what he had said to offend Tougal.

" 'Mr. Stewart,' says my grandfather, 'it wass not in my mind to anger you whateffer. Only I thought, from your asking me if I had some money, that you might be looking fir a wee bit of a loan, as many a gentleman has to do at times, and no shame to him at all,' said my grandfather.

" 'A loan?' says Tougal, sneering. 'A loan, is it? Where's your memory, Mr. McTavish! Are you not owing me half the price of the plow you've had these three years?'

" 'And wass you asking me for money for the other half of the plow?' says my grandfather, very astonished.

" 'Just that,' says Tougal.

" 'Have you no shame or honor in you?' says my grandfather, firing up. 'How could I feel able to pay that now, and me chust yesterday been giving my poor brother a funeral fit for the McTavishes' own grandnephew, that wass as good chentleman's plood as any Stewart in Glengarry. You saw the expense I wass at, for there you wass, and I thank you for the politeness of coming, Mr. Stewart,' says my grandfather, ending mild, for the anger would never stay in him more than a minute, so kind was the nature he had.

" 'If you can spend money on a funeral like that, you can pay me for my plow,' says Stewart; for with buying and selling he wass become a poor creature, and the heart of a Hielan' man wass half gone out of him, for all he wass so proud of his name of monarchs and kings.

"My grandfather had a mind to strike him down on the spot, so he often said; but he thought of the time when he hit Hamish Cochrane in anger, and he minded the penances the priest put on him for breaking the silly man's jaw with that blow, so he smothered the heat that wass in him, and turned away in scorn. With that Tougal went to court, and sued my grandfather, puir mean creature.

"You might think that Judge Jones—him that wass judge in Cornwall before Judge Jarvis that's dead—would do justice. But no, he made it the law that my grandfather must pay at once, though Tougal Stewart could not deny what the bargain wass.

" 'Your Honor,' says my grandfather, 'I said I'd pay when I felt able. And do I feel able now? No, I do not,' says he. 'It's a disgrace to Tougal Stewart to ask me, and himself telling you what the bargain wass,' said my grandfather. But Judge Jones said that he must pay, for all that he did not feel able.

" 'I will nefer pay one copper till I feel able,' says my grandfather; 'but I'll keep my Hielan' promise to my dying day, as I always done,' says he.

"And with that the old judge laughed, and said he would have to give judgment. And so he did; and after that Tougal Stewart got out an execution. But not the worth of a handful of oatmeal could the bailiff lay hands on, because my grandfather had chust exactly taken the precaution to give a bill of sale on his gear to his neighbor, Alexander Frazer, that could be trusted to do what was right after the law play was over.

"The whole settlement had great contempt for Tougal Stewart's conduct; but he wass a headstrong body, and once he begun to do wrong against my grandfather, he held on, for all that his trade fell away; and finally he had my grandfather arrested for debt, though you'll understand, sir, that he was owing Stewart nothing that he ought to pay when he didn't feel able.

"In those times prisoners for debt wass taken to jail in Cornwall, and if they had friends to give bail that they would not go beyond the posts that wass around the sixteen acres nearest the jail walls, the prisoners could go where they liked on that ground. This was called 'the privilege of the limits.' The limits, you'll understand, wass marked by cedar posts painted white about the size of hitching posts.

"The whole settlement wass ready to go bail for my grandfather if he wanted it, and for the health of him he needed to be in the open air, and so he gave Tuncan Macdonnell of the Greenfields, and Aeneas Macdonald of the

Sandfields, for his bail, and he promised, on his Hielan' word of honor, not to go beyond the posts. With that he went where he pleased, only taking care that he never put even the toe of his foot beyond a post, for all that some prisoners of the limits would chump ofer them and back again, or maybe swing round them, holding by their hands.

"Efery day the neighbors would go into Cornwall to give my grandfather the good word, and they would offer to pay Tougal Stewart for the other half of the plow, only that vexed my grandfather, for he wass too proud to borrow, and, of course, every day he felt less and less able to pay on account of him having to hire a man to be doing the spring plowing and seeding and making the kale yard.

"All this time, you'll mind, Tougal Stewart had to pay five shillings a week for my grandfather's keep, the law being so that if the debtor swore he had not five pounds' worth of property to his name, then the creditor had to pay the five shillings, and, of course, my grandfather had nothing to his name after he gave the bill of sale to Alexander Frazer. A great diversion it was to my grandfather to be reckoning up that if he lived as long as his father, that was hale and strong at ninety-six, Tougal would need to pay five or six hundred pounds for him, and there was only two pounds ten shillings to be paid on the plow.

"So it was like that all summer, my grandfather keeping heartsome, with the neighbors coming in so steady to bring him the news of the settlement. There he would sit, just inside one of the posts, for to pass his jokes and tell what he wished the family to be doing next. This way it might have kept going on for forty years, only it came about that my grandfather's youngest child—him that was my father—fell sick, and seemed like to die.

"Well, when my grandfather heard that bad news, he wass in a terrible way, to be sure, for he would be longing to hold the child in his arms, so that his heart was sore and like to break. Eat he could not, sleep he could not: all night he would be groaning, and all day he would be walking around by the posts, wishing that he had not passed his Hielan' word of honor not to go beyond a post; for he thought how he could have broken out like a chentleman, and gone to see his sick child, if he had stayed inside the jail wall. So it went on three days and three nights before the wise thought came into my grandfather's head to show him how he need not go beyond the posts to see his little sick boy. With that he went straight to one of the white cedar posts and pulled it up out of the hole, and started for home, taking great care to carry it in his hands pefore him, so he would not be beyond it one bit.

"My grandfather wass not half a mile out of Cornwall, which was only a little place in those days, when two of the turnkeys came after him.

" 'Stop, Mr. McTavish,' says the turnkeys.

" 'What for would I stop?' says my grandfather.

" 'You have broke your bail,' says they.

" 'It's a lie for you,' says my grandfather, for his temper flared up for anybody to say he would broke his bail. 'Am I beyond the post?' says my grandfather.

"With that they run in on him, only that he knocked the two of them over with the post, and went on rejoicing, like an honest man should, at keeping his word and over-coming them that would slander his good name. The only thing besides thoughts of the child that troubled him was questioning whether he had been strictly right in turning round for to use the post to defend himself in such a way that it was nearer the jail than he wass. But he remembered how the jailer never complained of prisoners of the limits chumping ofer the posts, if so that chumped back again in a moment, the trouble went out of his mind.

"Pretty soon after that he met Tuncan Macdonnell of Greenfields coming into Cornwall with the wagon.

" 'And how is this Glengatchie?' says Tuncan. 'For you were never the man to broke your bail.'

"Glengatchie, you'll understand, sir, is the name of my grandfather's farm.

" 'Never fear, Greenfields,' says my grandfather, 'for I'm not beyond the post.'

"So Greenfields looked at the post, and he looked at my grandfather, and he scratched his head a wee, and he seen it was so; and then he fell into a great admiration entirely.

" 'Get in with me, Glengatchie—it's proud I'll be to carry you home'; and he turned the team around. My grandfather did so, taking great care to keep the post in front of him all the time; and that way he reached home. Out comes my grandmother running to embrace him; but she had to throw her arms around the post and my grand-father's neck at the same time, he was that strict to be

within his promise. Pefore going ben the house, he went
to the back end of the kale yard which was farthest from
the jail, and there he stuck the post; and then he went back
to see his sick child, while all the neighbors that came
round was glad to see what a wise thought the saints
had put into his mind to save his bail and his promise.

"So there he stayed a week till my father got well. Of
course the constables came after my grandfather, but the
settlement would not let the creatures come within a mile
of Glengatchie. You might think, sir, that my grandfather
would have stayed with his wife and weans, seeing the
post was all the time in the kale yard, and him careful
not to go beyond it; but he was putting the settlement to a
great deal of trouble day and night to keep the constables
off, and he was fearful that they might take the post away,
if ever they got to Glengatchie, and give him the name of
false, which no McTavish ever had. So Tuncan Greenfields and Aeneas Sandfield drove my grandfather back to
the jail, him with the post behind him in the wagon, so as
he would be between it and the jail. Of course Tougal
Stewart tried his best to have the bail declared forfeited;
but old Judge Jones only laughed, and said my grandfather
was a Hielan' gentleman, with a very nice sense of honor,
and that was chust exactly the truth.

"How did my grandfather get free in the end? Oh, then,
that was because of Tougal Stewart being careless—him
that thought he knew so much of the law. The law was,
you will mind, that Tougal had to pay five shillings a week
for keeping my grandfather in the limits. The money wass
to be paid efery Monday, and it was to be paid in lawful
money of Canada, too. Well, would you belief that
Tougal paid in four shillings in silver one Monday, and one
shilling in coppers, for he took up the collection in church
the day pefore, and it wass not till Tougal had gone away
that the jailer saw that one of the coppers was a Brock
copper—a medal, you will understand, made at General
Brock's death, and not lawful money of Canada at all.
With that the jailer came out to my grandfather.

" 'Mr. McTavish,' says he, taking off his hat, 'you are a
free man, and I'm glad of it.' Then he told him what
Tougal had done.

" 'I hope you will not have any hard feelings toward
me, Mr. McTavish,' said the jailer; and a decent man he

wass, for all that there wass not a drop of Hielan' blood in him. 'I hope you will not think hard of me for not being hospitable to you, sir,' he says, 'but it's against the rules and regulations for the jailer to be offering the best he can command to the prisoners. Now that you are free, Mr. McTavish,' says the jailer, 'I would be a proud man if Mr. McTavish of Glengatchie would do me the honor of taking supper with me this night. I will be asking your leave to invite some of the gentlemen of the place, if you will say the word, Mr. McTavish,' says he.

"Well, my grandfather could never bear malice, the kind man he wass, and he seen how bad the jailer felt, so he consented, and a great company came in, to be sure, to celebrate the occasion.

"Did my grandfather pay the balance on the plow? What for should you suspicion, sir, that my grandfather would refuse his honest debt? Of course he paid for the plow, for the crop was good that fall.

" 'I would be paying you the other half of the plow now, Mr. Stewart,' says my grandfather comin' in when the store was full.

" 'Hoich, but *you* are the honest McTavish,' says Tougal, sneering.

"But my grandfather made no answer to the creature, for he thought it would be unkind to mention how Tougal had paid out six pounds four shillings and eleven pence to keep him in on account of a debt of two pound five that never was due till it was paid."

WHEN TWILIGHT FALLS
ON THE STUMP LOTS

Sir Charles G. D. Roberts

The wet, chill first of the spring, its blackness made tender by the lilac wash of the afterglow, lay upon the high, open stretches of the stump lots. The winter-whitened stumps, the sparse patches of juniper and bay just budding, the rough-mossed hillocks, the harsh boulders here and there upthrusting from the soil, the swampy hollows wherein a coarse grass began to show green, all seemed anointed, as it were, to an ecstasy of peace by the chrism of that paradisial color. Against the lucid immensity of the April sky the thin tops of five or six soaring rampikes aspired like violet flames. Along the skirts of the stump lots a fir wood reared a ragged-crested wall of black against the red amber of the horizon.

Late that afternoon, beside a juniper thicket not far from the center of the stump lots, a young black and white cow had given birth to her first calf. The little animal had been licked assiduously by the mother's caressing tongue till its color began to show, of a rich dark red. Now it had struggled to its feet, and with its disproportionately long, thick legs braced wide apart, was beginning to nurse. Its blunt wet muzzle and thick lips tugged eagerly, but somewhat blunderingly as yet, at the unaccustomed teats; and its tail lifted, twitching with delight, as the first warm streams of mother milk went down its throat. It was a pathetically awkward, unlovely little figure, not yet advanced to that youngling winsomeness which is the heritage, to some degree and at some period, of the infancy of all the kindreds that breathe upon the earth. But to the young mother's eyes it was the most beautiful of things. With her head twisted far around, she nosed and licked its heaving flanks as it nursed; and between deep, ecstatic breathings she uttered in her throat low murmurs, unspeakably tender, of encouragement and caress. The delicate but pervading flood of sunset color had the effect of blending the ruddy-hued calf into the tones of the landscape; but the cow's insistent blotches of black and white stood out sharply, refusing to harmonize. The drench of violet light was of no avail to soften their staring contrasts. They made her vividly conspicuous across the whole breadth of the stump lots, to eyes that watched her from the forest coverts.

The eyes that watched her—long, fixedly, hungrily—were small and red. They belonged to a lank she-bear, whose gaunt flanks and rusty coat proclaimed a season of famine in the wilderness. She could not see the calf, which was hidden by a hillock and some juniper scrub; but its presence was very legibly conveyed to her by the mother's solicitous watchfulness. After a motionless scrutiny from behind the screen of fir branches, the lean bear stole noiselessly forth from the shadows into the great wash of violet light. Step by step, and very slowly, with the patience that endures because confident of its object, she crept toward that oasis of mothering joy in the vast emptiness of the stump lots. Now crouching, now crawling, turning to this side and to that, taking advantage of every hollow, of every thicket, every hillock, every aggressive stump, her craft succeeded in eluding even the wild and menacing watchfulness of the young mother's eyes.

The spring had been a trying one for the lank she-bear. Her den, in a dry tract of hemlock wood some furlongs back from the stump lots, was a snug little cave under the uprooted base of a lone pine, which had somehow grown up among the alien hemlocks only to draw down upon itself at last, by its superior height, the fury of a passing hurricane. The winter had contributed but scanty snowfall to cover the bear in her sleep; and the March thaws, unseasonably early and ardent, had called her forth to activity weeks too soon. Then frosts had come with belated severity, sealing away the budding tubers, which are the bear's chief dependence for spring diet; and worst of all, a long stretch of intervale meadow by the neighboring river, which had once been rich in groundnuts, had been ploughed up the previous spring and subjected to the producing of oats and corn. When she was feeling the pinch of meager rations, and when the fat which a liberal autumn of blueberries had laid up about her ribs was getting as shrunken as the last snow in the thickets, she gave birth to two hairless and hungry little cubs. They were very blind, and ridiculously small to be born of so big a mother; and having so much growth to make during the next few months, their appetites were immeasurable. They tumbled, and squealed, and tugged at their mother's teats and grew astonishingly, and made huge haste to cover their bodies with fur of a soft and silken black; and all this vitality of theirs made a strenuous demand upon their mother's milk. There were no more bee trees left in the neighborhood. The long wanderings which she was forced to take in her search for roots and tubers were in themselves a drain upon her nursing powers. At last, reluctant though she was to attract the hostile notice of the settlement, she found herself forced to hunt on the borders of the sheep pastures. Before all else in life was it important to her that these two tumbling little ones in the den should not go hungry. Their eyes were open now—small and dark and whimsical, their ears quaintly large and inquiring for their roguish little faces. Had she not been driven by the unkind season to so much hunting and foraging, she would have passed near all her time rapturously in the den under the pine root, fondling those two soft miracles of her world.

With the killing of three lambs—at widely scattered points so as to mislead retaliation—things grew a little easier for the harassed bear; and presently she grew bolder in tampering with the creatures under man's protection. With one swift, secret blow of her mighty paw she struck down a young ewe which had strayed within reach of her hiding place. Dragging her prey deep into the woods, she fared well upon it for some days, and was happy with her growing cubs. It was just when she had begun to feel the fasting which came upon the exhaustion of this store that, in a hungry hour, she sighted the conspicuous markings of the black and white cow.

It is altogether unusual for the black bear of the eastern woods to attack any quarry so large as a cow, unless under the spur of fierce hunger or fierce rage. The she-bear was powerful beyond her fellows. She had the strongest possible incentive to bold hunting, and she had lately grown confident beyond her wont. Nevertheless, when she began her careful stalking of this big game which she coveted, she had no definite intention of forcing a battle with the cow. She had observed that cows, accustomed to the protection of man, would at times leave their calves asleep and stray off some distance in their pasturing. She had even seen calves left by themselves in a field from morning till night, and had wondered at such negligence in their mothers. Now she had a confident idea that sooner or later the calf would lie down to sleep, and the young mother roam a little wide in search of the scant young grass. Very softly, very self-effacingly, she crept nearer step by step, following up the wind, till at last, undiscovered, she was crouching behind a thick patch of juniper on the slope of a little hollow not ten paces distant from the cow and the calf.

By this time the tender violet light was fading to a grayness over hillock and hollow; and with the deepening of the twilight, the faint breeze, which had been breathing from the northward, shifted suddenly and came in slow, warm pulsations out of the south. At the same time the calf, having nursed sufficiently, and feeling his baby legs tired of the weight they had not yet learned to carry, laid himself down. On this the cow shifted her position. She turned half round, and lifted her head high. As she did so a scent of peril was borne upon her fine nostrils. She recognized it instantly. With a snort of anger she sniffed again, then stamped a challenge with her fore hoofs and leveled the lance points of her horns toward the menace. The next moment her eyes, made keen by the fear of love, detected the black outline of the bear's head through the coarse screen of the juniper. Without a second's hesitation, she flung up her tail, gave a short bellow, and charged.

The moment she saw herself detected, the bear rose upon her hindquarters; nevertheless she was in a measure surprised by the sudden, blind fury of the attack. Nimbly she swerved to avoid it, aiming at the same time a stroke with her mighty forearm, which, if it had found its mark, would have smashed her adversary's neck. But as she struck out, in the act of shifting her position, a depression of the ground threw her off-balance. The next instant one sharp horn caught her slantingly in the flank, ripping its way upward and inward, while the mad impact threw her upon her back.

Grappling, she had her assailant's head and shoulders in a trap, and her gigantic claws cut through the flesh and sinew like knives; but at the desperate disadvantage of her position she could inflict no disabling blow. The cow, on the other hand, though mutilated and streaming with blood, kept pounding with her whole massive weight, and with short tremendous shocks crushing the breath from her foe's ribs.

Presently, wrenching herself free, the cow drew off for another battering charge; and as she did so the bear hurled herself violently down the slope, and gained her feet behind a dense thicket of bay shrub. The cow, with one eye blinded and the other obscured by blood, glared around for her in vain, then in a panic of mother terror, plunged back to her calf.

Snatching at the respite, the bear crouched down, craving that invisibility which is the most faithful shield of the furtive kindred. Painfully, and leaving a drenched red trail behind her, she crept off from the disastrous neighborhood. Soon the deepening twilight sheltered her. But she could not make haste; and she knew that death was close upon her.

Once within the woods, she struggled straight toward the den that held her young. She hungered to die licking them. But destiny is as implacable as iron to the wilderness people, and even this was denied her. Just a half-score of paces from the lair in the pine root, her hour descended upon her. There was a sudden redder and fuller gush upon the trail; the last light of longing faded out of her eyes; and she lay down upon her side.

The merry little cubs within the den were beginning to expect her, and getting restless. As the night wore on and no mother came, they ceased to be merry. By morning they were shivering with hunger and desolate fear. But the doom of the ancient wood was less harsh than its wont, and spared them some days of starving anguish; for about noon a pair of foxes discovered the dead mother, astutely estimated the situation, and then with the boldness of good appetite, made their way into the unguarded den.

As for the red calf, its fortune was ordinary. Its mother,

for all her wounds, was able to nurse and cherish it through the night; and with morning came a searcher from the farm and took it, with the bleeding mother, safely back to the settlement. There it was tended and fattened, and within a few weeks found its way to the cool marble slabs of a city market.

LABRIE'S WIFE

Duncan Campbell Scott

[Being an excerpt from the manuscript journal of Archibald Muir, clerk of the honorable The Hudson's Bay Company, at Nepigon House in the year of our Lord 1815.]

May 22, 1815

Today something happened which is bound to be of consequence in this outlandish place, and that I will set down here and make of record. Alec, who is getting more gumption now, although as unsteady in all his performances as he ever was, returned from his trip to the Flat Rock, and arrived safe with his two canoes and Ogemah-ga-bow, little Needic, and his two sons. It appears they had, by reason of the rough weather, to lay by at Dry Beaver Islands and had like to have starved if the wind had not gone down, for these fools of Indians will never learn not to devour half their rations in the first day out from the Post. They came in looking like wasps, their belts girt so tightly about their middles.

I could tell the moment I clapped eyes upon Alec that he had some bee in his bonnet, for he can no more control his countenance than an otter can help fishing. His face was all of a jump, and he spoke as if he had no spittle under his tongue. I have a plan to let the youngster speak when he is ready, and by this means I have the enjoyment of witnessing him cast about to get me to question him and assist him out with his story. When we were having a bit of dinner he fairly simmered, but he did not boil until I lit my pipe. Then he could stand my coolness no longer.

"We're to have an opposition!" he blurted out. I did not

want to show any astonishment, but I nearly dropped my pipe, such a matter never having been thought of in the Nepigon before. "You see," he went on, "I determined when I was at that part of the lake to go over to Keg Island and see if the cache was all right, and on St. Paul's Island, when we went ashore to roast some fish, we found two canoes loaded, and a Frenchman and three Indians.

"He asked me if I was with the English, and I lied to him straight enough, and said, 'No! I am trading alone.' Then he wanted to know where our Post was, and I said it was beyond the large island to the west. He said his name was Labrie, and that he was for the North West Company and was sent in opposition to the English on the lake. So I decided to camp where I was and not to go to Keg Island, but to come on here. I told him to keep due west, and not to land until he struck the big island, which was Cariboo Island, and not for any reason to camp on a little flat island halfway there, which was full of snakes."

The youngster was mighty proud of himself at outwitting the Frenchman, but to take down his pride a bit, I provoked him saying, "Well, poor Donald used to call you a clavering idiot, but if he had lived to this day he'd have had to invent a new kind of word for you. If your Labrie is anything of a trader he watched you away in the morning, and he will treat us in good Hudson's Bay Company rum when we first meet, having visited your little flat island full of snakes." Off went Alec trying to bite his beard, aping Donald's manner, poor lad; but he has yet a beard no longer than a pinfeather.

May 23, 1815

I was up before sun this day, as I had a restless night, thinking what I should do now we were to have opposition on the lake, a thing new to me, who has scant experience. I determined to be smooth with them and observe them closely, and spoil them if I might with a fair face, and in all events to fight them with what weapons they may choose. I had wakened from a light doze with the sudden thought that I should possess myself of the point of land below the Post where I have always said the buildings should have been placed, which commands and oversees our present position. If it were seized by these pirates of Frenchmen, what then would become of our trade? They would eat it like a bear eats honeycomb. Alec could not see that it was a useless work and a weary waste of muscle. It is curious how blockheaded he is about all matters connected with trade; he has some acuteness belike, but of what sort God alone knows. In the end I was mightily satisfied to see a stout staff with the ensign flying, and a small boat landing with one of the boats moored. We had the work done before midday, and for the rest of the time I had pleasure in looking down at the Point, which had an inhabited and secure look under The Hudson's Bay Company's flag. If the Frenchmen have any idea of the shore about here there will be some *sacré*ing when they find the Point taken up, for northward there is no place for a foothold, and only in a cove, half a mile to the south, can they find level land enough for building upon. So when our Indians come down, and they should be here in a matter of four weeks, they are bound to reach the Post first, and I can keep my eye upon the rascals, who would, if they could, trade with the newcomers and forget old kindnesses and obligations.

May 24, 1815

Ogemah-ga-bow came up to say that one of Needic's boys had died last night, having overeaten himself after his fast on the Dry Beaver Islands. Rain today.

May 26, 1815

Sundown yesterday on my bench before the door, whereby Needic had made a smudge to keep off the flies, which are now very bad, when I saw a canoe that was none of ours land at the Point, and a man step out onto the new boat landing. He looked all about him as if he was making an inventory of the place, and then he came slowly up the hill. He was a stout-shouldered, low-set fellow, with a black beard and small bad eyes. Said I to myself as I saw him approach, "There is something mainly dishonest in your makeup, my man, and whatever one may have to do to keep trade from you it won't be very savory in the doing if your methods are to be used."

"My name's Labrie," he said, running his hand through his hair.

I got upon my legs and said politely, "I heard of your being in the lake from my man. Will you be seated?"

He said "No" and looked over his shoulder at the Point.

"You have the Point under your flag," he remarked.

"Aye," I said, as dry as I could.

"The work has marks of newness."

"You are right, it was only finished yesterday."

The blood came into his face in an ugly way.

"Well, there can be no great objection to my trading a little."

"Not there," said I bluntly. "Under my company's flag what we take we claim and keep."

He breathed rather heavily, but held his tongue, and was going to walk away.

"Hold on," said I. "Strangers are not treated so here. You must have a dram."

I called Alec, who brought the rum and the glasses. We drank healths courteously, we who were ready to cut one another's throats.

"Did you ever taste better than that?" I asked.

"I have as good," said he. "Though it is the best, I can match it."

"Match it!" said I in a tone of surprise, winking at Alec, who flew as red as a bubble jock. We parted then, but just as he was getting away he said over his shoulder, "Your man there has a damned queer idea of direction."

May 27, 1815

Sent Needic and his live boy and Ogemah-ga-bow's brother to Poplar Lodge to have news of the hunters. The Osnaburgh packs from the north should now be two weeks out, unless the ice is later this year than last. Tomorrow I will put Alec and Ogemah-ga-bow to work clearing out the storehouse and setting things to rights. I am much exercised in mind over my responsibilities. It was bad enough last year, but now I have the whole management and this opposition to contend with upon the back of it. I begin to be worn with it, what with loss of sleep at night and thinking about nought else in the day. No sign of Labrie or any of his party.

May 30, 1815

This morning Labrie came up to borrow an adze, which I lent to him without any question. He seemed to want to be civil enough. When I asked him, however, if Madame

Labrie had arrived, he seemed quite put about and mumbled something in his beard which sounded nearly like, "What affair is that of yours?" I paid no attention to him, not wishing to quarrel yet awhile, and without any further parley off he went with the adze, which I am fortunate if I ever see again.

Heat intense today, bringing on a great storm of thunder and much rain. Had a great debate with Alec, when we were indoors, as to when the Osnaburgh packs will be in. I calculate in three weeks; as the water is like to be high, they will take the route through Mud Lakes to Negodina, as I wrote Godfrey. The old route to Wabinosh would take them much longer, and what with broken water and two desperate, long carries, there is a great risk of loss by that way. Alec thinks they will be down sooner. There is no doubt they have had a fine winter, and if the pack can be safely landed it will be a great matter, and no doubt I shall hear good of it from the partners.

May 31, 1815

This morning when I was cleaning my pistols I heard a clear sound of laughter. Now, laughter is an uncommon thing in this country, visiting us very infrequently. To be sure the Indians laugh, but that to me always has an un-meaning sound, and sometimes a bestial. Moreover, this laughter was different in kind, and one must have listened to it however absorbed he might have been. It was high-pitched and very clear and had something merry and withal innocent about it. It was contagious also, and the mere sound of it made my very muscles twitch. There was no one visible, but after I had gazed awhile I saw Alec come up the steps from the warehouse. Not to appear interested before the lad I went back to my work. After a little he came in. I noticed his face was flushed and his manner excited. I paid no attention to him until he had knocked a dish off the table. It broke into three pieces. I was angry with him, good crockery not being by any means very plentiful in this country.

"Good God, man!" I cried. "If you're in such a state that you cannot avoid breaking the dishes, will you lie upon your bed for a while." He glared at me terribly, but had not a word to say. Then I kept quiet for as much as a quarter of an hour, and I could see it was fretting

Sharon — I put
3 Alice Munro books out.
That's all the room I have
for now.

Paul.

Paul

Could we have
these put out
on the special
shelf.

Thanks
Sharon $\longrightarrow$

him; he fidgeted about greatly. Then he got up and went to the door.

"It seems to me you take mighty small interest in things." I said never a word.

"Are you deaf this morning?"

I made no sound. He made no move for a minute, then he said, just as he was going out of the door, in an exasperated way, "That was Labrie's wife."

I could have laughed to myself, but when I had thought upon it for a time I began to perceive something bitter in his tone, and I reflected that of late I had treated him much as poor Donald used unthinkingly to treat me, and that he must be occupying my old position of complaint, and my heart was softened a bit, and I resolved to be more kind to him in future, who is in much a good boy and canny in a sort about many things.

June 1, 1815

I saw Labrie's wife for the first time this morning—an uncommon-looking wench, with black hair and eyes and a mouth full of white teeth. I discussed her thoroughly with Alec, who sticks up for it that she is a handsome one. So she is, after her manner, though that I do not acknowledge to Alec. She looked me all over as if I were for sale, and when I coolly turned my back on her that she might have a good look at that, she went off in a mighty huff.

Alec reports that there are two other women in Labrie's party, rather old and haggish. I have not clapped eyes upon them, not having visited the Cove. Although she went off in a huff, the young wench is a merry one, and it amuses her to hear Alec so aboundingly polite to her with his "Madame Labrie." "Madame Labrie" this and "Madame Labrie" that, whereupon she giggles or breaks out into wild laughter.

June 3, 1815

Needic back from Poplar Lodge, where everything is all right. Had an amusing conversation with the lad Alec anent Labrie's wife. The hussy comes about the house constantly, even when we are not here.

"Now what is she after?" said I.

"You have no understanding of women," he replied. "Of

course she will come back when you treat her in that way."

"Now in what way?" I asked. "Never do I look at her or pass the time of day with her."

"That is it," he retorts. "You are fairly insulting her, and she comes back."

"Do you try and be sweet to her and mayhap she would stay away."

"It is different with me," he says, biting his "whiskers" and shrugging up his shoulders, just as the wench does herself. He has taken on a sort of mincing, balancing, half-Frenchified accent and shrugs his shoulders.

"Are you afrait she would fall into love weez you, Alec?" I remarked, trying hard to imitate the accent.

"It is not me she will be in love with."

"No, who then? Needic?"

"Needic!" he cried, going off with a great French shrug.

June 4, 1815

No word from Godfrey about the packs. I am getting a trifle anxious. Alec says there are more guns than yardsticks in Labrie's quarters and makes out they are on for a fight. Labrie's wife came up at noon and made us an omelette with gull's eggs and fresh onion tops. She is a clever wench and sat looking at me as I devoured it. I talked a bit to her. After she left, Alec sat frowning.

"You were very free with her."

"I merely spoke to her, but then she made a good omelette."

"You said too much to her. You nearly told her we expected the packs at Negodina by the Mud Lake route this year instead of Wabinosh."

"Well, and if I did?"

"It is all she wanted to know."

"Well, you seem to be always ready to stand up for the spy, if she be one," said I, turning the French accent upon him. This made him wroth, as it always does.

"You never seem to understand that a woman's not like a man. The best of them you have to watch, and more particularly when one of them is in love with you."

"That does not apply here," I said, "unless you have her assurances yourself."

"I would not make love to a married woman," he said hotly.

"That's why you guard yourself so carefully, is it? You are mighty pious. It is a pity you are not like me. Now for me Mr. Labrie's wife has no attraction whatever, commandments or no commandments."

This set him off again.

"Be careful you, Archibald Muir—that is what I have to say to you."

We could hear the lady herself laughing down at the landing, and it sounded so innocent that I could not refrain from smiling at the boy.

June 5, 1815

We had a scene last night with Labrie's wife, for which Alec has to be thanked, and in which I think he had a small revenge for my baiting of him. I will set down the occurrence here although it be against myself and our national instrument. She had been hardly before the house, and it was in the dusk of the evening, when she asked me to play upon the pipes.

"Will you play upon the bagpipes, Mr. Muir?" she said in a very civil voice. "I have never heard the bagpipes."

Now, I am always at pains to oblige a lady, if it be possible, so I went in and got the pipes, hearing Alec urge me also, so I had two willing to be pleased.

Well, scarcely had I begun to get the skin filled with wind when Labrie's wife began to laugh. Now, I am willing to admit that the foreword to a performance on the pipes may be dispiriting, but I charge that what follows after, when the instrument is well controlled and when the melody pours forth in full cry, would serve to obliterate a greatly more dispiriting prelude. But in this case I did not get beyond that stage, for Labrie's wife laughed with so little judgment that I was put about. I saw something in Alec's face which led me to think that the whole matter was preconceived by him, and with that I laid down my pipes on the bench beside me. Not another note would I play. I am not much versed in women's ways, and what Labrie's wife did puzzled me. But of that I shall give Alec's explanation. At first she kept on laughing, and then she stopped suddenly and came forward looking sober enough, but with the wrinkles of the laughter not yet gone out of her face. There she stood about four feet from me with a bit of her dress in her hand, as I have seen schoolgirls stand abashed having been found at fault.

"You are angry because I laughed?" she asked.

I did not answer.

"Are you angry with me because I could not help laughing?"

I did not answer.

Then she came close to me and made as if to put her hands upon my shoulders, and when I looked straight upon her eyes she dropped her hands, made a sound in her throat, and turned and went away.

Then young Alec began to strut about like a bantam cock.

"I have to thank you for that performance," I said.

"Why would you prevent a woman from laughing?" he asks, in a rage. "Don't you know enough of women to let them laugh and let them talk?"

"I can lay no claim to such a knowledge as yourself," said I, in a mighty sneering voice. "In truth I know naught about them."

"You have proved that this night," retorted Alec.

"Expound that, you young oracle," said I.

"Expound? You have sent her away with a sore heart, and she was minded to be playful with you, and that cuts sore on a heart such as hers. Don't you see it, man?" he cried, sort of dashing his hands down.

"I see nothing of the sort. She was angry simply because I wouldn't speak back to her."

"You might have spoken to her or not spoken, and she would never have minded if you hadn't looked at her in the way you did."

I saw it was no use my trying to fathom the young donkey, so I would speak no more to him.

June 6, 1815

Labrie's wife was up last night but I would not go out to see her, being tired of the body and her endless chatter. Alec and she talked for an hour; the boy would be contented to go on vaporing forever, I believe. I pretended to be busy with my papers, and in the end she went away. She came to the window just before she went, and I heard her fingers on the sash, but I did not look up, and I heard her low gurgling laugh as she ran away from Alec, who would go down to the landing with her.

He is as polite to her and as formal as if he were living by a code of court etiquette. I twitted him with that.

"Well," he says, mighty stiff and pulling a solemn face, "she is a woman, and she is another man's wife."

"The last is her great virtue," said I, with a tone of sarcasm, at which he looked scornful and exceeding pious.

June 7, 1815

Good news yesterday. Toma came in with a message from Godfrey. The Osnaburgh packs are safe at Cache Point on the Mud Lake route. The water is high and they have not had a mishap. In three days they should reach Negodina at the end of the lake. It is, as I have always said, a route more clean and handy than the Wabinosh route, and it will be adopted now from this out.

June 8, 1815

Woke up with a mighty sore head this morning and had words with Alec. It is inconceivable how domineering that lad has become.

"You were drinking with Madame Labrie last night," he said.

"And my lord is jealous," I replied, sneering at him.

"Ye have made a fool of yourself. What did you tell her?"

"Nothing that I rightly remember. Since when were you ordained my catechist?"

"Now I have told you many times," he said in a parsoning way, "that you did not understand the nature of women, and that you would let slip something that Labrie wanted to know. Now you have done so, I believe, between a glass too much of whiskey and a pretty woman."

"Do you call yon a pretty woman?" I said, mocking his accent.

"I pity you!" he said, with great contempt.

He went away swinging his shoulders, much more the master than the man.

To set down the truth, although it be against myself, Labrie's wife came up in the evening of yesterday. I was more decent with the bitch, having had the good news, and I treated her to some whiskey, and drank with her. Alec was off watching Toma, as he thought Labrie might try to get hold of him. I do not just remember when she went away. God forgive me, I do not rightly remember anything about it.

Hardly had Alec dismissed himself when he came back very greatly excited, but in anger this time.

"They have gone," said he.

"Who?" I asked, not thinking for a moment.

"Who! My God! Who? Why, Labrie."

"Well, what of that?" I asked. "It is a good riddance of a vile lot of thieves out of God's country."

"That is all you see to it?" he asked.

"Well, what more?" I replied.

"I seem to see that last night you told Madame Labrie the packs were coming by the Mud Lake route to Negodina, and that they have gone to stop them. I have my doubt they will not barter with them. I seem to see that they will capture the furs and that by no very gentle means."

"You have said it before," I cried out, wroth with him and with myself. "So yon slut is what I have always supposed her to be."

A dark look came into his face. "Choose your words!" he cried, taking a step toward me.

"I'll neither pick nor choose my words," I said. "What do you call her then that would take our hospitality and then do us wrong?"

"Madeleine would do no such thing," he cried, strutting about in a way that looked comical to me. I laughed at him.

"Madeleine! Madeleine! We shall see what Madeleine will have done when we lose our furs. Why, man, you said out of your own mouth that she had done it."

"You lie," he cried, but it was here not impudence, so I paid no attention to him.

After some parley and conversation, I sent him with three canoes and all the able men, except Needic, to Negodina to see what had fallen out. He is to send me back a letter as soon as he can with the word. I am here now quite alone, and in mind very much put about. I have been striving to recall what passed between Labrie's wife and myself, but without any clear recollection. Ah, those

women! I well remember my father used to say, "At the
bottom of every trouble, there you will find a woman," and
my mother used to retort, "And likewise at the bottom of
every happiness." Whereupon he would kiss her.

June 10, 1815

Last night—waiting for word from Alec. This morning I
went down to Labrie's camp with Needic. They had left
two tents and some rubbish, and a little green box marked
"M.L." Turning the lot over I found two empty kegs
marked "H.B.Co.," once full of rum, which they had
stolen from the cache on Keg Island. So we heaped all together and set fire to it. It burned merrily, and they are at
least by that much the poorer.

June 11, 1815

I am in great spirits today. Last night I was wakened by
Needic, who had his boy with him. Everything had reached
Negodina safely, and there was no sign anywhere of La-
brie's party. They will push on at once.

June 12, 1815

This morning Labrie came back. Needic came up and told
me, so about noon I took my pistols and went down with
him to the cove. They had one tent up and the women were
making the fire. The men went off and none of them
would speak to us. I stood smiling in a taunting way, and
just as I was about to leave, Labrie's wife came over to
me. I perceived she had her arm wound in a cloth.

"Well, Madame Labrie, how did you hurt your arm?"

"Why do you call me Madame Labrie?"

"One must call you something. My boy Alec calls you
Madeleine."

Her face grew a darker red.

"You have been away for a while?"

"Yes," she said, "we were at Wabinosh, and I see you
burned my box when I was gone.

"Were you ever in love?" she asked suddenly.

"Never," said I, "praise be to God."

"When you are I pray heaven you may be tortured in it."

"I am thankful for your good wishes."

"The other night you told me your packs were coming
by Negodina. You understand? It was Labrie who shot me

through the arm. He wanted to kill me for taking them to Wabinosh, but the others would not let him."

"The low rascal," I said, "to shoot a woman."

"And you have nothing to say about me?" She looked at me curiously, and put an odd emphasis on the *you* and the *me.*

"It is fortunate you made a mistake."

"A mistake!" said she. "Your boy Alec is twice the man that you are."

The hussy said that with a fluff of pride.

"Good-bye," said I from my canoe.

"Is that all, Archibald Muir, is that all?"

"Good-bye," said I, "and I hope your husband won't shoot at you again."

I looked back when we had gone a bit, and she still stood there. She did not make any sign toward me, though I waved to her in courtesy. Then she covered up her face in her hands.

No word of Godfrey and Alec. I sent Needic to Labrie's wife with two gold guineas for the box I had burned, probably the only gold she ever clapped her eyes on, as it is unknown in this trade almost.

June 13, 1815

The packs came in yesterday evening—Godfrey and the men all well. I mixed a keg of spirits for them and they made a hideous night of it. Too busy to write much now, but can do nothing more tonight. Looking back in the store ledgers I can see no such winter's catch. Great good luck. Labrie's party still hanging around. Alec went down as soon as he got back, and stayed longer than he ought, so I berated him soundly. Tonight at supper he said:

"Labrie shot her through the arm because she had taken them to Wabinosh and had misled them."

I paid no attention to him. By and by he said, "You will be glad to know that she says you told her nothing about the packs."

"Did she?" I asked, puzzled, as she had told me the contrary.

"I don't believe her," he added.

"You're complimentary to the ladies," I remarked.

"Here is something she asked me to give you."

It was the money I had sent her for that box of hers I burned.

June 14, 1815

Busy all day between the storehouse and the fur press. Half the Indians are drunk yet. Alec says Labrie and his party have gone. May the devil's luck go with them. I thought Alec looked a trifle white in the face, and as if he was impatient to make me talk, but I had no time to be spending with him.

June 15, 1815

A wonderfully warm day, and the flies very bad, enough to madden one. Have pressed all the packs and now everything is in order for a move. What a grand night for the partners it will be when they see our canoes full of the finest come to land at Fort William. It should be of profit to me, and I expect to come back here or go somewhere a factor, if I comprehend the rules properly. About an hour ago I had just finished writing the last words when Alec's shadow came over the window. He seemed to stand there over long, and I was just on the point of crying out to him when he moved off. In a moment he came in to me. I did not look up from my writing when he flung a scrap of paper down before me.

"There!" he said, in an odd voice. "I found it under the sash. It fell face down, so, as I saw printing on the back, I thought it was but a scrap torn off a fur bill.

"Read it," said he.

I turned it over and observed that there were some words in writing on the other side. I made them out to be: "Why do you call me Labrie's wife? She is my aunt. Do you think I would marry an ugly fellow like Labrie? They brought me up here to help their plans. We shall see. If you want to know my name it's Madeleine Lesage. I learned to write from the Sister St. Theresa at Wikwemikong. Is it not pretty? M.L."

Then I recalled how she had come to the window one night not very long ago, when I opine she had left the paper there.

"Well!" I said coolly, "and what is it now that you have to say about Madeleine Lesage?"

His face had a tortured look upon it. He tried to speak. "She was—she was the bravest, the dearest—" He stopped there and hung down his head. "Oh, my God, you cannot understand. You can never understand!"

He moved away and stood by the door. I thought upon what he had said. No, I did not understand. Then I tried once more to go on with my page. But I was detained by a sound which is as uncommon as that of laughter in these outlandish parts. The sound of sobbing. Just for a moment it brought back to me the sound of my sister's voice as she sobbed for her lover when they brought him back dead and dripping out of the sea. I had a vision of it as if it were snapped upon my eye in a flash of lightning, she leaning her forehead upon her wrists against the wall. I looked up at Alec and there he was leaning at the door-post, his shoulders all moving with his sobs. I understood in a flash. I pray God to forgive me for the sin of blindness, and for always being so dead to others in my own affairs. I went toward him knowing that I could not give him any comfort. So he went out from the house and walked alone through the gloaming. I perceived that a change had come over him. I had always considered him a bit of a boy to be ordered about, but there was a man walking away from me, resolute in his steps, big in his bulk, and weighed down as if he was carrying a load, bearing it as if he were proud of it, with energy and trust in himself.

THE SPECULATIONS
OF JEFFERSON THORPE

Stephen Leacock

It was not until the mining boom, at the time when everybody went simply crazy over the Cobalt and Porcupine mines of the new silver country near the Hudson Bay, that Jefferson Thorpe reached what you might call public importance in Mariposa.

Of course everybody knew Jeff and his little barber shop that stood across the street from Smith's Hotel. Everybody knew him and everybody got shaved there. From early morning, when the commercial travelers off the 6:30 express got shaved into the resemblance of human beings, there were always people going in and out of the barber shop.

Mullins, the manager of the Exchange Bank, took his morning shave from Jeff as a form of resuscitation, with enough wet towels laid on his face to stew him and with Jeff moving about in the steam, razor in hand, as grave as an operating surgeon.

Then, as I think I said, Mr. Smith came in every morning and there was a tremendous outpouring of Florida water and rums, essences and revivers and renovators, regardless of expense. What with Jeff's white coat and Mr. Smith's flowered waistcoat and the red geranium in the window and the Florida water and the double extract of hyacinth, the little shop seemed multicolored and luxurious enough for the annex of a Sultan's harem.

But what I mean is that till the mining boom, Jefferson Thorpe never occupied a position of real prominence in Mariposa. You couldn't, for example, have compared him with a man like Golgotha Gingham, who, as undertaker, stood in a direct relation to life and death; or to Trelawney, the postmaster, who drew money from the Federal

Government of Canada and was regarded as virtually a member of the Dominion Cabinet.

Everybody knew Jeff and liked him, but the odd thing was that till he made money nobody took any stock in his ideas at all. It was only after he made the "clean up" that they came to see what a splendid fellow he was. "Level-headed" I think was the term; indeed, in the speech of Mariposa, the highest form of endowment was to have the head set on horizontally as with a theodolite.

As I say, it was when Jeff made money that they saw how gifted he was, and when he lost it—but still, there's no need to go into that. I believe it's something the same in other places, too.

The barber shop, you will remember, stands across the street from Smith's Hotel, and stares at it face to face.

It is one of those wooden structures—I don't know whether you know them—with a false front that sticks up above its real height and gives it an air at once rectangular and imposing. It is a form of architecture much used in Mariposa and understood to be in keeping with the pretentious and artificial character of modern business. There is a red, white, and blue post in front of the shop, and the shop itself has a large square window out of proportion to its little flat face.

Painted on the panes of the window are the remains of a legend that once spelled BARBER SHOP, executed with the flourishes that prevailed in the golden age of sign painting in Mariposa. Through the window you can see the geraniums in the window shelf and behind them Jeff Thorpe with his little black skull cap on and his spectacles drooped upon his nose as he bends forward in the absorption of shaving.

As you open the door, it sets in violent agitation a coiled spring up above and a bell that almost rings. Inside, there are two shaving chairs of the heavier, or electrocution, pattern, with mirrors in front of them and pigeon holes with individual shaving mugs. There must be ever so many of them, fifteen or sixteen. It is the current supposition of each of Jeff's customers that everyone else but himself uses a separate mug. One corner of the shop is partitioned off and bears the sign: HOT AND COLD BATHS, *50 cents*. There has been no bath inside the partition for twenty years—only old newspapers and a mop. Still, it lends distinction somehow, just as do the faded cardboard signs that hang against the mirror with the legends: TURKISH SHAMPOO, *75 cents,* and ROMAN MASSAGE, *$1.00.*

They said commonly in Mariposa that Jeff made money out of the barber shop. He may have, and it may have been that that turned his mind to investment. But it's hard to see how he could. A shave cost five cents, and a haircut fifteen (or the two, if you liked, for a quarter), and at that it is hard to see how he could make money, even when he had both chairs going and shaved first in one and then in the other.

You see, in Mariposa, shaving isn't the hurried, perfunctory thing that it is in the city. A shave is looked upon as a form of physical pleasure and lasts anywhere from twenty-five minutes to three-quarters of an hour.

In the morning hours, perhaps, there was a semblance of haste about it, but in the long quiet of the afternoon, as Jeff leaned forward toward the customer and talked to him in a soft, confidential monotone, like a portrait painter, the razor would go slower and slower, and pause and stop, move and pause again, till the shave died away into the mere drowse of conversation.

At such hours, the Mariposa barber shop would become a very Palace of Slumber, and as you waited your turn in one of the wooden armchairs beside the wall, what with the quiet of the hour, and the low drone of Jeff's conversation, and the buzzing of the flies against the windowpane, and the measured tick of the clock above the mirror, your head sank dreaming on your breast, and *The Mariposa Newspacket* rustled unheeded on the floor. It makes one drowsy just to think of it!

The conversation, of course, was the real charm of the place. You see, Jefferson's forte, or specialty, was information. He could tell you more things within the compass of a half hour's shave than you get in days of laborious research in an encyclopedia. Where he got it all, I don't know, but I am inclined to think it came more or less out of the newspapers.

In the city, people never read the newspapers, not really, only little bits and scraps of them. But in Mariposa it's different. There they read the whole thing from cover to cover, and they build up on it, in the course of years, a range of acquirement that would put a college president to the blush. Anybody who has ever heard Henry Mullins and Peter Glover talk about the future of China will know just what I mean.

And, of course, the peculiarity of Jeff's conversation was that he could suit it to his man every time. He hⁿd a kind of divination about it. There was a certain kind of man that Jeff would size up sideways as he stropped the razor, and in whose ear he would whisper, "I see where Saint Louis has took four straight games off Chicago—" and so hold him fascinated to the end.

In the same way he would say to Mr. Smith, "I see where it says that this 'Flying Squirl' run a dead heat for the King's Plate."

To a humble intellect like mine he would explain in full the relations of the Keesar to the German Rich Dog.

But first, and foremost, Jeff's specialty in the way of conversation was finance and the money market, the huge fortunes that a man with the right kind of head could make.

I've known Jefferson to pause in his shaving with the razor suspended in the air as long as five minutes while he described, with his eyes half closed, exactly the kind of a head a man needed in order to make a "haul" or a "cleanup." It was evidently simply a matter of the head, and as far as one could judge, Jeff's own was the very type required.

I don't know just at what time or how Jefferson first began his speculative enterprises. It was probably in him from the start. There is no doubt that the very idea of such things as Traction Stock and Amalgamated Asbestos went to his head; and whenever he spoke of Mr. Carnegie and Mr. Rockefeller, the yearning tone of his voice made it as soft as lathered soap.

I suppose the most rudimentary form of his speculation was the hens. That was years ago. He kept them out at the back of his house—which itself stood up a grass plot behind and beyond the barber shop—and in the old days Jeff would say, with a certain note of pride in his voice, that The Woman had sold as many as two dozen eggs in a day to the summer visitors.

But what with reading about Amalgamated Asbestos and Consolidated Copper and all that, the hens began to seem pretty small business, and in any case, the idea of two dozen eggs at a cent apiece almost makes one blush. I suppose a good many of us have felt just as Jeff did about our poor little earnings. Anyway, I remember Jeff telling me one day that he could take the whole lot of the hens and sell them off and crack the money into Chicago wheat on margin and turn it over in twenty-four hours. He did it, too. Only somehow when it was turned over it came upside down on top of the hens.

After that the hen house stood empty and The Woman had to throw away chicken feed every day, at a dead loss of perhaps a shave and a half. But it made no difference to Jeff, for his mind had floated away already on the possibilities of what he called "displacement" mining on the Yukon.

So you can understand that when the mining boom struck Mariposa, Jefferson Thorpe was in it right from the very start. Why, no wonder; it seemed like the finger of Providence. Here was this great silver country spread out to north of us, where people had thought there was only a wilderness. And right at our very doors! You could see, as I saw, the night express going north every evening; for all one knew Rockefeller or Carnegie or anyone might be on it! Here was the wealth of Calcutta, as *The Mariposa Newspacket* put it, poured out at our very feet.

So no wonder the town went wild! All day in the street you could hear men talking of veins and smelters and dips and deposits and faults—the town hummed with it like a geology class on examination day. And there were men about the hotels with mining outfits and theodolites and dunnage bags, and at Smith's bar they would hand chunks of rock up and down, some of which would run as high as ten drinks to the pound.

The fever just caught the town and ran through it! Within a fortnight they put a partition down Robertson's Coal and Wood Office and opened the Mariposa Mining Exchange, and just about every man on Main Street started buying scrip. Then presently young Fizzlechip, who had been teller in Mullins's Bank and whom everybody had thought a worthless jackass before, came back from the Cobalt country with a fortune and loafed around in the Mariposa House in English khaki and a horizontal hat, drunk all the time, and everybody holding him up as an example of what it was possible to do if you tried.

They all went in. Jim Eliot mortgaged the inside of the drugstore and jammed it into Twin Tamagami. Pete Glover at the hardware store bought Nippewa stock at thirteen cents and sold it to his brother at seventeen and bought it back in less than a week at nineteen. They didn't care! They took a chance. Judge Pepperleigh put the rest of his wife's money into Temiskaming Common, and Lawyer Macartney got the fever, too, and put every cent that his sister possessed into Tulip Preferred.

And even when young Fizzlechip shot himself in the back room of the Mariposa House, Mr. Gingham buried him in a casket with silver handles, and it was felt that there was a Monte Carlo touch about the whole thing.

They all went in—or all except Mr. Smith. You see, Mr. Smith had come down from there, and he knew all about rocks and mining and canoes and the north country. He knew what it was to eat flour-baked dampers under the lee side of a canoe propped among the underbrush, and to drink the last drop of whiskey within fifty miles. Mr. Smith had mighty little use for the north. But what he did do was to buy up enough early potatoes to send fifteen carload lots into Cobalt at a profit of five dollars a bag.

Mr. Smith, I say, hung back. But Jeff Thorpe was in the mining boom right from the start. He bought in on the Nippewa mine even before the interim prospectus was out. He took a block of 100 shares of Abbitibbi Development at fourteen cents, and he and Johnson, the livery stablekeeper next door, formed a syndicate and got a thousand shares of Metagami Lake at 3¼ cents and then unloaded them on one of the sausage men at Netley's butcher shop at a clear cent percent advance.

Jeff would open the little drawer below the mirror in the barber shop and show you all kinds and sorts of Cobalt country mining certificates—blue ones, pink ones, green ones, with outlandish and fascinating names on them that ran clear from the Mattawa to the Hudson Bay.

And right from the start he was confident of winning.

"There ain't no difficulty to it," he said, "there's lots of silver up there in that country and if you buy some here and some there you can't fail to come out somewhere. I don't say," he used to continue, with the scissors open and ready to cut, "that some of the greenhorns won't get bit.

But if a feller knows the country and keeps his head level, he can't lose."

Jefferson had looked at so many prospectuses and so many pictures of mines and pine trees and smelters, that I think he'd forgotten that he'd never been in the country. Anyway, what's two hundred miles!

To an onlooker it certainly didn't seem so simple. I never knew the meanness, the trickery, of the mining business, the sheer obstinate determination of the bigger capitalists not to make money when they might, till I heard the accounts of Jeff's different mines. Take the case of the Corona Jewel. There was a good mine simply going to ruin for lack of common sense.

"She ain't been developed," Jeff would say. "There's silver enough in her so you could dig it out with a shovel. She's full of it. But they won't get at her and work her."

Then he'd take a look at the pink and blue certificates of the Corona Jewel and slam the drawer on them in disgust.

Worse than that was the Silent Pine—a clear case of stupid incompetence! Utter lack of engineering skill was all that was keeping the Silent Pine from making a fortune for its holders.

"The only trouble with that mine," said Jeff, "is they won't go deep enough. They followed the vein down to where it kind o' thinned out and then they quit. If they'd just go right into her good, they'd get it again. She's down there all right."

But perhaps the meanest case of all was the Northern Star. That always seemed to me, every time I heard of it, a straight case for the criminal law. The thing was so evidently a conspiracy.

"I bought her," said Jeff, "at thirty-two, and she stayed right there tight, like she was stuck. Then a bunch of these fellers in the city started to drive her down and they got her pushed down to twenty-four, and I held on to her and they shoved her down to twenty-one. This morning they've got her down to sixteen, but I don't mean to let go. No, sir."

In another fortnight they shoved her, the same unscrupulous crowd, down to nine cents, and Jefferson still held on.

"They're working her down," he admitted, "but I'm holding her."

No conflict between vice and virtue was ever grimmer. "She's at six," said Jeff, "but I've got her. They can't squeeze me."

A few days after that, the same criminal gang had her down further than ever.

"They've got her down to three cents," said Jeff, "but I'm with her. Yes, sir, they think they can shove her clean off the market, but they can't do it. I've boughten in Johnson's shares, and the whole of Netley's, and I'll stay with her till she breaks."

So they shoved and pushed and clawed her down— that unseen nefarious crowd in the city—and Jeff held on to her and they writhed and twisted at his grip, and then—

And then—well, that's just the queer thing about the mining business. Why, sudden as a flash of lightning, it seemed, the news came over the wire to *The Mariposa Newspacket* that they had struck a vein of silver in the Northern Star as thick as a sidewalk, and that the stock had jumped to seventeen dollars a share, and even at that you couldn't get it! And Jeff stood there flushed and half staggered against the mirror of the little shop, with a bunch of mining scrip in his hand that was worth forty thousand dollars!

Excitement! It was all over the town in a minute. They ran off a news extra at *The Mariposa Newspacket*, and in less than no time there wasn't standing room in the barber shop, and over in Smith's Hotel they had three extra barkeepers working on the lager beer pumps.

They were selling mining shares on Main Street in Mariposa that afternoon and people were just clutching for them. Then at night there was a big oyster supper in Smith's cafe, with speeches, and the Mariposa band outside.

And the queer thing was that the very next afternoon was the funeral of young Fizzlechip, and Dean Drone had to change the whole text of his Sunday sermon at two days' notice for fear of offending public sentiment.

But I think what Jeff liked best of it all was the sort of public recognition that it meant. He'd stand there in the shop, hardly bothering to shave, and explain to the men in the armchairs how he held her, and they shoved her, and he clung to her, and what he'd said to himself—a perfect Iliad—while he was clinging to her.

The whole thing was in the city papers a few days after

with a photograph of Jeff, taken specially at Ed Moore's studio (upstairs over Netley's). It showed Jeff sitting among palm trees, as all mining men do, with one hand on his knee, and a dog, one of those regular mining dogs, at his feet, and a look of piercing intelligence in his face that would easily account for forty thousand dollars.

I say that the recognition meant a lot to Jeff for its own sake. But no doubt the fortune meant quite a bit to him, too, on account of Myra.

Did I mention Myra, Jeff's daughter? Perhaps not. That's the trouble with the people in Mariposa; they're all so separate and so different—not a bit like the people in the cities—that unless you hear about them separately and one by one you can't for a moment understand what they're like.

Myra had golden hair and a Greek face and would come bursting through the barber shop in a hat at least six inches wider than what they wear in Paris. As you saw her swinging up the street to the Telephone Exchange in a suit that was straight out of *The Delineator* and brown American boots, there was style written all over her—the kind of thing that Mariposa recognized and did homage to. And to see her in the Exchange—she was one of the four girls that I spoke of—on her high stool with a steel cap on, jabbing the connecting plugs in and out as if electricity cost nothing—well, all I mean is that you could understand why it was that the commercial travelers would stand round in the Exchange calling up all sorts of impossible villages, and waiting about so pleasant and genial! It made one realize how naturally good-tempered men are. And then when Myra would go off duty and Miss Cleghorn, who was sallow, would come on, the commercial men would be off again like autumn leaves.

It just shows the difference between people. There was Myra who treated lovers like dogs and would slap them across the face with a banana skin to show her utter independence. And there was Miss Cleghorn, who was sallow and who bought a forty-cent *Ancient History* to improve herself; and yet if she'd hit any man in Mariposa with a banana skin, he'd have had her arrested for assault.

Mind you, I don't mean that Myra was merely flippant and worthless. Not at all. She was a girl with any amount of talent. You should have heard her recite "The Raven" at the Methodist Social! Simply genius! And when she acted

Portia in the trial scene of the *Merchant of Venice* at the high-school concert, everybody in Mariposa admitted that you couldn't have told it from the original.

So, of course, as soon as Jeff made the fortune, Myra had her resignation in next morning and everybody knew that she was to go to a dramatic school for three months in the fall and become a leading actress.

But, as I said, the public recognition counted a lot for Jeff. The moment you begin to get that sort of thing it comes in quickly enough. Brains, you know, are recognized right away. That was why, of course, within a week from this Jeff received the first big packet of stuff from the Cuban Land Development Company, with colored pictures of Cuba, and fields of bananas, and haciendas, and insurrectos with machetes, and Heaven knows what. They heard of him, somehow—it wasn't for a modest man like Jefferson to say how. After all, the capitalists of the world are just one and the same crowd. If you're in it, you're in it, that's all! Jeff realized why it is that of course men like Carnegie or Rockefeller and Morgan all know one another. They have to.

For all I know, this Cuban stuff may have been sent from Morgan himself. Some of the people in Mariposa said yes, others said no. There was no certainty.

Anyway, they were fair and straight, this Cuban crowd that wrote to Jeff. They offered him to come right in and be one of them. If a man's got the brains, you may as well recognize it straight away. Just as well write him to be a director now as wait and hesitate till he forces his way into it.

Anyhow, they didn't hesitate, these Cuban people that wrote to Jeff from Cuba—or from a post-office box in New York—it's all the same thing, because Cuba being so near to New York the mail is all distributed from there. I suppose in some financial circles they might have been slower, wanted guarantees of some sort, and so on, but these Cubans, you know, have got a sort of Spanish warmth of heart that you don't see in businessmen in America, and that touches you. No, they asked no guarantee. Just send the money—whether by express order or by bank draft or check, they left that entirely to oneself, as a matter between Cuban gentlemen.

And they were quite frank about their enterprise—

bananas and tobacco in the plantation district reclaimed from the insurrectos. You could see it all there in the pictures—the tobacco plants and the insurrectos—everything. They made no rash promises, just admitted straight out that the enterprise might realize four hundred percent, or might conceivably make less. There was no hint of more.

So within a month, everybody in Mariposa knew that Jeff Thorpe was "in Cuban lands" and would probably clean up half a million by New Year's. You couldn't have failed to know it. All round the little shop there were pictures of banana groves and the harbor of Havana, and Cubans in white suits and scarlet sashes, smoking cigarettes in the sun and too ignorant to know that you can make four hundred percent by planting a banana tree.

I liked it about Jeff that he didn't stop shaving. He went on just the same. Even when Johnson, the livery stable man, came in with five hundred dollars and asked him to see if the Cuban Board of Directors would let him put it in, Jeff laid it in the drawer and then shaved him for five cents in the same old way. Of course, he must have felt proud when, a few days later, he got a letter from the Cuban people, from New York, accepting the money straight without a single question and without knowing anything more of Johnson except that he was a friend of Jeff's. They wrote most handsomely. Any friends of Jeff's were friends of Cuba. All money they might send would be treated just as Jeff's would be treated.

One reason, perhaps, why Jeff didn't give up shaving was because it allowed him to talk about Cuba. You see, everybody knew in Mariposa that Jeff Thorpe had sold out of Cobalts and had gone into Cuban Renovated Lands, and that spread round him a kind of halo of wealth and mystery and outlandishness—oh, something Spanish. Perhaps you've felt it about people you know. Anyhow, they asked him about the climate, and yellow fever, and what the Negroes were like, and all that sort of thing.

"This Cubey, it appears, is an island," Jeff would explain. Of course, everybody knows how easily islands lend themselves to making money—"and for fruit, they say it comes up so fast you can't stop it." And then he would pass into details about the Hash-enders and the resurrectos and technical things like that till it was thought a wonder how he could know it. Still, it was realized that a man with money has got to know these things. Look at Morgan and Rockefeller and all the men that make a pile. They know just as much as Jeff does about the countries where they make it. It stands to reason.

Did I say that Jeff shaved in the same old way? Not quite. There was something even dreamier about it now, and a sort of new element in the way Jeff fell out of his monotone into lapses of thought that perhaps getting so much money—well, you know the way it acts on people in the larger cities. It seemed to spoil one's idea of Jeff that copper and asbestos and banana lands should form the goal of his thought, when, if he knew it, the little shop and the sunlight of Mariposa was so much better.

In fact, I had perhaps borne him a grudge for what seemed to me his perpetual interest in the great capitalists. He always had some item out of the paper about them.

"I see where this here Carnegie has give fifty thousand dollars for one of them observatories," he would say.

And another day he would pause in the course of shaving, and almost whisper, "Did you ever see this Rockefeller?"

It was only by a sort of accident that I came to know that there was another side to Jefferson's speculation that no one in Mariposa ever knew, or will ever know now.

I knew it because I went in to see Jeff in his house one night. The house—I think I said it—stood out behind the barber shop. You went out of the back door of the shop and through a grass plot with petunias beside it, and the house stood at the end. You could see the light of the lamp behind the blind and through the screen door as you came along. And it was here that Jefferson used to sit in the evenings when the shop got empty.

There was a round table that The Woman used to lay for supper, and after supper there used to be a checkered cloth on it and a lamp with a shade. And beside it Jeff would sit, with his spectacles on and the paper spread out, reading about Carnegie and Rockefeller. Near him, but away from the table, was The Woman doing needlework; and Myra, when she wasn't working in the Telephone Exchange, was there, too, with her elbows on the table reading Marie Corelli—only now, of course, after the fortune, she was reading the prospectuses of dramatic schools.

So this night—I don't know just what it was in the paper that caused it—Jeff laid down what he was reading and started to talk about Carnegie.

"This Carnegie, I bet you, would be worth," said Jeff, closing up his eyes in calculation, "as much as perhaps two million dollars, if you was to sell him up. And this Rockefeller and this Morgan, either of them, to sell them up clean would be worth another couple of million—"

I may say in parentheses that it was a favorite method in Mariposa, if you wanted to get at the real worth of a man, to imagine him clean sold up, put up for auction, as it were. It was the only way to test him.

"And now look at 'em," Jeff went on. "They make their money and what do they do with it? They give it away. And who do they give it to? Why, to those as don't want it, every time. They give it to these professors and to this research and that, and do the poor get any of it? Not a cent and never will.

"I tell you, boys," continued Jeff—there were no boys present, but in Mariposa all really important speeches are addressed to an imaginary audience of boys—"I tell you, if I was to make a million out of this Cubey, I'd give it straight to the poor, yes, sir—divide it up into a hundred lots of a thousand dollars each and give it to the people that hadn't nothing."

So always after that I knew just what those bananas were being grown for.

Indeed, after that, though Jefferson never spoke of his intentions directly, he said a number of things that seemed to bear on them. He asked me one day, for instance, how many blind people it would take to fill one of these blind homes and how a feller could get a hold of them. And at another time he asked whether if a feller advertised for some of these incurables a feller could get enough of them to make a showing. I know for a fact that he got Nivens, the lawyer, to draw up a document that was to give an acre of banana land in Cuba to every idiot in Missinaba county.

But still, what's the use of talking of what Jeff meant to do? Nobody knows or cares about it now.

The end of it was bound to come. Even in Mariposa some of the people must have thought so. Else how was it that Henry Mullins made such a fuss about selling a draft for forty thousand on New York? And why was it that Mr. Smith wouldn't pay Billy, the desk clerk, his back wages when he wanted to put it into Cuba?

Oh, yes, some of them must have seen it. And yet when it came it seemed so quiet—ever so quiet—not a bit like the Northern Star mine and the oyster supper and the Mariposa band. It is strange how quiet these things look the other way round.

You remember the Cuban Land frauds in New York, and Porforio Gomez shooting the detective, and him and Maximo Morez getting clear away with two hundred thousand? No, of course you don't; why, even in the city papers it only filled an inch or two of type, and anyway the names were hard to remember. That was Jeff's money —part of it. Mullins got the telegram from a broker or someone, and he showed it to Jeff just as he was going up the street with an estate agent to look at a big empty lot on the hill behind the town—the very place for these incurables.

And Jeff went back to the shop so quiet—have you ever seen an animal that is stricken through, how quiet it seems to move?

Well, that's how he walked.

And since that, though it's quite a little while ago, the shop's open till eleven every night now, and Jeff is shaving away to pay back that five hundred that Johnson, the livery man, sent to the Cubans, and—

Pathetic? Tut, tut! You don't know Mariposa. Jeff has to work pretty late, but that's nothing—nothing at all if you've worked hard all your lifetime. And Myra is back at the Telephone Exchange—they were glad enough to get her—and she says now that if there's one thing she hates, it's the stage, and she can't see how the actresses put up with it.

Anyway, things are not so bad. You see it was just at this time that Mr. Smith's café opened, and Mr. Smith came to Jeff's Woman and said he wanted seven dozen eggs a day, and wanted them handy, and so the hens are back, and more of them, and they exult so every morning over the eggs they lay that if you wanted to talk of Rockefeller in the barber shop you couldn't hear his name for the cackling.

SNOW

Frederick Philip Grove

Toward morning the blizzard had died down, though it was still far from daylight. Stars without number blazed in the dark blue sky, which presented that brilliant and uncompromising appearance always characterizing, on the northern plains of America, those nights in the dead of winter when the thermometer dips to its lowest levels.

In the west Orion was sinking to the horizon. It was between five and six o'clock.

In the bush fringe of the Big Marsh, sheltered by thick but bare bluffs of aspens, stood a large house, built of logs, whitewashed, solid—such as a settler who is still single would put up only when he thinks of getting married. It, too, looked ice-cold, frozen in the night. Not a breath stirred where it stood; a thin thread of whitish smoke, reaching up to the level of the tree tops, seemed to be suspended into the chimney rather than to issue from it.

Through the deep snow of the yard, newly packed, a man was fighting his way to the door. Arrived there, he knocked and knocked, first tapping with his knuckles, then hammering with his fists.

Two, three minutes passed. Then a sound awoke in the house, as of somebody stirring, getting out of bed.

The figure on the door slab—a medium-sized, slim man in sheepskin and high rubber boots into which his trousers were tucked, with the ear flaps of his cap pulled down—stood and waited, bent over, hands thrust into the pockets of the short coat, as if he wished to shrink into the smallest possible space so as to offer the smallest possible surface to the attack of the cold. In order to get rid of the dry, powdery snow which filled every crease of his foot gear and trousers, he stamped his feet. His chin was drawn deep into the turned-up collar on whose points his breath had settled in the form of a thick layer of hoarfrost.

At last a bolt was withdrawn inside.

The face of a man peered out, just discernible in the starlight.

Then the door was opened; in ominous silence the figure from the outside entered, still stamping its feet.

Not a word was spoken till the door had been closed. Then a voice sounded through the cold and dreary darkness of the room.

"Redcliff hasn't come home. He went to town about noon and expected to get back by midnight. We're afraid he's lost."

The other man, quite invisible in the dark, had listened, his teeth chattering with the cold. "Are you sure he started out from town?"

"Well," the newcomer answered hesitatingly, "one of the horses came to the yard."

"One of his horses?"

"Yes. One of those he drove. The woman worked her way to my place to get help."

The owner of the house did not speak again. He went in the dark to the door in the rear and opened it. There, he groped about for matches, and finding them, lighted a lamp. In the room stood a big stove, a coal stove of the self-feeder type; but the fuel used was wood. He opened the drafts and shook the grate clear of ashes; there were two big blocks of spruce in the firebox, smoldering away for the night. In less than a minute they blazed up.

The newcomer entered, blinking in the light of the lamp, and looked on. Before many minutes the heat from the stove began to tell.

"I'll call Bill," the owner of the house said. He was himself of medium height or only slightly above it, but of enormous breadth of shoulder—a figure built for lifting loads. By his side the other man looked small, weakly, dwarfed.

He left the room, and returning through the cold, bare hall in front, went upstairs.

A few minutes later a tall, slender, well-built youth bolted into the room where the newcomer was waiting.

Bill, Carroll's hired man, was in his underwear and carried his clothes, thrown in a heap over his arm. Without loss of time, but jumping, stamping, swinging his arms, he began at once to dress.

He greeted the visitor. "Hello, Mike! What's that Abe tells me? Redcliff got lost?"

"Seems that way," said Mike listlessly.

"By gringo," Bill went on, "I shouldn't wonder. In that storm! I'd have waited in town! Wouldn't catch me going out in that kind of weather!"

"Didn't start till late in the afternoon," Mike Sobotski said in his shivering way.

"No. And didn't last long either," Bill agreed while he shouldered into his overalls. "But while she lasted—"

At this moment Abe Carroll, the owner of the farm, re-entered, with a sheepskin, fur cap, and long woollen scarf on his arm. His deeply lined, striking, square face bore a settled frown while he held the inside of his sheepskin to the stove to warm it up. Then, without saying a word, he got deliberately into it.

Mike Sobotski still stood bent over, shivering, though he had opened his coat and, on his side of the stove, was catching all the heat it afforded.

Abe, with the least motion needed to complete dressing, made for the door. In passing Bill, he flung out an elbow which touched the young man's arm. "Come on," he said; and to the other, pointing to the stove, "Close the drafts."

A few minutes later a noise as of rearing and snorting horses in front of the house. . . .

Mike, buttoning up his coat and pulling his mitts over his hands, went out.

They mounted three unsaddled horses. Abe leading, they dashed through the new drifts in the yard and out through the gate to the road. Here, where the shelter of the bluffs screening the house was no longer effective, a light but freshening breeze from the northwest made itself felt as if fine little knives were cutting into the flesh of their faces.

Abe dug his heels into the flank of his rearing mount. The horse was unwilling to obey his guidance, for Abe wanted to leave the road and to cut across wild land to the southwest.

The darkness was still inky black, though here and there, where the slope of the drifts slanted in the right direction, starlight was dimly reflected from the snow. The drifts were six, eight, in places ten feet high; and the snow was once more crawling up their flanks, it was so light and fine. It would fill the tracks in half an hour. As the horses plunged through, the crystals dusted up in clouds, flying aloft over horses and riders.

In less than half an hour they came to two little log buildings that seemed to squat on their haunches in the snow. Having entered the yard through a gate, they passed one of the buildings and made for the other, a little stable; their horses snorting, they stopped in its lee.

Mike dismounted, throwing the halter shank of his horse to Bill. He went to the house, which stood a hundred feet or so away. The shack was even smaller than the stable, twelve by fifteen feet perhaps. From its flue pipe a thick, white plume of smoke blew to the southeast.

Mike returned with a lantern; the other two sprang to the ground; and they opened the door to examine the horse which the woman had allowed to enter.

The horse was there, still excited, snorting at the leaping light and shadows from the lantern, its eyes wild, its nostrils dilated. It was covered with white frost and fully harnessed, though its traces were tied up to the back band.

"He let him go," said Mike, taking in these signs. "Must have stopped and unhitched him."

"Must have been stuck in a drift," Bill said, assenting.

"And tried to walk it," Abe added.

For a minute or so they stood silent, each following his own gloomy thoughts. Weird, luminous little clouds issued fitfully from the nostrils of the horse inside.

"I'll get the cutter," Abe said at last.

"I'll get it," Bill volunteered. "I'll take the drivers along. We'll leave the filly here in the stable."

"All right."

Bill remounted, leading Abe's horse. He disappeared into the night.

Abe and Mike, having tied the filly and the other horse in their stalls, went out, closed the door, and turned to the house.

There, by the light of a little coal-oil lamp, they saw the woman sitting at the stove, pale, shivering, her teeth achatter, trying to warm her hands, which were cold with fever, and looking with lackluster eyes at the men as they entered.

The children were sleeping; the oldest, a. girl, on the floor, wrapped in a blanket and curled up like a dog; four others in one narrow bed with hay for a mattress, two at the head, two at the foot; the baby on, rather than in, a sort of cradle made of a wide board slung by thin ropes to the pole roof of the shack.

The other bed was empty and unmade. The air was stifling from a night of exhalations.

"We're going to hunt for him," Mike said quietly. "We've sent for a cutter. He must have tried to walk."

The woman did not answer. She sat and shivered.

"We'll take some blankets," Mike went on. "And some whisky if you've got any in the house."

He and Abe were standing by the stove, opposite the woman, and warming their hands, their mitts held under their armpits.

The woman pointed with a look to a homemade little cupboard nailed to the wall and apathetically turned back to the stove. Mike went, opened the door of the cupboard, took a bottle from it, and slipped it into the pocket of his sheepskin. Then he raised the blankets from the empty bed, rolled them roughly into a bundle, dropped it, and returned to the stove where, with stiff fingers, he fell to rolling a cigarette.

Thus they stood for an hour or so.

Abe's eye was fastened on the woman. He would have liked to say a word of comfort, of hope. What was there to be said?

She was the daughter of a German settler in the bush, some six or seven miles northeast of Abe's place. Her father, an oldish, unctuous, bearded man had, some ten years ago, got tired of the hard life in the bush where work meant clearing, picking stones, and digging stumps. He had sold his homestead and bought a prairie farm, half a section, on crop payments, giving notes for the equipment which he needed to handle the place. He had not been able to make it a "go." His bush farm had fallen back on his hands; he had lost his all and returned to the place. He had been counting on the help of his two boys— big, strapping young fellows—who were to clear much land and to raise crops which would lift the debt. But the boys had refused to go back to the bush; they could get easy work in town. Ready money would help. But the ready money had melted away in their hands. Redcliff, the old people's son-in-law, had been their last hope. They were on the point of losing even their bush farm. Here they might perhaps still have found a refuge for their old age—though Redcliff's homestead lay on the sandflats bordering on the marsh where the soil was thin, dreadfully thin; it drifted when the scrub brush was cleared off. Still, with Redcliff living, this place had been a hope. What were they to do if he was gone? And this woman, hardly more than a girl in spite of her six children!

The two tiny, square windows of the shack began to turn gray.

At last Abe, thinking he heard a sound, went to the door and stepped out. Bill was there; the horses were shaking the snow out of their pelts; one of them was pawing the ground.

Once more Abe opened the door and gave Mike a look for a signal. Mike gathered the bundle of blankets into his arms, pulled on his mitts, and came out.

Abe reached for the lines, but Bill objected.

"No. Let me drive. I found something."

And as the two older men had climbed in, squeezing into the scant space on the seat, he clicked his tongue.

"Get up there!" he shouted, hitting the horses' backs with his lines. And with a leap they darted away.

Bill turned, heading back to the Carroll farm. The horses plunged, reared, snorted, and then, throwing their heads, shot along in a gallop, scattering snow slabs right and left and throwing wingwaves of the fresh, powdery snow, especially on the lee side. Repeatedly they tried to turn into the wind, which they were cutting at right angles. But Bill plied the whip and guided them expertly.

Nothing was visible anywhere; nothing but the snow in the first gray of dawn. Then, like enormous ghosts, or like evanescent apparitions, the trees of the bluff were adumbrated behind the lingering veils of the night.

Bill turned to the south, along the straight trail which bordered Abe Carroll's farm. He kept looking out sharply to right and left. But after a while he drew his galloping horses in.

"Whoa!" he shouted, tearing at the lines in seesaw fashion. And when the rearing horses came to a stop, excited and breathless, he added, "I've missed it." He turned.

"What is it?" Abe asked.

"The other horse," Bill answered. "It must have had the scent of our yard. It's dead . . . frozen stiff."

A few minutes later he pointed to a huge white mound on top of a drift to the left. "That's it," he said, turned the horses into the wind, and stopped.

To the right, the bluffs of the farm slowly outlined themselves in the morning grayness.

The two older men alighted, and with their hands, shoveled the snow away. There lay the horse, stiff and cold, frozen into a rocklike mass.

"Must have been here a long while," Abe said.

Mike nodded. "Five, six hours." Then he added, "Couldn't have had the smell of the yard. Unless the wind has turned."

"It has," Abe answered, and pointed to a fold in the flank of the snowdrift which indicated that the present drift had been superimposed on a lower one whose longitudinal axis ran to the northeast.

For a moment longer they stood and pondered.

Then Abe went back to the cutter and reached for the lines. "I'll drive," he said.

Mike climbed in.

Abe took his bearings, looking for landmarks. They were only two or three hundred feet from his fence. That enabled him to estimate the exact direction of the breeze. He clicked his tongue. "Get up!"

And the horses, catching the infection of a dull excitement, shot away. They went straight into the desert of drifts to the west, plunging ahead without any trail, without any landmark in front to guide them.

They went for half an hour, an hour, and longer.

None of the three said a word. Abe knew the sandflats better than any other; Abe reasoned better than they. If anyone could find the missing man, it was Abe.

Abe's thought ran thus: The horse had gone against the wind. It would never have done so without good reason; that reason could have been no other than a scent to follow. If that was so, however, it would have gone in as straight a line as it could. The sandflats stretched away to the southwest for sixteen miles with not a settlement, not a farm but Redcliff's. If Abe managed to strike that line of scent, it must take him to the point whence the horses had started.

Clear and glaring, with an almost indifferent air, the sun rose to their left.

And suddenly they saw the wagon box of the sleigh sticking out of the snow ahead of them.

Abe stopped, handed Bill the lines, and got out. Mike followed. Nobody said a word.

The two men dug the tongue of the vehicle out of the snow and tried it. This was part of the old, burned-over bushland south of the sandflats. The sleigh was tightly wedged in between several charred stumps which stuck up through the snow. That was the reason why the man had unhitched the horses and turned them loose. What else, indeed, could he have done?

The box was filled with a drift which, toward the tail-gate, was piled high, for there three bags of flour were standing on end and leaning against a barrel half filled with small parcels, the interstices between which were packed with mealy snow.

Abe waded all around the sleigh, reconnoitering; and as he did so, wading at the height of the upper edge of the wagon box, the snow suddenly gave way beneath him; he broke in; the drift was hollow.

A suspicion took hold of him; with a few quick reaches of his arm he demolished the roof of the drift all about.

And there, in the hollow, lay the man's body as if he were sleeping, a quiet expression, as of painless rest, on his face. His eyes were closed; a couple of bags were wrapped about his shoulders. Apparently he had not even tried to walk! Already chilled to the bone, he had given in to that desire for rest, for shelter at any price, which overcomes him who is doomed to freeze.

Without a word the two men carried him to the cutter and laid him down on the snow.

Bill, meanwhile, had unhitched the horses and was hooking them to the tongue of the sleigh. The two others looked on in silence. Four times the horses sprang, excited because Bill tried to make them pull with a sudden twist. The sleigh did not stir.

"Need an axe," Mike said at last, "to cut the stumps. We'll get the sleigh later."

Mike hitched up again and turned the cutter. The broken snowdrifts through which they had come gave the direction.

Then they laid the stiff, dead body across the floor of their vehicle, leaving the side doors open, for it protruded both ways. They themselves climbed up on the seat and crouched down, so as not to put their feet on the corpse.

Thus they returned to Abe Carroll's farm, where, still in silence, they deposited the body in the granary.

That done, they stood for a moment as if in doubt. Then Bill unhitched the horses and took them to the stable to feed.

"I'll tell the woman," said Mike. "Will you go tell her father?"

Abe nodded. "Wait for breakfast," he added.

It was ten o'clock; and none of them had eaten since the previous night.

On the way to Altmann's place in the bush, drifts were no obstacles to driving. Drifts lay on the marsh, on the open sandflats.

Every minute of the time Abe, as he drove along, thought of that woman in the shack; the woman, alone, with six children, and with the knowledge that her man was dead.

Altmann's place in the bush looked the picture of peace and comfort; a large log house of two rooms. Window frames and doors were painted green. A place to stay with, not to leave. . . .

When Abe knocked, the woman, whom he had seen but once in his life, at the sale where they had lost their possessions, opened the door—an enormously fat woman, overflowing her clothes. The man, tall, broad, with a long, rolling beard, now gray, stood behind her, peering over her shoulder. A visit is an event in the bush!

"Come in," he said cheerfully when he saw Abe. "What a storm that was!"

Abe entered the kitchen, which was also the dining and living room. He sat down on the chair which was pushed forward for him and looked at the two old people, who remained standing.

Suddenly, from the expression of his face, they anticipated something of his message. No use dissembling.

"Redcliff is dead," he said. "He was frozen to death last night on his way home from town."

The two old people also sat down; it looked as if their knees had given way beneath them. They stared at him, dumbly, a sudden expression of panic fright in their eyes.

"I thought you might want to go to your daughter," Abe added sympathetically.

The man's big frame seemed to shrink as he sat there. All the unctuousness and the conceit of the handsome man dwindled out of his bearing. The woman's eyes had already filled with tears.

Thus they remained for two, three minutes.

Then the woman folded her fat, pudgy hands; her head sank low on her breast; and she sobbed, "God's will be done!"

MRS. GOLIGHTLY AND THE FIRST CONVENTION

Ethel Wilson

Mrs. Golightly was a shy woman. She lived in Vancouver. Her husband, Tommy Golightly, was not shy. He was personable and easy to like. He was a consulting engineer who was consulted a great deal by engineering firms, construction firms, logging firms in particular, any firm that seemed to have problems connected with traction. When he was not being consulted he played golf, tennis, or bridge according to whether the season was spring, summer, autumn, or winter. Any time that was left over he spent with his wife and three small children, of whom he was very fond. When he was with them, it seemed that that was what he liked best. He was a very extroverted sort of man, easy and likable, and his little wife was so shy that it just was not fair. But what can you do?

At the period of which I write, Conventions had not begun to take their now-accepted place in life on the North American continent. I am speaking of Conventions with a capital C. Conventions with a small c have, of course, always been with us, but not as conspicuously now as formerly. In those days, when a man said rather importantly I am going to a Convention, someone was quite liable to ask, What is a Convention? Everyone seemed to think that they must be quite a good thing, which of course they are. We now take them for granted.

Now Mr. Golightly was admirably adapted to going to Conventions. His memory for names and faces was good; he liked people, both in crowds and separately; he collected acquaintances who rapidly became friends. Everyone liked him.

One day he came home and said to his wife, How would you like a trip to California?

Mrs. Golightly gave a little gasp. Her face lighted up and she said, Oh Tom! . . .

There's a Western and Middle-Western Convention meeting at Del Monte the first week of March, and you and I are going down, said Mr. Golightly.

Mrs. Golightly's face clouded and she said in quite a different tone and with great alarm, Oh Tom! . . .

Well what? said her husband.

Mrs. Golightly began the sort of hesitation that so easily overcame her. Well, Tom, she said, I'd have to get a hat, and I suppose a suit and a dinner dress, and Emmeline isn't very good to leave with the children and you know I'm no good with crowds and people, I never know what to say and—

Well, get a new hat, said her husband, get one of those hats I see women wearing with long quills on. And get a new dress. Get twenty new dresses. And Emmeline's fine with the children and what you need's a change and I'm the only one in my profession invited from British Columbia. You get a hat with the longest feather in town and a nice dinner dress! Mr. Golightly looked fondly at his wife and saw with new eyes that she appeared anxious and not quite as pretty as she sometimes was. He kissed her and she promised that she would get the new hat, but he did not know how terrified she was of the Convention and all the crowds of people, and that she suffered at the very thought of going. She could get along all right at home, but small talk with strangers—oh poor Mrs. Golightly! These things certainly are not fair. However, she got the dress, and a new hat with the longest quill in town. She spent a long time at the hairdresser's; and how pretty she looked and how disturbed she felt; I'll break the quill every time I get into the car, Tom, she said.

Non*sense,* said her husband, and they set off in the car for California.

Mrs. Golightly traveled in an old knitted suit and a felt hat well pulled down on her head in observance of a theory which she had inherited from her mother that you must never wear good clothes when traveling. The night before arriving at Del Monte a car passing them at high speed sideswiped them ever so little, but the small damage and fuss that resulted from that delayed them a good deal. The result was that they got late to bed that night, slept little, rose early, and had to do three hundred miles before lunch. Mrs. Golightly began to feel very tired in spite of some mounting excitement, but this did not make her forget to ask her husband to stop at the outskirts of Del Monte so that she could take her new hat out of the bag and put it on. Mr. Golightly was delighted with the way his wife was joining in the spirit of the thing. Good girl, he said, which pleased her, and neither of them noticed that nothing looked right about Mrs. Golightly except her hat, and even smart hats, worn under those circumstances, look wrong.

How impressive it was to Mrs. Golightly, supported by her hat, to approach the portals of the fashionable Del Monte Hotel. Large cars reclined in rows, some sparkling, some dimmed by a film of dust, all of them costly. Radiant men and women, expensively dressed (the inheritors of the earth evidently) strolled about without a care in the world, or basked on the patio, scrutinizing new arrivals with experienced eyes. Mrs. Golightly had already felt something formidably buoyant in the air of California, accustomed as she was to the mild, soft, and (to tell the truth) sometimes deliciously drowsy air of the British Columbia coast. The air she breathed in California somehow alarmed her. Creatures customarily breathing this air must, she thought, by nature be buoyant, self-confident—all the things that Mrs. Golightly was not. Flowers bloomed, trees threw their shade, birds cleft the air, blue shone the sky, and Mrs. Golightly, dazzled, knocked her hat crooked as she got out of the car, and she caught the long quill on the door. She felt it snick. Oh, she thought, my darling quill.

No sooner had they alighted from their car, which was seized on all sides by hotel minions of great competence, than her husband was surrounded by prosperous men who said, Well Tom! And how's the boy! Say Tom this is great! And Tom turned from side to side, greeting, expansive, the most popular man in view. Mrs. Golightly had no idea that Tom had so many business friends that loved him dearly. And then with one accord these prosperous men turned their kindly attention to Mrs. Golightly. It overwhelmed her, but it really warmed her heart to feel that they were all so pleased that she had come, and that she had come so far; and although she felt shy, travel-worn, and tired, she tried to do her best and her face shone sweetly with a desire to please.

Now, said the biggest of the men, the boys are waiting for you Tom. Up in one three three. Yes in one three three. And Mrs. Golightly I want you to meet Mrs. Allyman of the Ladies' Committee. Mrs. Allyman meet Mrs. Tom Golightly from British Columbia. Will you just register her please, we've planned a good time for the ladies, Tom . . . we'll take good care of Tom, Mrs. Golightly. And Mr. Golightly said, But my wife . . . and then a lot of people streamed in, and Tom and the other men said, Well, well, well, so here's Ed! Say Ed . . . the words streamed past Mrs. Golightly and Tom was lost to her view.

A lump that felt large came in her throat because she was so shy and Tom was not to be seen, but Mrs. Allyman was very kind and propelled her over to a group of ladies and said, Oh this is the lady from British Columbia, the name is Golightly isn't it? Mrs. Golightly I want you to meet Mrs. Finkel and Mrs. Connelly and Mrs. Magnus and pardon me I didn't catch the name Mrs. Sloper from Colorado. Oh there's the President's wife Mrs. Bagg. Well Mrs. Bagg did you locate Mr. Bagg after all, no doubt, he's in one three three. Mrs. Golightly I'd like to have you meet Mrs. Bagg and Mrs. Simmons, Mrs. Bagg, Mrs. Finkel, Mrs. Bagg, and Mrs. Sloper, Mrs. Bagg. Mrs. Golightly is all the way from British Columbia, I think that's where you come from Mrs. Golightly? Mrs. Allyman, speaking continually, seemed to say all this in one breath. By the time that Mrs. Golightly's vision had cleared (although she felt rather dizzy) she saw that all these ladies were chic, and that they wore hats with very long quills, longer even than hers, which made her feel much more secure. However, her exhilaration was passing, she realized that she was quite tired, and she said smiling sweetly, I *think* I'd better find my room. The hubbub in the hotel rotunda increased and increased.

When she reached her room she found that Tom had sent the bags up, and she thought she would unpack, and lie down for a bit to get rested, and then go down and have a quiet lunch. Perhaps she would see Tom somewhere. But first she went over to the window and looked out upon the incredible radiance of blue and green and gold, and the shine of the ethereal air. She looked at the great oak trees and the graceful mimosa trees and she thought, After I've tidied up and had some lunch I'll just go and sit under one of those beautiful mimosa trees and drink in this . . . this largesse of air and scent and beauty. Mrs. Golightly had never seen anything like it. The bright air dazzled her, and made her sad and gay. Just then the telephone rang. A man's strong and purposeful voice said, Pardon me, but may I speak to Tom?

Oh I'm sorry, said Mrs. Golightly, Tom's not here.

Can you tell me where I can get him? asked the voice very urgently.

I'm so sorry . . . faltered Mrs. Golightly.

Sorry to troub— said the voice and the telephone clicked off.

There. The Convention had invaded the bedroom, the azure sky, and the drifting grace of the mimosa tree outside the bedroom window.

I think, said Mrs. Golightly to herself, if I had a bath it would freshen me, I'm beginning to have a headache. She went into the bathroom and gazed with pleasure on its paleness and coolness and shiningness, on the lavish array of towels, and an uneven picture entered and left her mind of the bathroom at home, full, it seemed to her, of the essentials for cleaning and dosing a father and mother and three small children, nonstop. The peace! The peace of it! She lay in the hot water regarding idly and alternately the soap which floated agreeably upon the water, and the window through which she saw blue sky of an astonishing azure.

The telephone rang.

Is that Mrs. Goodman? purred a voice.

No, no, not Mrs. Goodman, said Mrs. Golightly, wrapped in a towel.

I'm so sorry, purred the voice.

Mrs. Golightly got thankfully into the bath and turned on some more hot water.

The telephone rang.

She scrambled out, Hello, hello?

There's a wire at the desk for Mr. Golightly, said a voice, shall we send it up?

Oh dear, oh dear, said Mrs. Golightly wrapped in a towel, well . . . not yet . . . not for half an hour.

Okay, said the voice.

She got back into the bath. She closed her eyes in disturbed and recovered bliss.

The telephone rang.

Hello, hello, said Mrs. Golightly plaintively, wrapped in a very damp towel.

Is that Mrs. Golightly? asked a kind voice.

Yes, oh yes, agreed Mrs. Golightly.

Well, this is Mrs. Porter speaking and we'd be pleased if you'd join Mrs. Bagg and Mrs. Wilkins and me in the Tap Room and meet some of the ladies and have a little drink before lunch.

Oh thank you, thank you, that will just be lovely, I'd love to, said Mrs. Golightly. Away went the sky, away went the birds, away went the bath, and away went the mimosa tree.

Well, that will be lovely, said Mrs. Porter, in about half an hour?

Oh thank you, thank you, that will be lovely! . . . said Mrs. Golightly, repeating herself considerably.

She put on her new gray flannel suit, which was only slightly rumpled, and straightened the tip of her quill as best she could. She patted her rather aching forehead with cold water and felt somewhat refreshed. She paid particular and delicate attention to her face, and left her room looking and feeling quite pretty but agitated.

When she got down to the Tap Room everyone was having Old-Fashioneds and a little woman in gray came up and said, Pardon me but are you Mrs. Golightly from British Columbia? Mrs. Golightly, I'd like to have you meet Mrs. Bagg (our President's wife) and Mrs. Gillingham from Saint Louis, Mrs. Wilkins from Pasadena, Mrs. Golightly, Mrs. Finkel and—pardon me?—Mrs. Connelly and Mrs. Allyman of Los Angeles.

Mrs. Golightly felt confused, but she smiled at each lady in turn, saying How do you do, but neglected to remember or repeat their names because she was so inexperienced. She slipped into a chair and a waiter brought her an Old-Fashioned. She then looked round and tried hard to memorize the ladies, nearly all of whom had stylish hats with tall quills on. Mrs. Bagg very smart. Mrs. Wilkins with pince-nez. Little Mrs. Porter in gray. Mrs. Simmons, Mrs. Connelly, and Mrs. Finkel in short fur capes. Mrs.

Finkel was lovely, of a gorgeous pale beauty. Mrs. Golightly sipped her Old-Fashioned and tried to feel very gay indeed. She and Mrs. Connelly who came from Chicago found that each had three small children, and before they had finished talking, a waiter brought another Old-Fashioned. Then Mrs. Connelly had to speak to a lady on her other side, and Mrs. Golightly turned to the lady on her left. This lady was not talking to anyone but was quietly sipping her Old-Fashioned. By this time Mrs. Golightly was feeling unusually bold and responsible, and quite like a woman of the world. She thought to herself, Come now, everyone is being so lovely and trying to make everyone feel at home, and I must try too.

So she said to the strange lady, I don't think we met, did we? My name is Mrs. Golightly and I come from British Columbia. And the lady said, I'm pleased to meet you. I'm Mrs. Gampish and I come from Toledo, Ohio. And Mrs. Golightly said, Oh isn't this a beautiful hotel and wouldn't you like to see the gardens, and then somehow everyone was moving.

When Mrs. Golightly got up she felt as free as air, but as if she was stepping a little high. When they reached the luncheon table there must have been about a hundred ladies and of course everyone was talking. Mrs. Golightly was seated between two perfectly charming people, Mrs. Carillo from Little Rock, Arkansas, and Mrs. Clark from Phoenix, Arizona. They both said what a cute English accent she had and she had to tell them because she was so truthful that she had never been to England. It was a little hard to talk as there was an orchestra and Mrs. Golightly and Mrs. Carillo and Mrs. Clark were seated just below the saxophones. Mrs. Golightly couldn't quite make out whether she had no headache at all, or the worst headache of her life. This is lovely, she thought as she smiled back at her shouting companions, but how nice it will be to go upstairs and lie down. Just for half an hour after lunch, before I go and sit under the mimosa tree.

But when the luncheon was over, Mrs. Wilkins clapped her hands and said, Now Ladies, cars are waiting at the door and we'll assemble in the lobby for the drive. And Mrs. Golightly said, Oh hadn't I better run upstairs and see whether my husband— But Mrs. Wilkins said, Now

Ladies! So they all gathered in the lobby, and for one moment, one moment, Mrs. Golightly was still.

Oh, she thought, I feel awful, and I am so sleepy, and I feel a little queer. But she soon started smiling again, and they all got into motorcars.

She got into a nice car with some other ladies whom she did not know. They all had tall quills on their hats, which made it awkward. Mrs. Golightly was the smallest and sat in the middle. She turned from side to side with great politeness. Flick, flick went the quills, smiting against each other. Well, we'd better introduce ourselves, she thought. But the lady on her right had already explained that she was Mrs. Johnson from Seattle, so she turned to her left and said to the other stranger, Do tell me your name? I'm Mrs. Golightly and I come from British Columbia.

The other lady said a little stiffly, Well, I'm Mrs. Gampish and I come from Toledo, Ohio, and Mrs. Golightly felt awful and said, Oh Mrs. Gampish, how stupid of me, we met in the Tap Room, of course! So many people! Oh, it's quite all right, said Mrs. Gampish rather coldly. But she and Mrs. Johnson soon found that their husbands both had gastric ulcers and so they had a very very interesting conversation. Mrs. Golightly did not join in because she had nothing to offer in the way of an ulcer, as she and Tom and the children never seemed to be ill and the ladies did not appear to need sympathy. She dodged this way and that behind Mrs. Gampish and Mrs. Johnson, interfering with their quills, and peering at gleaming Spanish villas enfolded in green, blazing masses of flowers, a crash and white spume of breakers, a twisted Monterey pine—they all rushed dazzling past the car windows—villas, pines, ocean, and all. If I were courageous or even tactful, thought Mrs. Golightly, I could ask to sit beside the window where I want to be, and these ladies could talk in comfort (the talk had moved from ulcers to their sons' fraternities), which is what they wish, but she knew that she was not skillful in such matters, and it would not do. Oh, she yearned, if I could ever be a woman of the world and achieve these simple matters!

Then all the cars stopped at a place called Point Lobos, and everybody got out.

Mrs. Golightly sped swiftly alone toward the cliffs. She

stood on a high rock overlooking the vast ocean, and the wind roared and whistled about her. She took off her hat as the whistling, beating broken quill seemed to impede her. She looked down and could hardly believe the beauty that lay below her. Green ocean crashed and broke in towering spray on splintered rocky islets, on the cliffs where she stood, and into swirling, sucking, rock-bound bays and caves. In the translucent green waves played joyous bands of seals, so joyous that they filled her with rapture. Bellowing seals clambered upon the rocks, but the din of wind and ocean drowned their bellowing. The entrancement of sea and sky and wind and the strong playing bodies of the seals so transported Mrs. Golightly that she forgot to think, Oh I must tell the children, and how Tom would love this! She was one with the rapture of that beautiful unexpected moment. She felt someone beside her and turned. There was Mrs. Carillo with a shining face. They shouted at each other, laughing with joy, but could not hear each other, and stood arm in arm braced against the wind, looking down at the playing bands of seals.

As the party assembled again, Mrs. Golightly stepped aside and waited for Mrs. Gampish and Mrs. Johnson to get in first. Then she got in, and sat down beside the window. Conversation about Point Lobos and the seals became general, and Mrs. Johnson, who was in the middle, found herself turning from side to side, bending and catching her quill. They then became quiet, and the drive home was peaceful. I shall never forget, thought Mrs. Golightly, as the landscape and seascape flashed past her rather tired eyes, the glory of Point Lobos, and the strong bodies of the seals playing in the translucent water. Whatever happens to me on earth, I shall never never forget it.

When she arrived at the hotel she discovered that she was nearly dead with excitement and noise and fatigue and when Tom came in she said, because she was so simple and ignorant, Oh darling, can we have dinner somewhere quietly tonight, I must tell you about all those seals. And Tom looked quite shocked, and he said, Seals? But darling, aren't you having a good time? I was just talking to Mr. Bagg and he tells me that you made a great hit with his wife. This is a Convention you know, he said reprovingly, and you can't do that kind of thing! Seals indeed! Where's your program? Yes, Ladies' Dinner in the Jacobean Room,

and I'll be at the Men's. And Mrs. Golightly said, Oh
Tom . . . yes, of course, I know, how stupid of me . . . I'm
having the loveliest time, Tom, and we had the loveliest
drive, and now I'm really going to have a proper bath
and a rest before I dress. And Tom said, Fine! But can
I have the bathroom first because— And then the telephone
rang and Tom said, Yes? Yes, Al, what's that? In the Tap
Room? In fifteen minutes? Make it twenty Al, I want to
bathe and change. Okay Al. . . . That was Al, dear. I'll
have to hurry but you have a good rest. And then the
telephone rang and it was Mrs. Wilkins and she said, Oh
Mrs. Golightly will you join Mrs. Porter and me and some
of the ladies in my room one seven five for cocktails at
six o'clock. I do hope it won't rush you. One seven five.
Oh that will be lovely. Oh, yes, that will be lovely, said
Mrs. Golightly. She put her hands to her face and then
she took out her blue dinner dress and began pressing it,
and away went the bath and away went the rest and away
went the mimosa tree. And Tom came out of the bathroom and said, Why ever aren't you lying down? That's
the trouble with you, you never will rest! Well so long
darling, have a good time. And he went, and she finished
pressing her dress and put it on.

The next time Mrs. Golightly saw Tom was downstairs
in the hotel lobby as she waited with some of the other
ladies to go into the ladies' dinner. Tom was in the middle
of a group of men who walked down the center of the
lobby. They walked almost rolling with grandeur or something down the lobby, owning it, sufficient unto themselves,
laughing together at their own private jokes and unaware
of anyone else. But Mr. Golightly's eyes fell on his wife.
He saw how pretty she looked and was delighted with
her. He checked the flow of men down the lobby and
stepped forward and said, Terry I want you to meet Mr.
Flanagan, Bill this is my wife. And a lively and powerful
small man seized Mrs. Golightly's hand and held it and
looked admiringly at her and said, Well, Mrs. Golightly,
I certainly am pleased to meet you. I've just got Tom here
to promise that you and he will come and stay with Mrs.
Flanagan and me this fall when the shooting's good up
at our little place in Oregon—now, no argument, it's all
settled, you're coming! What a genial host! It would be a
pleasure to stay with Mr. Flanagan.

Tom beamed in a pleased way, and Mrs. Golightly's face sparkled with pleasure. Oh, Mr. Flanagan, she said, how kind! Tom and I will just love to come. (Never a word or thought about What shall we do with the children—just We'd love to come.) So that's settled, said Mr. Flanagan breezily and the flow of men down the hotel lobby was resumed.

At dinner Mrs. Golightly sat beside a nice woman from San Francisco called Mrs. de Kay who had once lived in Toronto, so of course they had a lot in common. Before dinner everyone had had one or two Old-Fashioneds, and as the mists cleared a bit, Mrs. Golightly had recognized Mrs. Bagg, Mrs. Connelly, dear Mrs. Carillo, and beautiful Mrs. Finkel. How lovely was Mrs. Finkel sitting in blond serenity amidst the hubbub, in silence, looking around her with a happy gentle gaze. You could never forget Mrs. Finkel. Her face, her person, her repose, her shadowed eyes invited scrutiny. You gazed with admiration and sweetly she accepted your admiration. While all around her were vivacious, Mrs. Finkel sat still. But now Mrs. Finkel and Mrs. Carillo were far down the table and Mrs. Golightly conversed with Mrs. de Kay as one woman of the world to another. How well I'm coming along! she thought, and felt puffed up.

During the sweet course she became hot with shame! She had not spoken a word to the lady on her left who wore a red velvet dress. She turned in a gushing way and said to the lady in the red dress who, she realized, was not speaking to anyone at the moment, Isn't this a delightful dinner! We haven't had a chance of a word with each other, have we, and I don't believe we've met, but I'm Mrs. Golightly from British Columbia.

The lady in the red cut-velvet dress turned toward Mrs. Golightly and said clearly, I am Mrs. Gampish, and I come from Toledo, Ohio. Their eyes met.

Mrs. Golightly remained silent. Blushes flamed over her. She thought, this is, no doubt, some dreadful dream from which I shall soon awake. And still the chatter and clatter and music went on. Mrs. Golightly could not think of anything to say. Mrs. Gampish continued to eat her dessert. Mrs. Golightly attempted to smile in a society way, but it was no good, and she couldn't say a thing.

After dinner there was bridge and what do you suppose?

Mrs. Golightly was set to play with Mrs. Magnus and Mrs. Finkel and Mrs. Gampish. Trembling a little, she stood up.

I think I will go to bed, she said. She could not bear to think of Mrs. Gampish being compelled to play bridge with her.

No, I shall go to bed, said Mrs. Gampish.

No, do let me go to bed, cried Mrs. Golightly, I simply insist on going to bed.

And I insist on going to bed too, said Mrs. Gampish firmly, in any case I have a headache. Mrs. Magnus and Mrs. Finkel looked on in amazement.

No, no, I shall go to bed, said Mrs. Golightly in distress.

No, I shall go to bed, said Mrs. Gampish. It was very absurd.

Mrs. Bagg hurried up. Everything all set here? she said in a hostess voice.

Mrs. Gampish and Mrs. Golightly said, speaking together, I am going to bed.

Oh, don't both go to bed, pleaded Mrs. Bagg, unaware of any special feeling. If one of you must go to bed, do please one of you stay, and I will make the fourth.

Mrs. Golightly considered and acted quickly. If Mrs. Gampish really wants to go to bed, she said, timidly but with effect, I will stay . . . a slight headache . . . she said bravely fluttering her fingers and batting her eyelashes which were rather long.

Mrs. Gampish did not argue any more. She said good night to the ladies and left.

Oh do excuse me a minute, said Mrs. Golightly, flickering her eyelashes, and she caught Mrs. Gampish at the elevator. Mrs. Gampish looked at her with distaste.

I want to tell you, Mrs. Gampish, said Mrs. Golightly with true humility, and speaking very low, that I have never been to a Convention before, and I want to confess to you my stupidity. I am not really rude, only stupid and so shy although I have three children that I am truly in a whirl. Will you be able ever to forgive me? . . . It would be very kind of you if you feel that you could. Oh, please do try.

There was a silence between them as the elevators came and went. Then Mrs. Gampish gave a wan smile.

You are too earnest, my child, she said. (Oh how

good you are! breathed Mrs. Golightly.) I wouldn't myself know one person in this whole Convention—except Mrs. Finkel and no one could forget her—continued Mrs. Gampish, and I never knew you each time you told me who you were until you told me, so you needn't have worried. If you want to know why I'm going to bed, it's because I don't like bridge and anyway, I do have a headache.

Oh I'm so glad you really have a headache, no I mean I'm so sorry, and I think you're perfectly sweet, Mrs. Gampish, and if ever you come to Canada . . . and she saw the faintly amused smile of Mrs. Gampish going up in the elevator. Well I never, she said, but she felt happier.

She turned and there was Tom hurrying past. Oh Tom, she called. He stopped.

Having a good time darling? he said in a hurry. D'you want to come to the meeting at Salt Lake City next year? and he smiled at her encouragingly. Oh Tom, she said, I'd adore it! (What a changed life. Del Monte, Mr. Flanagan's shooting lodge, Salt Lake City, all in a minute, you might say.)

Well, well! said Tom in surprise and vanished.

On the way to her bedroom that night Mrs. Golightly met Mr. Flanagan walking very slowly down the hall.

How do you do Mr. Flanagan! said Mrs. Golightly gaily. She felt that he was already her host at his shooting lodge.

Mr. Flanagan stopped and looked at her seriously as from a great distance. It was obvious that he did not know her. How do you do, he said very carefully and with a glazed expression. Did we meet or did we meet. In any case, how do you do. And he continued walking with the utmost care down the corridor.

Oh . . . said Mrs. Golightly, her eyes wide open . . . oh. . . . It was probable that Mr. Flanagan invited everyone to the shooting lodge. The shooting lodge began to vanish like smoke.

When she entered the bedroom she saw that in her hurry before dinner she had not put her hat away. The quill was twice bent, and it dangled. She took scissors and cut it short. There, she thought, caressing and smoothing the feather, it looks all right, doesn't it? She had felt for a moment very low, disintegrated, but now as she sat on the bed in her blue dinner dress she thought, Mr. Flanagan isn't a bit afraid to be him and Mrs. Gampish isn't a bit afraid to be her and now I'm not a bit afraid to be me . . . at least, not much. As she looked down, smoothing her little short feather, a dreamy smile came on her face. Seals swam through the green waters of her mind. Mrs. Finkel passed and repassed in careless loveliness. Mrs. Gampish said austerely, Too earnest, my child, too earnest. The ghost of the mimosa tree drifted, drifted. Salt Lake City, she thought fondly . . . and then . . . where? . . . anticipation . . . a delicious fear . . . an unfamiliar pleasure.

Mrs. Golightly was moving out of the class for beginners. She is much more skillful now (How agile and confiding are her eyelashes!) and when her husband says, There's going to be a Convention in Mexico City (or Chilliwack or Trois Rivières), she says with delight, Oh Tom! . . .

ONE SPRING NIGHT

Morley Callaghan

They had been to an eleven-o'clock movie. Afterward, as they sat very late in the restaurant, Sheila was listening to Bob Davis, liking all the words he used and showing by the quiet gladness that kept coming into her face the deep enjoyment she felt in being with him. She was the young sister of his friend, Jack Staples. Every time Bob had been at their apartment, she had come into the room, they had laughed and joked with her, they had teased her about the new way she wore her clothes, watching her growing, and she had always smiled and answered them in a slow, measured way.

Bob had taken her out a few times when he had felt like having some girl to talk to who knew him and liked him. And tonight he was leaning back good-humoredly, telling her one thing and then another with the wise self-assurance he usually had when with her; but gradually, as he watched her, he found himself talking more slowly, his voice grew serious and much softer, and then finally he leaned across the table toward her as though he had just discovered that her neck was full and soft with her spring coat thrown open, and that her face under her little black straw hat tilted back on her head had a new, eager beauty. Her warm, smiling softness was so close to him that he smiled a bit shyly.

"What are you looking at, Bob?" she said.

"What is there about you that seems different tonight?" he said, and they both began to laugh lightly, as if sharing the same secret.

When they were outside, walking along arm in arm and liking the new night air, Sheila said quickly, "It's awfully nice out tonight. Let's keep walking awhile, Bob," and she held his arm as though very sure of him.

"All right," he said. "We'll walk till we get so tired we'll have to sit on the curb. It's nearly two o'clock, but it doesn't seem to matter much, does it?"

Every step he took with Sheila leaning on his arm in this new way, and with him feeling now that she was a woman he hardly knew, made the excitement grow in him, and yet he was uneasy. He was much taller than Sheila and he kept looking down at her, and she always smiled back with frank gladness. Then he couldn't help squeezing her arm tight, and he started to talk recklessly about anything that came into his head, swinging his free arm and putting passionate eloquence into the simplest words. She was listening as she used to listen when he talked with her brother and father in the evenings, only now she wanted him to see how much she liked having it tonight all for herself. Almost pleading, she said, "Are you having a good time, Bob? Don't you like the streets at night, when there's hardly anybody on them?"

They stopped and looked along the wide avenue and up the towering, slanting faces of the buildings to the patches of night sky. Holding out her small, gloved hand in his palm, he patted it with his other hand, and they both laughed as though he had done something foolish but charming. The whole city was quieter now, the streets flowed away from them without direction, but there was always the hum underneath the silence like something restless and stirring and really touching them, as the soft, spring night air of the streets touched them, and at a store door he pulled her into the shadow and kissed her warmly, and when she didn't resist he kept on kissing her. Then they walked on again happily. He didn't care what he talked about; he talked about the advertising agency where he had gone to work the year before, and what he planned to do when he got more money, and each word had a feeling of reckless elation behind it.

For a long time they walked on aimlessly like this before he noticed that she was limping. Her face kept on turning up to him, and she laughed often, but she was really limping badly. "What's the matter, Sheila? What's the matter with your foot?" he said.

"It's my heel," she said, lifting her foot off the ground.

"My shoe has been rubbing against it." She tried to laugh. "It's all right, Bob," she said, and she tried to walk on without limping.

"You can't walk like that, Sheila."

"Maybe if we just took it off for a minute, Bob, it would be all right," she said as though asking a favor of him.

"I'll take it off for you," he said, and he knelt down on one knee while she lifted her foot and balanced herself with her arm on his shoulder. He drew off the shoe gently.

"Oh, the air feels so nice and cool on my heel," she said. No one was coming along the street. For a long time he remained kneeling, caressing her ankle gently and looking up with his face full of concern. "Try and put it on now, Bob," she said. But when he pushed the shoe over the heel, she said, "Good heavens, it seems tighter than ever." She limped along for a few steps. "Maybe we should never have taken it off. There's a blister there," she said.

"It was crazy to keep on walking like this," he said. "I'll call a taxi as soon as one comes along." They were standing by the curb, with her leaning heavily on his arm, and he was feeling protective and considerate, for with her heel hurting her, she seemed more like the young girl he had known. "Look how late it is. It's nearly four o'clock," he said. "Your father will be wild."

"It's terribly late," she said.

"It's my fault. I'll tell him it was all my fault."

For a while she didn't raise her head. When she did look up at him, he thought she was frightened. She was hardly able to move her lips. "What will they say when I go home at this hour, Bob?"

"It'll be all right. I'll go right in with you," he said.

"Wouldn't it be better . . . don't you think it would be all right if I stayed the night with Alice—with my girl friend?"

She was so hesitant that it worried him, and he said emphatically, "It's nearly morning now, and anyway, your father knows you're with me."

"Where'll we say we've been till this hour, Bob?"

"Just walking."

"Maybe he won't believe it. Maybe he's sure by this time I'm staying with Alice. If there was some place I could go. . . ." While she waited for him to answer, all that had been growing in her for such a long time was showing in the softness of her dark, eager face.

There was a breathless excitement in him and something like a slow unfolding that was all lost in guilty uneasiness. Then a half-ashamed feeling began to come over him and he began thinking of himself at the apartment, talking with Jack and the old man, and with Sheila coming in and listening with her eager face full of seriousness. "Why should you think there'll be trouble?" he asked. "Your father will probably be in bed."

"I guess he will," she said quickly. "I'm silly. I ought to know that. There was nothing . . . I must have sounded silly." She began to fumble for words, and then her confusion was so deep that she could not speak.

"I'm surprised you don't know your father better than that," he said rapidly, as though offended. He was anxious to make it an argument between them over her father. He wanted to believe this himself, so he tried to think only of the nights when her father, with his white head and moustaches, had talked in his good-humored way about the old days in New York and the old eating places, but every one of these conversations, every one of these nights that came into his thoughts, had Sheila there, too, listening and watching. Then it got so that he could remember nothing of those times but her intense young face, which kept rising before him, although he had never been aware that he had paid much attention to her. So he said desperately, "There's the friendliest feeling in the world between your people and me. Leave it to me. We'll go back to the corner, where we can see a taxi."

They began to walk slowly to the corner, with her still limping though he held her arm firmly. He began to talk with a soft persuasiveness, eager to have her respond readily, but she only said, "I don't know what's the matter. I feel tired or something." When they were standing on the street corner, she began to cry a little.

"Poor little Sheila," he said.

Then she said angrily, "Why 'poor little Sheila'? There's nothing the matter with me. I'm just tired." And they both kept looking up and down the street for a taxi.

Then one came, they got in, and he sat with his arm along the back of the seat, just touching her shoulder. He dared not tighten his arm around her, though never before had he wanted so much to be gentle with anyone; but with the street lights sometimes flashing on her face and showing the frightened, bewildered whiteness that was in it, he was scared to disturb her. His heart began to beat with slow heaviness and he was glad when the ride was over.

As soon as they opened the apartment door and lit the lights in the living room, they heard her father come shuffling from his bedroom. His white moustaches were working up and down furiously as he kept wetting his lips, and his hair, which was always combed nicely, was mussed over his head because he had been lying down. "Where have you been till this hour, Sheila?" he asked. "I kept getting up all the time. Where have you been?"

"Just walking with Bob," she said. "I'm dead tired, Dad. We lost all track of time." She spoke very calmly and then she smiled, and Bob saw how well she knew that her father loved her. Her father's face was full of concern while he peered at her, and she only smiled openly, showing no worry and saying, "Poor Daddy, I never dreamed you'd get up. I hope Jack is still sleeping."

"Jack said if you were with Bob, you were all right," Mr. Staples said. Glancing at Bob, he added curtly, "She's only eighteen, you know. I thought you had more sense."

"I guess we were fools to walk for hours like that, Mr. Staples," Bob said. "Sheila's got a big blister on her foot." Bob shook his head as if he couldn't understand why he had been so stupid.

Mr. Staples looked a long time at Sheila, and then he looked shrewdly at Bob; they were both tired and worried, and they were standing close together. Mr. Staples cleared his throat two or three times and said, "What on earth got into the pair of you?" Then he grinned suddenly and said, "Isn't it extraordinary what young people do? I'm so wide awake now I can't sleep. I was making myself a cup of coffee. Won't you both sit down and have a cup with me? Eh, Bob?"

"I'd love to," Bob said heartily.

"You go ahead. I won't have any coffee. It would keep me awake," Sheila said.

"The water's just getting hot," Mr. Staples said. "It will be ready in a minute." Still chuckling and shaking his head, for he was glad Sheila had come in, he said, "I kept telling myself she was all right if she was with you, Bob."

Bob and Mr. Staples grinned broadly at each other.

But when her father spoke like this, Sheila raised her head, and Bob thought that he saw her smile at him. He wanted to smile, too, but he couldn't look at her and had to turn away uneasily. And when he did turn to her again, it was almost pleadingly, for he was thinking, "I did the only thing there was to do. It was the right thing, so why should I feel ashamed now?" and yet he kept on remembering how she had cried a little on the street corner. He longed to think of something to say that might make her smile agreeably—some gentle, simple, friendly remark that would make her feel close to him—but he could only go on remembering how yielding she had been.

Her father was saying cheerfully, "I'll go and get the coffee now."

"I don't think I'd better stay," Bob said.

"It'll only take a few minutes," Mr. Staples said.

"I don't think I'll wait," Bob said, but Mr. Staples, smiling and shaking his head, went on into the kitchen to get the coffee.

Bob kept on watching Sheila, who was supporting her head with her hand and frowning a little. There was some of the peacefulness in her face now that had been there days ago, only there was also a new, full softness; she was very quiet, maybe feeling again the way he had kissed her, and then she frowned again as though puzzled, as though she was listening and overhearing herself say timidly, "If there was some place I could go. . . ."

Growing more and more uneasy, Bob said, "It turned out all right, don't you see, Sheila?"

"What?" she said.

"There was no trouble about coming home," he said.

As she watched him without speaking, she was not at all like a young girl. Her eyes were shining. All the feeling of the whole night was surging through her; she could hardly hold within her all the mixed-up feeling that was stirring her, and then her face grew warm with shame and she said savagely, "Why don't you go? Why do you want to sit there talking, talking, talking?"

"I don't know," he said.

"Go on. Please go. Please," she said.

"All right, I'll go," he muttered, and he got up clumsily, looking around for his hat and coat. As he started to go, his face got hot with humiliation. He longed to look back at her, and when she did not call out to him as he went, he was full of a wild resentment.

In the cold, early morning light, with heavy trucks rumbling on the street, he felt terribly tense and nervous. He could hardly remember anything that had happened. Inside him there was a wide, frightening emptiness. He wanted to reach out desperately and hold that swift, ardent, yielding joy that had been so close to him. For a while he could not think at all. And then he felt that slow unfolding coming in him again, making him quick with wonder.

THE PAINTED DOOR

Sinclair Ross

Straight across the hills it was five miles from John's farm to his father's. But in winter, with the roads impassable, a team had to make a wide detour and skirt the hills, so that from five the distance was more than trebled to seventeen.

"I think I'll walk," John said at breakfast to his wife. "The drifts in the hills wouldn't hold a horse, but they'll carry me all right. If I leave early I can spend a few hours helping him with his chores, and still be back by supper-time."

She went to the window, and thawing a clear place in the frost with her breath, stood looking across the snow-swept farmyard to the huddle of stables and sheds. "There was a double wheel around the moon last night," she countered presently. "You said yourself we could expect a storm. It isn't right to leave me here alone. Surely I'm as important as your father."

He glanced up uneasily, then drinking off his coffee tried to reassure her. "But there's nothing to be afraid of—even supposing it does start to storm. You won't need to go near the stable. Everything's fed and watered now to last till night. I'll be back at the latest by seven or eight."

She went on blowing against the frosted pane, carefully elongating the clear place until it was oval-shaped and symmetrical. He watched her a moment or two longer, then more insistently repeated, "I say you won't need to go near the stable. Everything's fed and watered, and I'll see that there's plenty of wood in. That will be all right, won't it?"

"Yes—of course—I heard you—" It was a curiously cold voice now, as if the words were chilled by their contact with the frosted pane. "Plenty to eat—plenty of wood to keep me warm—what more could a woman ask for?"

"But he's an old man—living there all alone. What is it, Ann? You're not like yourself this morning."

She shook her head without turning. "Pay no attention to me. Seven years a farmer's wife—it's time I was used to staying alone."

Slowly the clear place on the glass enlarged: oval, then round, then oval again. The sun was risen above the frost mists now, so keen and hard a glitter on the snow that instead of warmth its rays seemed shedding cold. One of the two-year-old colts that had cantered away when John turned the horses out for water stood covered with rime at the stable door again, head down and body hunched, each breath a little plume of steam against the frosty air. She shivered, but did not turn. In the clear, bitter light the long white miles of prairie landscape seemed a region strangely alien to life. Even the distant farmsteads she could see served only to intensify a sense of isolation. Scattered across the face of so vast and bleak a wilderness it was difficult to conceive them as a testimony of human hardihood and endurance. Rather they seemed futile, lost, to cower before the implacability of snow-swept earth and clear pale sun-chilled sky.

And when at last she turned from the window there was a brooding stillness in her face as if she had recognized this mastery of snow and cold. It troubled John. "If you're really afraid," he yielded, "I won't go today. Lately it's been so cold, that's all. I just wanted to make sure he's all right in case we do have a storm."

"I know—I'm not really afraid." She was putting in a fire now, and he could no longer see her face. "Pay no attention to me. It's ten miles there and back, so you'd better get started."

"You ought to know by now I wouldn't stay away," he tried to brighten her, "no matter how it stormed. Before we were married—remember? Twice a week I never missed and we had some bad blizzards that winter, too."

He was a slow, unambitious man, content with his farm and cattle, naively proud of Ann. He had been bewildered by it once, her caring for a dull-witted fellow like him; then assured at last of her affection he had relaxed against it gratefully, unsuspecting it might ever be less constant than his own. Even now, listening to the restless brooding in her voice, he felt only a quick, unformulated kind of pride that after seven years his absence for a day should still concern her. While she, his trust and earnestness controlling her again:

"I know. It's just that sometimes when you're away I get lonely. . . . There's a long cold tramp in front of you. You'll let me fix a scarf around your face."

He nodded. "And on my way I'll drop in at Steven's place. Maybe he'll come over tonight for a game of cards. You haven't seen anybody but me for the last two weeks."

She glanced up sharply, then busied herself clearing the table. "It will mean another two miles if you do. You're going to be cold and tired enough as it is. When you're gone I think I'll paint the kitchen woodwork. White this time—you remember we got the paint last fall. It's going to make the room a lot lighter. I'll be too busy to find the day long."

"I will though," he insisted, "and if a storm gets up you'll feel safer, knowing that he's coming. That's what you need, maybe—someone to talk to besides me."

She stood at the stove motionless a moment, then turned to him uneasily. "Will you shave then, John—now—before you go?"

He glanced at her questioningly, and avoiding his eyes she tried to explain, "I mean—he may be here before you're back—and you won't have a chance then."

"But it's only Steven—he's seen me like this—"

"He'll be shaved, though—that's what I mean—and I'd like you to spend a little time on yourself."

He stood up, stroking the heavy stubble on his chin. "Maybe I should—only it softens up the skin too much. Especially when I've got to face the wind."

She nodded and began to help him dress, bringing heavy socks and a big woolen sweater from the bedroom, wrapping a scarf around his face and forehead. "I'll tell Steven to come early," he said, as he went out. "In time for supper. Likely there'll be chores for me to do, so if I'm not back by six don't wait."

From the bedroom window she watched him nearly a mile along the road. The fire had gone down when at last she turned away, and already through the house there was an encroaching chill. A blaze sprang up again when the drafts were opened, but as she went on clearing the table her movements were furtive and constrained. It was the silence weighing upon her—the frozen silence of the bitter fields and sun-chilled sky—lurking outside as if alive, relentlessly in wait, mile-deep between her now and John. She listened to it, suddenly tense, motionless. The fire crackled and the clock ticked. Always it was there. "I'm a fool," she whispered, rattling the dishes in defiance, going back to the stove to put in another fire. "Warm and safe— I'm a fool. It's a good chance when he's away to paint. The day will go quickly. I won't have time to brood."

Since November now the paint had been waiting warmer weather. The frost in the walls on a day like this would crack and peel it as it dried, but she needed something to keep her hands occupied, something to stave off the gathering cold and loneliness. "First of all," she said aloud, opening the paint and mixing it with a little turpentine, "I must get the house warmer. Fill up the stove and open the oven door so that all the heat comes out. Wad something along the window sills to keep out the drafts. Then I'll feel brighter. It's the cold that depresses."

She moved briskly, performing each little task with careful and exaggerated absorption, binding her thoughts to it, making it a screen between herself and the surrounding snow and silence. But when the stove was filled and the windows sealed it was more difficult again. Above the quiet, steady swishing of her brush against the bedroom door the clock began to tick. Suddenly her movements became precise, deliberate, her posture self-conscious, as if someone had entered the room and were watching her. It was the silence again, aggressive, hovering. The fire spit and crackled at it. Still it was there. "I'm a fool," she repeated. "All farmers' wives have to stay alone. I mustn't give in this way. I mustn't brood. A few hours now and they'll be here."

The sound of her voice reassured her. She went on, "I'll get them a good supper—and for coffee after cards bake some of the little cakes with raisins that he likes. . . . Just three of us, so I'll watch, and let John play. It's better with four, but at least we can talk. That's all I need—someone to talk to. John never talks. He's stronger—he doesn't understand. But he likes Steven—no matter what the neighbors say. Maybe he'll have him come again, and some other young people, too. It's what we need, both of us, to help keep young ourselves. . . . And then before we know it we'll be into March. It's cold still in March sometimes, but you never mind the same. At least you're beginning to think about spring."

She began to think about it now. Thoughts that outstripped her words, that left her alone again with herself and the ever-lurking silence. Eager and hopeful first, then clenched, rebellious, lonely. Windows open, sun and thawing earth again, the urge of growing, living things. Then the days that began in the morning at half-past four and lasted till ten at night; the meals at which John gulped his food and scarcely spoke a word; the brute-tired stupid eyes he turned on her if ever she mentioned town or visiting.

For spring was drudgery again. John never hired a man to help him. He wanted a mortgage-free farm, then a new house and pretty clothes for her. Sometimes, because with the best of crops it was going to take so long to pay off anyway, she wondered whether they mightn't better let the mortgage wait a little. Before they were worn out, before their best years were gone. It was something of life she wanted, not just a house and furniture; something of John, not pretty clothes when she would be too old to wear them. But John of course couldn't understand. To him it seemed only right that she should have the pretty clothes—only right that he, fit for nothing else, should slave away fifteen hours a day to give them to her. There was in his devotion a baffling, insurmountable humility that made him feel the need of sacrifice. And when his muscles ached, when his feet dragged stolidly with weariness, then it seemed that in some measure at least he was making amends for his big hulking body and simple mind. Year after year their lives went on in the same little groove. He drove his horses in the field; she milked the cows and hoed potatoes. By dint of his drudgery he saved a few months' wages, added a few dollars more each fall to his payments on the mortgage; but the only real difference that it all made was to deprive her of his companionship, to make him a little duller, older, uglier than he might otherwise have been. He never saw their lives objectively. To him it was not what he actually accomplished by means of the sacrifice that mattered, but the sacrifice itself, the gesture—something done for her sake.

And she, understanding, kept her silence. In such a gesture, however futile, there was a graciousness not to be shattered lightly. "John," she would begin sometimes, "you're doing too much. Get a man to help you—just for a month—" But smiling down at her he would answer simply, "I don't mind. Look at the hands on me. They're made for work." While in his voice there would be a stalwart ring to tell her that by her thoughtfulness she had made him only the more resolved to serve her, to prove his devotion and fidelity.

They were useless, such thoughts. She knew. It was his very devotion that made them useless, that forbade her to rebel. Yet over and over, sometimes hunched still before their bleakness, sometimes her brush making swift sharp strokes to pace the chafe and rancor that they brought, she persisted in them.

This now, the winter, was their slack season. She could sleep sometimes till eight, and John till seven. They could linger over their meals a little, read, play cards, go visiting the neighbors. It was the time to relax, to indulge and enjoy themselves; but instead, fretful and impatient, they kept on waiting for the spring. They were compelled now, not by labor, but by the spirit of labor—a spirit that pervaded their lives and brought with idleness a sense of guilt. Sometimes they did sleep late, sometimes they did play cards, but always uneasily, always reproached by the thought of more important things that might be done. When John got up at five to attend to the fire he wanted to stay up and go out to the stable. When he sat down to a meal he hurried his food and pushed his chair away again from habit, from sheer work instinct, even though it was only to put more wood in the stove, or go down to the cellar to cut up beets and turnips for the cows.

And anyway, sometimes she asked herself, why sit trying to talk with a man who never talked? Why talk when there was nothing to talk about but crops and cattle, the weather and the neighbors? The neighbors, too—why go visiting them when still it was the same—crops and cattle, the weather and the other neighbors? Why go to the dances in the schoolhouse to sit among the older women, one of them now, married seven years, or to waltz with the work-bent, tired old farmers to a squeaky fiddle tune? Once she had danced with Steven six or seven times in the evening, and they had talked about it for as many months. It was easier to stay at home. John never danced or enjoyed himself. He was always uncomfortable in his good suit and shoes. He didn't like shaving in the cold weather oftener than once or twice a week. It was easier to stay at home, to stand at the window staring out across the bitter fields, to count the days and look forward to another spring.

But now, alone with herself in the winter silence, she saw the spring for what it really was. This spring—next spring—all the springs and summers still to come. While they grew old, while their bodies warped, while their minds kept shriveling dry and empty like their lives. "I mustn't," she said aloud again. "I married him—and he's a good man. I mustn't keep on this way. It will be noon before long, and then time to think about supper. . . . Maybe he'll come early—and as soon as John is finished at the stable we can all play cards."

It was getting cold again, and she left her painting to put in more wood. But this time the warmth spread slowly. She pushed a mat up to the outside door, and went back to the window to pat down the woolen shirt that was wadded along the sill. Then she paced a few times round the room, then poked the fire and rattled the stove lids, then paced again. The fire crackled, the clock ticked. The silence now seemed more intense than ever, seemed to have reached a pitch where it faintly moaned. She began to pace on tiptoe, listening, her shoulders drawn together, not realizing for a while that it was the wind she heard, thin-strained and whimpering through the eaves.

Then she wheeled to the window, and with quick short breaths thawed the frost to see again. The glitter was gone. Across the drifts sped swift and snakelike little tongues of snow. She could not follow them, where they sprang from, or where they disappeared. It was as if all across the yard the snow were shivering awake—roused by the warnings of the wind to hold itself in readiness for the impending storm. The sky had become a somber, whitish gray. It, too, as if in readiness, had shifted and lay close to earth. Before her as she watched a mane of powdery snow reared up breast-high against the darker background of the stable, tossed for a moment angrily, and then subsided again as if whipped down to obedience and restraint. But another followed, more reckless and impatient than the first. Another reeled and dashed itself against the window where she watched. Then ominously for a while there were only the angry little snakes of snow. The wind rose, creaking the troughs that were wired beneath the eaves. In the distance, sky and prairie now were merged into one another linelessly. All round her it was gathering; already in its press and whimpering there strummed a boding of eventual fury. Again she saw a mane of snow spring up, so dense and high this time that all the sheds and stables were obscured. Then others followed, whirling fiercely out of hand; and when at last they cleared, the stables seemed in dimmer outline than before. It was the snow beginning, long lancet shafts of it, straight from the north, borne almost level by the straining wind. "He'll be there soon," she whispered, "and coming home it will be in his back. He'll leave again right away. He saw the double wheel— he knows the kind of storm there'll be."

She went back to her painting. For a while it was easier, all her thoughts half-anxious ones of John in the blizzard, struggling his way across the hills; but petulantly again she soon began, "I knew we were going to have a storm— I told him so—but it doesn't matter what I say. Big stubborn fool—he goes his own way anyway. It doesn't matter what becomes of me. In a storm like this he'll never get home. He won't even try. And while he sits keeping his father company I can look after his stable for him, go plowing through snowdrifts up to my knees—nearly frozen—"

Not that she meant or believed her words. It was just an effort to convince herself that she did have a grievance, to justify her rebellious thoughts, to prove John responsible for her unhappiness. She was young still, eager for excitement and distractions; and John's steadfastness rebuked her vanity, made her complaints seem weak and trivial. She went on fretfully, "If he'd listen to me sometimes and not be so stubborn we wouldn't be living still in a house like this. Seven years in two rooms—seven years and never a new stick of furniture. . . . There—as if another coat of paint could make it different anyway."

She cleaned her brush, filled up the stove again, and went back to the window. There was a void white moment that she thought must be frost formed on the windowpane; then, like a fitful shadow through the whirling snow, she recognized the stable roof. It was incredible. The sudden, maniac raging of the storm struck from her face all its pettishness. Her eyes glazed with fear a little; her lips blanched. "If he starts for home now—" she whispered silently. "But he won't—he knows I'm safe—he knows Steven's coming. Across the hills he would never dare."

She turned to the stove, holding out her hands to the warmth. Around her now there seemed a constant sway and tremor, as if the air were vibrating with shudderings of the walls. She stood quite still, listening. Sometimes the wind struck sharp, savage blows. Sometimes it bore down in a sustained, minute-long blast, silent with effort and intensity; then with a foiled shriek of threat wheeled away to gather and assault again. Always the eaves troughs creaked and sawed. She started toward the window again, then detecting the morbid trend of her thoughts, prepared fresh coffee and forced herself to drink a few mouthfuls. "He would never dare," she whispered again. "He wouldn't leave the old man anyway in such a storm. Safe in here—there's nothing for me to keep worrying about. It's after one already. I'll do my baking now, and then it will be time to get supper ready for Steven."

Soon, however, she began to doubt whether Steven would come. In such a storm even a mile was enough to make a man hesitate. Especially Steven, who was hardly the one to face a blizzard for the sake of someone else's chores. He had a stable of his own to look after anyway. It would be only natural for him to think that when the storm rose John had turned again for home. Another man would have—would have put his wife first.

But she felt little dread or uneasiness at the prospect of spending the night alone. It was the first time she had been left like this on her own resources, and her reaction, now that she could face and appraise her situation calmly, was gradually to feel it a kind of adventure and responsibility. It stimulated her. Before nightfall she must go to the stable and feed everything. Wrap up in some of John's clothes—take a ball of string in her hand, one end tied to the door, so that no matter how blinding the storm she could at least find her way back to the house. She had heard of people having to do that. It appealed to her now because suddenly it made life dramatic. She had not felt the storm yet, only watched it for a minute through the window.

It took nearly an hour to find enough string, to choose the right socks and sweaters. Long before it was time to start out she tried on John's clothes, changing and rechanging, striding around the room to make sure there would be play enough for pitching hay and struggling over snowdrifts; then she took them off again, and for a while busied herself baking the little cakes with raisins that he liked.

Night came early. Just for a moment on the doorstep she shrank back, uncertain. The slow dimming of the light clutched her with an illogical sense of abandonment. It was like the covert withdrawal of an ally, leaving the alien miles unleashed and unrestrained. Watching the hurricane of writhing snow rage past the little house she forced herself, "They'll never stand the night unless I get them fed. It's nearly dark already, and I've work to last an hour."

Timidly, unwinding a little of the string, she crept out from the shelter of the doorway. A gust of wind spun her forward a few yards, then plunged her headlong against a drift that in the dense white whirl lay invisible across her path. For nearly a minute she huddled, still, breathless, and dazed. The snow was in her mouth and nostrils, inside her scarf and up her sleeves. As she tried to straighten a smothering scud flung itself against her face, cutting off her breath a second time. The wind struck from all sides, blustering and furious. It was as if the storm had discovered her, as if all its forces were concentrated upon her extinction. Seized with panic suddenly she threshed out a moment with her arms, then stumbled back and sprawled her length across the drift.

But this time she regained her feet quickly, roused by the whip and batter of the storm to retaliative anger. For a moment her impulse was to face the wind and strike back blow for blow; then, as suddenly as it had come, her frantic strength gave way to limpness and exhaustion. Suddenly, a comprehension so clear and terrifying that it struck all thoughts of the stable from her mind, she realized in such a storm her puniness. And the realization gave her new strength, stilled this time to a desperate persistence. Just for a moment the wind held her, numb and swaying in its vise; then slowly, buckled far forward, she groped her way again toward the house.

Inside, leaning against the door, she stood tense and still a while. It was almost dark now. The top of the stove glowed a deep, dull red. Heedless of the storm, self-absorbed and self-satisfied, the clock ticked on like a glib little idiot. "He shouldn't have gone," she whispered silently. "He saw the double wheel—he knew. He shouldn't have left me here alone."

For so fierce now, so insane and dominant did the blizzard seem, that she could not credit the safety of the house. The warmth and lull around her was not real yet, not to be relied upon. She was still at the mercy of the storm. Only her body pressing hard like this against the door was staving it off. She didn't dare move. She didn't dare ease the ache and strain. "He shouldn't have gone," she repeated, thinking of the stable again, reproached by her helplessness. "They'll freeze in their stalls—and I can't reach them. He'll say it's all my fault. He won't believe I tried."

Then Steven came. Quickly, startled to quietness and control, she let him in and lit the lamp. He stared at her a moment, then flinging off his cap crossed to where she stood by the table and seized her arms. "You're so white —what's wrong? Look at me——" It was like him in such little situations to be masterful. "You should have known better—for a while I thought I wasn't going to make it here myself——"

"I was afraid you wouldn't come—John left early, and there was the stable——"

But the storm had unnerved her, and suddenly at the assurance of his touch and voice the fear that had been gripping her gave way to a hysteria of relief. Scarcely aware of herself she seized his arm and sobbed against it. He remained still a moment, unyielding, then slipped his other arm around her shoulder. It was comforting and she relaxed against it, hushed by a sudden sense of lull and safety. Her shoulders trembled with the easing of the strain, then fell limp and still. "You're shivering——" He drew her gently toward the stove. "It's all right—nothing to be afraid of. I'm going to see to the stable."

It was a quiet, sympathetic voice, yet with an undertone of insolence, a kind of mockery even, that made her draw away quickly and busy herself putting in a fire. With his lips drawn in a little smile he watched her till she looked at him again. The smile, too, was insolent, but at the same time companionable—Steven's smile, and therefore difficult to reprove. It lit up his lean, still-boyish face with a peculiar kind of arrogance: features and smile that were different from John's, from other men's—willful and derisive, yet naively so—as if it were less the difference itself he was conscious of than the long-accustomed privilege that thereby fell his due. He was erect, tall, square-shouldered. His hair was dark and trim, his lips curved, soft, and full. While John—she made the comparison swiftly—was thick-set, heavy-jowled, and stooped. He always stood before her helpless, a kind of humility and wonderment in his attitude. And Steven now smiled on her appraisingly with the worldly-wise assurance of one for whom a woman holds neither mystery nor illusion.

"It was good of you to come, Steven," she responded, the words running into a sudden, empty laugh. "Such a storm to face—I suppose I should feel flattered."

For his presumption, his misunderstanding of what had been only a momentary weakness, instead of angering, quickened her, roused from latency and long disuse all the instincts and resources of her femininity. She felt eager, challenged. Something was at hand that hitherto had always eluded her, even in the early days with John, something vital, beckoning, meaningful. She didn't understand, but she knew. The texture of the moment was satisfyingly dreamlike: an incredibility perceived as such, yet acquiesced in. She was John's wife—she knew—but also she knew that Steven standing here was different from John. There was no thought or motive, no understanding of herself as the knowledge persisted. Wary and poised round a sudden little core of blind excitement she evaded him, "It's nearly dark—hadn't you better hurry if you're going to do the chores? But don't trouble—I can get them off myself—"

An hour later when he returned from the stable she was in another dress, hair rearranged, a little flush of color in her face. Pouring warm water for him from the kettle into the basin, she said evenly, "By the time you're washed supper will be ready. John said we weren't to wait for him."

He looked at her a moment, "You don't mean you're expecting John tonight? The way it's blowing—"

"Of course." As she spoke she could feel the color deepening in her face. "We're going to play cards. He was the one that suggested it."

He went on washing, and then as they took their places at the table, resumed, "So John's coming. When are you expecting him?"

"He said it might be seven o'clock—or a little later." Conversation with Steven at other times had always been brisk and natural, but now suddenly she found it strained. "He may have work to do for his father. That's what he said when he left. Why do you ask, Steven?"

"I was just wondering—it's a rough night."

"You don't know John. It would take more than a storm to stop him."

She glanced up again and he was smiling at her. The same insolence, the same little twist of mockery and appraisal. It made her flinch suddenly, and ask herself why she was pretending to expect John—why there should be this instinct of defense to force her. This time, instead of poise and excitement, it brought a reminder that she had changed her dress and rearranged her hair. It crushed in a sudden silence, through which she heard the whistling wind again, and the creaking saw of the eaves. Neither spoke now. There was something strange, almost frightening, about this Steven and his quiet, unrelenting smile; but strangest of all was the familiarity—the Steven she had never seen or encountered, and yet had always known, always expected, always waited for. It was less Steven himself that she felt than his inevitability, just as she had felt the snow, the silence, and the storm. She kept her eyes lowered, on the window past his shoulder, on the stove, but his smile now seemed to exist apart from him, to merge and hover with the silence. She clinked a cup, listened to the whistle of the storm—always it was there. He began to speak, but her mind missed the meaning of his words. Swiftly she was making comparisons again—his face so different from John's, so handsome and young and clean-shaven—swiftly, helplessly, feeling the imperceptible and relentless ascendancy that thereby he was gaining over her, sensing sudden menace in this new, more vital life, even as she felt drawn toward it.

The lamp between them flickered as an onslaught of the storm sent shudderings through the room. She rose to build up the fire again and he followed her. For a long time they stood close to the stove, their arms almost touching. Once as the blizzard creaked the house she spun around sharply, fancying it was John at the door; but quietly he intercepted her. "Not tonight—you might as well make up your mind to it. Across the hills in a storm like this— it would be suicide to try."

Her lips trembled suddenly in an effort to answer, to parry the certainty in his voice, then set thin and blood-less. She was afraid now. Afraid of his face so different from John's, of his smile, of her own helplessness to re-buke it. Afraid of the storm, isolating her here alone with him. They tried to play cards, but she kept starting up at every creak and shiver of the walls. "It's too rough a night," he repeated, "even for John. Just relax a few min-utes—stop worrying and pay a little attention to me."

But in his tone there was a contradiction to his words, for it implied that she was not worrying—that her only concern was lest it really might be John at the door.

And the implication persisted. He filled up the stove for her, shuffled the cards—won, shuffled—still it was there. She tried to respond to his conversation, to think of the game, but helplessly into her cards instead she began to ask, Was he right? Was that why he smiled? Why he seemed to wait, expectant and assured?

The clock ticked, the fire crackled. Always it was there. Furtively for a moment she watched him as he deliberated over his hand. John, even in the days before they were married, had never looked like that. Only this morning she had asked him to shave. Because Steven was coming— because she had been afraid to see them side by side—be-cause deep within herself she had known even then. The same knowledge, furtive and forbidden, that was flaunted now in Steven's smile. "You look cold," he said at last, dropping his cards and rising from the table. "We're not playing, anyway. Come over to the stove for a few minutes and get warm."

"But first I think we'll hang blankets over the door. When there's a blizzard like this we always do." It seemed that in sane, commonplace activity there might be release, a moment or two in which to recover herself. "John has nails to put them on. They keep out a little of the draft."

He stood on a chair for her, and hung the blankets that

she carried from the bedroom. Then for a moment they stood silent, watching the blankets sway and tremble before the blade of wind that spurted around the jamb. "I forgot," she said at last, "that I painted the bedroom door. At the top there, see—I've smeared the blankets coming through."

He glanced at her curiously, and went back to the stove. She followed him, trying to imagine the hills in such a storm, wondering whether John would come. "A man couldn't live in it." Suddenly he answered her thoughts, lowering the oven door and drawing up their chairs one on each side of it. "He knows you're safe. It isn't likely that he'd leave his father, anyway."

"The wind will be in his back," she persisted. "The winter before we were married—all the blizzards that we had that year—and he never missed—"

"Blizzards like this one? Up in the hills he wouldn't be able to keep his direction for a hundred yards. Listen to it a minute and ask yourself."

His voice seemed softer, kindlier now. She met his smile a moment, its assured little twist of appraisal, then for a long time sat silent, tense, careful again to avoid his eyes.

Everything now seemed to depend on this. It was the same as a few hours ago when she braced the door against the storm. He was watching her, smiling. She dared not move, unclench her hands, or raise her eyes. The flames crackled, the clock ticked. The storm wrenched the walls as if to make them buckle in. So rigid and desperate were all her muscles set, withstanding, that the room around her seemed to swim and reel. So rigid and strained that for relief at last, despite herself, she raised her head and met his eyes again.

Intending that it should be for only an instant, just to breathe again, to ease the tension that had grown unbearable—but in his smile now, instead of the insolent appraisal that she feared, there seemed a kind of warmth and sympathy. An understanding that quickened and encouraged her—that made her wonder why but a moment ago she had been afraid. It was as if the storm had lulled, as if she had suddenly found calm and shelter.

Or perhaps—the thought seized her—perhaps instead of his smile it was she who had changed. She who, in the long, wind-creaked silence, had emerged from the increment of codes and loyalties to her real, unfettered self. She who now felt suddenly an air of appraisal as nothing more than an understanding of the unfulfilled woman that until this moment had lain within her brooding and un-admitted, reproved out of consciousness by the insistence of an outgrown, routine fidelity.

For there had always been Steven. She understood now. Seven years—almost as long as John—ever since the night they first danced together.

The lamp was burning dry, and through the dimming light, isolated in the fastness of silence and storm, they watched each other. Her face was white and struggling still. His was handsome, clean-shaven, young. Her eyes were fanatic, believing desperately, fixed upon him as if to exclude all else, as if to find justification. His were cool, bland, drooped a little with expectancy. The light kept dimming, gathering the shadows round them, hushed, conspiratorial. He was smiling still. Her hands again were clenched up white and hard.

"But he always came," she persisted. "The wildest, cold-est nights—even such a night as this. There was never a storm—"

"Never a storm like this one." There was a quietness in his smile now, a kind of simplicity almost, as if to reassure her. "You were out in it yourself for a few minutes. He would have five miles, across the hills. . . . I'd think twice myself, on such a night, before risking even one."

Long after he was asleep she lay listening to the storm. As a check on the draft up the chimney they had left one of the stovelids partly off, and through the open bedroom door she could see the flickerings of flame and shadow on the kitchen wall. They leaped and sank fantastically. The longer she watched the more alive they seemed to be. There was one great shadow that struggled toward her threateningly, massive and black and engulfing all the room. Again and again it advanced, about to spring, but each time a little whip of light subdued it to its place among the others on the wall. Yet though it never reached her, still she cowered, feeling that gathered there was all the frozen wilderness, its heart of terror and invincibility.

Then she dozed awhile, and the shadow was John. In-terminably he advanced. The whips of light still flicked and coiled, but now suddenly they were the swift little snakes that this afternoon she had watched twist and shiver across the snow. And they, too, were advancing. They writhed and vanished and came again. She lay still, paralyzed. He was over her now, so close that she could have touched him. Already it seemed that a deadly tightening hand was on her throat. She tried to scream but her lips were locked. Steven beside her slept on heedlessly.

Until suddenly as she lay staring up at him a gleam of light revealed his face. And in it was not a trace of threat or anger—only calm, and stonelike hopelessness.

That was like John. He began to withdraw, and frantically she tried to call him back. "It isn't true—not really true—listen, John—" but the words clung frozen to her lips. Already there was only the shriek of wind again, the sawing eaves, the leap and twist of shadow on the wall.

She sat up, startled now and awake. And so real had he seemed there, standing close to her, so vivid the sudden age and sorrow in his face, that at first she could not make herself understand she had been only dreaming. Against the conviction of his presence in the room it was necessary to insist over and over that he must still be with his father on the other side of the hills. Watching the shadows she had fallen asleep. It was only her mind, her imagination, distorted to a nightmare by the illogical and unadmitted dread of his return. But he wouldn't come. Steven was right. In such a storm he would never try. They were safe, alone. No one would ever know. It was only fear, morbid and irrational, only the sense of guilt that even her new-found and challenged womanhood could not entirely quell.

She knew now. She had not let herself understand or acknowledge it as guilt before, but gradually through the wind-torn silence of the night his face compelled her. The face that had watched her from the darkness with its stonelike sorrow—the face that was really John—John more than his features of mere flesh and bone could ever be.

She wept silently. The fitful gleam of light began to sink. On the ceiling and wall at last there was only a faint dull flickering glow. The little house shuddered and quailed, and a chill crept in again. Without wakening Steven she slipped out to build up the fire. It was burned to a few spent embers now, and the wood she put on seemed a long time catching light. The wind swirled through the blankets they had hung around the door, and then, hollow and moaning, roared up the chimney again, as if against its will drawn back to serve still longer with the onrush of the storm.

For a long time she crouched over the stove, listening. Earlier in the evening, with the lamp lit and the fire crackling, the house had seemed a stand against the wilderness, a refuge of feeble walls wherein persisted the elements of human meaning and survival. Now, in the cold, creaking darkness, it was strangely extinct, looted by the storm and abandoned again. She lifted the stovelid and fanned the embers till at last a swift little tongue of flame began to lick around the wood. Then she replaced the lid, extended her hands, and as if frozen in that attitude stood waiting.

It was not long now. After a few minutes she closed the drafts, and as the flames whirled back upon each other, beating against the top of the stove and sending out flickers of light again, a warmth surged up to relax her stiffened limbs. But shivering and numb it had been easier. The bodily well-being that the warmth induced gave play again to an ever more insistent mental suffering. She remembered the shadow that was John. She saw him bent toward her, then retreating, his features pale and overcast with unaccusing grief. She relived their seven years together, and in retrospect found them to be years of worth and dignity. Until crushed by it all at last, seized by a sudden need to suffer and atone, she crossed to where the draft was bitter, and for a long time stood unflinching on the icy floor.

The storm was close here. Even through the blankets she could feel a sift of snow against her face. The eaves sawed, the walls creaked, and the wind was like a wolf in howling flight.

And yet, suddenly, she asked herself, hadn't there been other storms, other blizzards? And through the worst of them hadn't he always reached her?

Clutched by the thought she stood rooted a minute. It was hard now to understand how she could have so deceived herself—how a moment of passion could have quieted within her not only conscience, but reason and discretion, too. John always came. There could never be a storm to stop him. He was strong, inured to the cold. He had crossed the hills since his boyhood, knew every creek bed and gully. It was madness to go on like this— to wait. While there was still time she must waken Steven, and hurry him away.

But in the bedroom again, standing at Steven's side, she hesitated. In his detachment from it all, in his quiet, even breathing, there was such sanity, such realism. For him nothing had happened; nothing would. If she wakened him he would only laugh and tell her to listen to the storm. Already it was long past midnight; either John had lost his way or not set out at all. And she knew that in his devotion there was nothing foolhardy. He would never risk a storm beyond his endurance, never permit himself a sacrifice likely to endanger her lot or future. They were both safe. No one would ever know. She must control herself—be sane like Steven.

For comfort she let her hand rest awhile on Steven's shoulder. It would be easier were he awake now, with her, sharing her guilt; but gradually as she watched his handsome face in the glimmering light she came to understand that for him no guilt existed. Just as there had been no passion, no conflict. Nothing but the sane appraisal of their situation, nothing but the expectant little smile, and the arrogance of features that were different from John's. She winced deeply, remembering how she had fixed her eyes on those features, how she had tried to believe that so handsome and young, so different from John's, they must in themselves be her justification.

In the flickering light they were still young, still handsome. No longer her justification—she knew now, John was the man—but wistfully still, wondering sharply at their power and tyranny, she touched them a moment with her fingertips again.

She could not blame him. There had been no passion, no guilt; therefore there could be no responsibility. Looking down at him as he slept, half smiling still, his lips relaxed in the conscienceless complacency of his achievement, she understood that thus he was revealed in his entirety—all there ever was or ever could be. John was the man. With him lay all the future. For tonight, slowly and contritely through the days and years to come, she would 'ry to make amends.

Then she stole back to the kitchen, and without thought, impelled by overwhelming need again, returned to the door where the draft was bitter still. Gradually toward morning the storm began to spend itself. Its terror blast became a feeble, worn-out moan. The leap of light and shadow sank, and a chill crept in again. Always the eaves creaked, tortured with wordless prophecy. Heedless of it all the clock ticked on in idiot content.

They found him the next day, less than a mile from home. Drifting with the storm he had run against his own pasture fence and, overcome, had frozen there, erect still, both hands clasping fast the wire.

"He was south of here," they said wonderingly when she told them how he had come across the hills. "Straight south—you'd wonder how he could have missed the buildings. It was the wind last night, coming every way at once. He shouldn't have tried. There was a double wheel around the moon."

She looked past them a moment, then as if to herself said simply, "If you knew him, though—John would try."

It was later, when they had left her awhile to be alone with him, that she knelt and touched his hand. Her eyes dimmed, it was still such a strong and patient hand; then, transfixed, they suddenly grew wide and clear. On the palm, white even against its frozen whiteness, was a little smear of paint.

UNDER THE VOLCANO

Malcolm Lowry

I

As they walked up the Calle Nicaragua toward the bus stop Hugh and Yvonne turned to watch the marmalade-colored birds trapezing in the vines. But her father, afflicted by their raucous cries, strode on austerely through the blue, hot November afternoon.

The bus was not very full at first and soon was rolling like a ship in a heavy sea.

Now out of one window, now out of another, they could see the great mountain, Popocatapetl, round whose base clouds curled like smoke drawn from a train.

They passed tall, hexagonal stands with advertisements for the Morelos Cinema: *Los Manos de Orlac: con Peter Lorre.* Elsewhere, as they clattered through the little town, they noticed posters of the same film, showing a murderer's hands laced with blood.

"Like Paris," Yvonne said to Hugh, pointing to the kiosks, " 'Kub,' 'Oxygenée,' do you remember?"

Hugh nodded, stammering out something, and the careening of the bus made him swallow every syllable.

". . . Do you remember Peter Lorre in 'M'?"

But they had to give it up. The patient floor boards were creaking too loudly. They were passing the undertakers: *Inhumaciones.* A parrot, head cocked, eyed them from its perch at the entrance. *Quo Vadis?* asked a notice above it.

"Marvelous," the Consul said.

At the market they stopped for Indian women with baskets of poultry. They had strong faces the color of dark earthenware. There was a massiveness in their movements as they settled themselves. Two or three had cigarette stubs behind their ears, another chewed an old pipe. Their good-humored faces of old idols were wrinkled with sun, but they did not smile.

Then someone laughed, and the faces of the others slowly cracked into mirth; the *camión* was welding the old women into a community. Two even managed to hold an anxious conversation in spite of the racket.

The Consul, nodding to them politely, wished he, too, were going home. And he wondered who had suggested making this ghastly trip to the fiesta at Chapultepec when their car was laid up and there were no taxis to be had! The effort of going without a drink for a day, even for the benefit of his daughter and her young man, who had arrived that morning from Acapulco, was far greater than he had expected. Perhaps it was not the effort of merely being sober that told so much as that of coping with the legacy of impending doom recent unprecedented bouts had left him. When Yvonne pointed out Popocatapetl to him for the fifth time he smiled wanly. Chimborozo, Cotopaxi —and there it was! To the Consul the volcano had taken on a sinister aspect: like a sort of Moby Dick, it had the air of beckoning them on, as it swung from one side of the horizon to the other, to some disaster, unique and immedicable.

The bus lurched away from the *mercado,* where the clock on the main building sheltering the stalls stood at seven minutes past two—it had struck eleven; the Consul's watch said a quarter to four—then bumped down a steep cobbled incline and began to cross a little bridge over a ravine.

Was this the same *arroyo,* Yvonne wondered, that cut through her father's garden? The Consul was indicating that it was. The bottom was immensely far below; one looked down at it as from the main-truck of a sailing ship, though dense foliage and wide leaves partly concealed the real treachery of the drop. Its steep banks were piled with refuse, which even hung on the foliage; from the precipitous slope beyond the bridge, turning round, Yvonne could see a dead dog right down at the bottom, with white bones showing through, nuzzling the refuse.

"How's the raja hangover, Dad?" she asked, smiling.

" 'Taut over chaos,' " the Consul gritted his teeth, " 'crammed with serried masks.' "

"Just a little longer."

"No. I shall never drink again. Nevermore."

The bus went on. Halfway up the slope, beyond the ravine, outside a gaudily decorated little *cantina* named El Amor de los Amores waited a man in a blue suit, swaying gently and eating á melon.

As they approached, the Consul thought he recognized him as the part owner of the *cantina,* which was not, however, on his beat; from the interior came the sound of drunken singing.

When the bus stopped, the Consul thirstily caught sight, over the jalousied doors, of a bartender leaning over the bar and talking with intensity to a number of roaring policemen.

The *camión* throbbed away to itself while the driver went into the *cantina.* He emerged almost immediately to hurl himself back on his vehicle. Then, with an amused glance at the man in the blue suit, whom he apparently knew, he jammed the bus into gear and drove away.

The Consul watched the man, fascinated. The latter was very drunk indeed, and he felt a queer envy of him, albeit it was perhaps a stir of fellowship. As the bus drew in sight of the brewery, the Cerveceria de Quahnahuac, the Consul, his too sober gaze on the other's large, trembling hands, thrust his own hands into his pockets guiltily, but he had found the word wanted to describe him: *pelado.*

Pelados, he thought, the peeled ones, were those who did not have to be rich to prey on the really poor. They were also those half-breed politicians who work like slaves to get into office for one year, just one year, in which year they hope to put by enough to forswear work for the rest of their lives. *Pelado*—it was an ambiguous word, to be sure. The Consul chuckled. A Spaniard could interpret it as meaning Indian—the Indian whom he despised, used, and filled with—ah—"poisonous" liquor. While to that Indian it might mean Spaniard, or, employed by either with an amiable contempt, simply anyone who made a show of himself.

But whatever it might or might not mean, the Consul judged, his eyes still fixed on his man with the blue suit, it was fair to consider that the word could have been distilled only from such a venture as the Conquest, suggesting as it did on the one hand exploiter, and on the other, thief; and neither was it difficult to understand why it had come in time to describe the invaders as well as their victims. Interchangeable ever were the terms of abuse with which the aggressor publicly discredited those about to be ravaged!

The *pelado* then, who for a time had been talking thickly to himself, was now sunk in stupor. There was no conductor this trip, fares were paid to the driver on getting off; none bothered him. The dusty blue suit with its coat, tight at the waist but open, the broad trousers, pointed shoes shined that morning and soiled with the saloon's sawdust, indicated a confusion in his mind the Consul well understood: whom shall I be today, Jekyll or Hyde? His purple shirt, open at the neck and showing a crucifix, had been torn and was partially hanging out over the top of his trousers. For some reason he wore two hats, a kind of cheap homburg fitting neatly over the broad crown of his *sombrero*.

Soon they were passing the Hotel Casino de la Selva and they stopped once more. Colts with glossy coats were rolling on a slope. The Consul recognized Dr. Vigil's back moving among the trees on the tennis court; it was as if he were dancing a grotesque dance all by himself there.

Presently they were getting out into the country. At first there were rough stone walls on either side, then, after crossing the narrow gauge railway, where the Pearce oil tanks were pillowed along the embankment against the trees, leafy hedges full of bright wildflowers with deep royal blue bells. Green and white clothing hung on the cornstalks outside the low, grass-roofed houses. Now the bright blue flowers grew right into the trees, already snowy with blooms, and all this beauty the Consul noted with horror.

The road became smoother for a time, so that it was possible for Hugh and Yvonne to talk; then, just as Hugh was saying something about the convolvuli, it grew much worse again.

"It's like a Canterbury bell," the Consul was trying to say, only the *camión* bumped over a pothole at that moment and it was as if the jolt had thrown his soul up into his teeth. He steadied himself on the seat and the wood sent a piercing pain through his body. His knees knocked together. With Popocatepetl always following or preceding them they jogged into very rough country indeed. The

Consul felt that his head had become an open basket swarming with crabs. Now it was the ravine that was haunting him, creeping after them with a gruesome patience, he thought, winding always around the road on one side or the other. The crabs were at the back of his eyes, yet he forced himself to be hearty.

"Where's old Popeye gone to now?" he would exclaim as the volcano slid out of sight past the window to the left, for though he was afraid of it, he felt somehow better when it was there.

"This is like driving over the moon," Hugh tried to whisper to Yvonne, but ended up by shouting.

"Maybe all covered with spinach!" Yvonne was answering her father.

"Right down Archimedes this time! Look out!"

Then for a while they were passing through flat, wooded country with no volcano in sight, nothing to be seen but pines, stones, fircones, black earth. But when they looked more closely they noticed that the stones were volcanic, the earth was parched-looking, that everywhere were attestations to Popocatapetl's presence and antiquity.

After, the mountain itself would stride into view again, magnificent, or appearing sad, slate gray as despair, poised over his sleeping woman, Ixtaccihuatl, now permanently contiguous, which perhaps accounted for it, the Consul decided, feeling that Popo had also an annoying quality of looking as though it knew people expected it to be about to do, or mean, something—as if to be the most beautiful mountain in the world were not enough.

Gazing around the *camión,* which was somewhat fuller, Hugh took stock of his surroundings. He noticed the drunk, the old women, the men in their white trousers with purple shirts, and now the men in black trousers with their white Sunday shirts—for it was a holiday—and one or two younger women in mourning. He attempted to take an interest in the poultry. The hens and cocks and turkeys imprisoned in their baskets, and those that were still loose, had all alike submitted. With only an occasional flutter to show they were alive they crouched passively under the seats, their emphatic spindly claws bound with cord. Two pullets lay, frighted and quivering, between the handbrake and the clutch, their wings linked, it seemed, with the levers. Hugh was bored with all this finally. The thought of Yvonne sagged down his mind, shook his brain, permeating the *camión,* the very day itself, with nervous passion.

He turned away from her nearness and looked out, only to see her clear profile and sleeked fair hair sailing along reflected in the window.

The Consul was suffering more and more intensely. Each object on which his glance fell appeared touched with a cruel, supersensual significance. He knew the very wood of the seat to be capable of hurting his hands. And the words which ran across the entire breadth of the bus over the windscreen: *Su salva estara a salvo no escapiendo en el interior de este vehículo;* the driver's round mirror, the legend above it, *Cooperación de la Cruz Roja;* beside which hung three postcards of the Virgin Mary and a fire extinguisher; the two slim vases of marguerites fixed over the dashboard; the dungaree jacket and whiskbroom under the seat opposite where the *pelado* was sitting—all seemed to him actually to be alive, to be participating, with evil animation, in their journey.

And the *pelado?* The shaking of the *camión* was making it difficult for him to remain seated. With his eyes shut, and swaying from side to side, he was trying to tuck his shirt in. Now he was methodically buttoning his coat on the wrong buttons. The Consul smiled, knowing how meticulous one could be when drunk: clothes mysteriously hung up, cars driven by a seventh sense, police eluded by an eighth. Now the *pelado* had found room to lie down full length on the seat. And all this had been superbly accomplished without once opening his eyes!

Stretched out—a corpse—he still preserved the appearance of being uncannily aware of all that was going on. In spite of his stupor, he was a man on his guard; half a melon slipped out of his hand, the segments full of seeds like raisins rolled to and fro on the seat, yet with eyeless sight those dead eyes saw it; his crucifix was slipping off, but he was conscious of it; the homburg fell from his *sombrero,* slipped to the floor, and though making no attempt to pick it up, he obviously knew it was there. He was guarding himself against theft while gathering strength for more debauchery. In order to get into somebody else's *cantina* he might have to walk straight. His prescience was worthy of admiration.

Yvonne was enjoying herself. For the time being she was freed by the fact of Hugh's presence from the tyranny of thinking exclusively about him. The *camión* was traveling very much faster, rolling, swaying, jumping; the men were smiling and nodding; two boys, hanging at the back of the bus were whistling; and the bright shirts, the brighter serpentine confetti of tickets, red, yellow, green, blue, dangling from a loop on the ceiling—all contributed a certain sense of gaiety to their trip. They might have been going to a wedding.

But when the boys dropped off, some of this gaiety departed. That predominance of purple in the men's shirts gave a disquieting glare to the day. There seemed something brutal to her, too, about those candelabra cacti swinging by. And about those other cacti, further away, like an army advancing uphill under machine-gun fire. All at once there was nothing to see outside but a ruined church full of pumpkins, caves for doors, windows bearded with grass. The exterior was blackened as by fire and it had an air of being damned. It was as though Hugh had left her again, and the pain of him slid back into her heart, momentarily possessing her.

Buses bobbed by in the other direction—buses to Tetecala, to Jujuta; buses to Xiutepec, to Xochitepec—

At a great pace they swerved into a side road. Popocatapetl appeared, off to the right, with one side beautifully curved as a woman's breast, the other jagged and ferocious. The drifted clouds were massing, high-piled behind it.

Everyone felt at last that they were really going somewhere; they had become self-enclosed, abandoned to the tumultuous will of the vehicle.

They thundered on, passing little pigs trotting along the road, an Indian screening sand. Advertisements on ruined walls swam by. *Atchis! Instantia! Resfria dos Dolores. Cafiaspirina. Rechaches Imitaciones. Los Manos de Orlac: con Peter Lorre.*

When there was a bad patch the bus rattled ominously and sometimes they ran off the road. But its determination outweighed these waverings; all were pleased to have transferred their responsibilities to it, and to be lulled into a state from which it would be pain to awaken.

As a partner in this, it was with a freezing, detached

calm that the Consul found himself able to think as they
bucked and bounded over an interminable series of teeth-
rattling potholes, even of the terrible night which doubtless awaited him, of his room shaking with demonic or-
chestras, of the snatches of fearful sleep, interrupted by
imaginary voices outside which were dogs barking, or by
his own name being continually repeated with scorn by
imaginary parties arriving.

The *camión* pitched and rolled on.

They spelled out the word *Deviación* but made the detour too quickly, with a yelping of tires and brakes. As
they swerved into alignment once more the Consul noticed
a man apparently lying fast asleep under the hedge by the
right side of the road.

Both Hugh and Yvonne appeared oblivious to this. Nor
did it seem likely to the Consul that in this country anyone
else was going to think it extraordinary a man should
choose to sleep in the sun by the side of the road, or even
in the middle of the road.

The Consul looked back again. No mistake. The man,
receding quickly now, lay with his hat over his eyes, his
arms stretched out toward a wayside cross. Now they were
passing a riderless horse, munching the hedge.

The Consul leaned forward to call out but hesitated.
What if it were simply a hallucination? This might prove
very embarrassing. However, he did call out, tapping the
driver on the shoulder; almost at the same moment the
bus leaped to a standstill.

Guiding the whining vehicle swiftly, steering an erratic
course with one hand, the driver, who was craning right
out of his seat watching the corners behind and before
with quick yet reluctant turns of the head, reversed along
the dusty detour.

There was the friendly, overpowering smell of exhaust
gases tempered with the hot smell of tar from the repairs,
though no one was at work on the road, everybody having knocked off; and there was nothing to be seen there,
just the soft indigo carpet sparkling and sweating by itself.
But a little further back, to one side by the hedge, was a
stone cross, and beneath it were a milk bottle, a funnel, a
sock, and part of an old suitcase.

Now they could see the man quite plainly, lying with
his arms stretched out toward this wayside cross.

II

As the bus jerked to another stop the *pelado* almost slid
from his seat to the floor but, managing to recover himself,
not only reached his feet and an equilibrium he contrived
remarkably to maintain, but in doing so had arrived halfway
to the door in one strong movement, crucifix fallen safely
into place around his neck, hats in one hand, melon in the
other. He nodded gravely, and with a look that might have
withered at its inception any thought of stealing them,
placed the hats carefully on a vacant seat near the door,
and with exaggerated care, let himself down to the road.
His eyes were still only half-open, preserving that dead
glaze, yet there could be no doubt he had taken in the
whole situation. Throwing away the melon he walked
over toward the man in the road. Even though he stepped
as if over imaginary obstacles his course was straight and
he held himself erect.

Yvonne, Hugh, the Consul, and two of the passengers
followed him. None of the old women had moved from
their seats.

Halfway across the road Yvonne gave a nervous cry,
turning on her heel abruptly. Hugh gripped her arm.

"Are you all right?"

"Yes," she said, freeing herself. "Go on. It's just that I
can't stand the sight of blood, damn it."

She was climbing back into the *camión* as Hugh came
up with the Consul and the two passengers.

The *pelado* was swaying gently over the recumbent man.

Although the latter's face was covered by his hat, it
could be seen that he was an Indian of the *peón* class.
There seemed no doubt that he was dying. His chest
heaved like a spent swimmer's, his stomach contracted
and dilated rapidly, yet there was no sign of blood. One
clenched fist spastically thumped the dust.

The two foreigners stood there helplessly, each waiting
for the other to remove the *peón's* hat, to expose the wound
they all felt must be there, each checked from some such
action by a common reluctance, an obscure courtesy.
Each knew the other was also thinking it would be,
naturally, even better still should the *pelado* or one of the
passengers examine the man. But as nobody made any

move Hugh became impatient. He shifted from foot to foot. He looked at the Consul with supplication. The Consul had been here long enough to know what could be done; moreover he was the one among them most nearly representing authority. But the Consul, who was trying to prevent himself saying, "Go ahead, after all, Spain invaded Mexico first," made no move either. At last Hugh could stand it no longer. Stepping forward impulsively he made to bend over the *peón* when one of the passengers plucked at his sleeve.

"Mistair, have you thrown away your cigarette?"

"What!" Hugh turned around, astonished.

"I don't know," said the Consul. "Forest fires, probably."

"Better throw your cigarette, *Señor*. They have prohibidated it."

Hugh dropped his cigarette and stamped it out, bewildered and irritated. He was about to bend over the man once more when the passenger plucked his sleeve again. Hugh straightened up.

"They have prohibidated it, *Señor*," the other said politely, tapping his nose. He gave an odd little laugh. *"Positivamente!"*

"I no comprendo, gnädige *Señor*," Hugh tried desperately to produce some Spanish.

"He means you can't touch this chap because you'd be an accessory after the fact," nodded the Consul, beginning to sweat and wishing profoundly he could get as far away from this scene as possible, if necessary even by means of the *peón's* horse, to somewhere where great gourds of mescal crouched. "Leave well enough alone is not only the watchword, Hugh, it's the law."

The man's breathing and thumping was like the sea dragging itself down a stone beach.

Then the *pelado* went down on one knee and whipped off the dying man's hat.

They all peered over, seeing the terrible wound in the side of his head, the blood from which had almost coagulated; and before they stood back, before the *pelado* replaced the hat and drawing himself erect, made a hopeless gesture with hands blotched with half-dried blood, they caught a glimpse of a sum of money, four or five silver pesos and a handful of centavos, which had been

placed neatly under the man's collar, by which it was
partly obscured.

"But we can't let the poor fellow die," Hugh said
despairingly, looking after the *pelado* as he returned to the
bus, and then down once more at this life gasping away
from them all. "We'll have to get a doctor."

This time from the *camión,* the *pelado* again made that
gesture of hopelessness, which might have been also a gesture of sympathy.

The Consul was relieved to see that by now their
presence had exampled approach to the extent that two
peasants, hitherto unnoticed, had come up to the dying
man, while another passenger was also standing beside the
body.

"*Pobrecito,*" said one.

"*Chingar,*" muttered the other.

And gradually the others took up these remarks as a
kind of refrain, a quiet seething of futility, of whispers, in
which the dust, the heat, the bus with its load of immobile
old women and doomed poultry, even the terrible beauty
and mystery of the country itself, seemed to be conspiring,
while only these two words, the one of tender compassion,
the other of fiendish contempt, were audible above the
thudding and the gasping, until the driver, as if satisfied
that all was now as it should be, began impatiently blowing
his horn.

A passenger shouted to him to shut up, but possibly
thinking the admonition was in jesting approval, the
driver continued to blow, punctuating the seething, which
soon developed into a general argument in which suspi-
cions and suggestions canceled each other out, to a heckling
accompaniment of contemptuous blasts.

Was it murder? Was it robbery? Or both? The *peón*
had ridden from the market with more than that four or
five pesos; possibly he'd been in possession of *mucho
dinero,* so that a good way to avoid suspicion of theft
was to leave a little of the money, as had been done. Perhaps it was not robbery at all; had he only been thrown
from his horse? The horse had kicked him? Possible? Impossible! Had the police been called? An ambulance—the
Cruz Roja? Where was the nearest phone? Should one of
them, now, go for the police? But it was absurd to suppose they were not on their way. How could they be on

their way when half of them were on strike? They would be on their way all right, though. An ambulance? But here it was impertinent of a *gringo* to interfere. Surely the Red Cross were perfectly capable of looking after such a matter themselves. But was there any truth in the rumor that the Servicio de Ambulante had been suspended? It was not a red but a green cross, and their business began only when they were informed. Perhaps it was imprudent of a *gringo* to assume they hadn't been informed. A personal friend, Dr. Vigil, why not call him? He was playing tennis. Call the Casino de la Selva then? There was no phone; oh, there was one once, but it had decomposed. Get another doctor, Dr. Gomez? *Un hombre noble.* Too far, and anyhow, probably he was out. Well, perhaps he was back!

At last Hugh and the Consul became aware that they had reached an impasse upon which the driver's horn still made a most adequate comment. Neither could presume, from the appearance of it, that the *peón's* fate was not being taken care of in some way "by one of his own kind." Well, it certainly didn't look as though his own kind had been any too generous to him! On the contrary, the same person who placed him at the side of the road, who placed the money in the *peón's* collar, was probably even now going for help!

These sentiments got up and knocked each other down again; and although their voices were not raised, although Hugh and the Consul were not quarreling, it was as if they were actually knocking each other down physically and getting up again, each time more weary than the last time down, each time with a practical or psychic obstruction toward cooperating or even acting singly, the most potent and final of all of which obstructions being that it was not their business at all but somebody else's.

Yet on looking around them they realized that this, too, was only what the others were arguing. It is not my business, nor yours, they said as they shook their heads, but someone else's, their answers becoming more and more involved, more and more theoretical, so that finally the discussion began to take a political turn.

To the Consul, time suddenly seemed to be moving at different speeds; the speed at which the *peón* was dying contrasting oddly with that at which everyone was arriving at the conclusion it was impossible to make up their minds. Aware that the discussion was by no means closed and that the driver, who had stopped blowing his horn and was conversing with some of the women over his shoulder, would not think of leaving without first taking their fares, the Consul excused himself to Hugh and walked over to the Indian's horse, which, with its bucket saddle and heavy iron sheathes for stirrups, was calmly chewing the convolvulus in the hedge, looking as innocent as only one of its species can when suspected, even wrongfully, of throwing its rider or kicking a man to death. He examined it carefully, without touching it, noticing its wicked, friendly, plausible eyes, the sore on its hipbone, the number seven branded on its rump, as if for some clue to what had happened. Well, what had happened? Parable of a too late hour! More important, what was going to happen—to them all? What was going to happen to him was that he was going to have fifty-seven drinks at the earliest opportunity.

The bus was hooting with real finality now that two cars were held up behind it; and the Consul, observing that Hugh was standing on the step of one of them, walked back shaking his head as the *camión* came toward him to stop at a wider part of the road. The cars, wild with impatience, thrust past and Hugh dropped off the second one. Bearing tin plates under their numbers with the warning *Diplomático* they disappeared ahead in a cloud of dust.

"It's the diplomatic thing, doubtless," said the Consul, with one foot on the step of the *camión*. "Come on, Hugh, there's nothing we can do."

The other passengers were getting on board and the Consul stood to one side to talk to Hugh. The periodicity of the honking now had become much slower. There was a bored, almost amused resignation in the sound.

"You'll only be hauled into gaol and entangled in red tape for God knows how long," the Consul persisted. "Come on, Hugh. What do you think you're going to do?"

"If I can't get a doctor here, God damn it, I'll take him to one."

"They won't let you on the bus."

"The hell they won't! Oh—here come the police," he added, as three smiling vigilantes came tramping through the dust at that moment, their holsters slapping their thighs.

"No, they're not," the Consul said unfortunately. "At least, they're just from the *policía de seguridad*, I think. They can't do anything much either, just tell you to go away or—"

Hugh began to expostulate with them while the Consul watched him apprehensively from the step of the *camión*. The driver was wearily honking. One of the policemen began to push Hugh toward the bus. Hugh pushed back. The policeman drew back his hand. Hugh raised his fist. The policeman dropped his hand and began to fumble with his holster.

"Come on Hugh, for God's sake," the Consul pleaded, grasping him again. "Do you want to land us all in the gaol? Yvonne—"

The policeman was still fumbling with his holster when suddenly Hugh's face collapsed like a heap of ashes. He let his hands fall limply to his sides, and with a scornful laugh boarded the bus, which was already moving away.

"Never mind, Hugh," said the Consul, on the step with him, a drop of sweat falling on his toe. "It would have been worse than the windmills."

"What windmills?" Hugh looked about him, startled.

"No, no," the Consul said, "I meant something else, only that Don Quixote wouldn't have hesitated that long."

And he began to laugh.

Hugh stood for a moment cursing under his breath and looking back at the scene, the *peón's* horse munching the hedge, the police enveloped in the dust, the *peón* far beyond thumping the road, and now, hovering high above all, what he hadn't noticed before, the obvious cartoon birds, the *xopilotes*, who wait only for the ratification of death.

III

The bus plunged on.

Yvonne was flaccid with shame and relief. She tried to catch Hugh's eyes, but he crammed himself into his seat so furiously she was afraid to speak to him or even to touch him.

She sought some excuse for her own behavior in the thought of the silent, communal decision of the old women to have nothing to do with the whole affair. With what sodality, scenting danger, they had clenched their baskets of poultry to them, or peered around to identify their property! Then they had sat, as now, motionless. It was as if, for them, through the various tragedies of Mexican history, pity, the impulse to approach, and terror, the impulse to escape (as she had learned at college), had been reconciled finally by prudence, the conviction it is better to stay where you are.

And the other passengers? The men in their purple shirts who had a good look at what was going on but didn't get out either? Who wanted to be arrested as an accomplice? they seemed to be saying to her now. *Frijoles* for all; *Tierra, Libertad, Justicia y Ley.* Did all that mean anything? *Quién sabe?* They were not sure of anything save that it was foolish to get mixed up with the police, who had their own way of looking at the law.

Yvonne clutched Hugh's arm but he did not look at her. The *camión* rolled and swayed as before, some more boys jumped on the back of the bus; they began to whistle, the bright tickets winked with their bright colors; and the men looked at each other with an air as of agreement that the bus was outdoing itself. It had never before gone so fast, which must be because it, too, knew today was a holiday.

Dust filtered in through the windows, a soft invasion of dissolution, filling the vehicle.

Then they were at Chapultepec.

The driver kept his hand on the screaming emergency brake as they circled down into the town, which was already invested with the Consul's abhorrence because of his past excesses there. Popocatapetl seemed impossibly close to them now, crouching over the jungle, which had begun to draw the evening over its knees.

For a moment there was a sort of twilight calm in the bus. The stars were out now: the Scorpion had come out of its hole and waited low on the horizon.

The Consul leaned forward and nudged Hugh. "Do you see what I see?" he asked him, inclining his head toward the *pelado,* who had been sitting bolt upright all this time, fidgeting with something in his lap, and wearing much the same expression as before, though he was evidently somewhat rested and sobered.

As the bus stopped in the square, pitching Hugh to his feet, he saw that the *pelado* clutched in his fist a sad, blood-stained pile of silver pesos and centavos, the dying man's money—

The passengers began to crowd out. Some of them looked at the *pelado*, incredulous but always preoccupied. Grinning round at them he perhaps half hoped that some comment would be made. But there was no comment.

The *pelado* paid his fare with part of the blood-stained money, and the driver accepted it. Then he went on taking the other fares.

The three of them stood in the warm evening in the little *zócalo*. The old women had disappeared; it was as if they had been sucked down into the earth.

From a street nearby the crashing, plangent chords of a guitar sounded. And from further away came the bangs and cries of the fiesta.

Yvonne took Hugh's arm. As they walked away they saw the driver, now ostensibly knocked off for the day, and the *pelado*, stepping high and with a fatuous smile of triumph on his face, swagger into a *pulqueria*. The three stared after them and at the name of the saloon, after its doors had swung shut: the Todos-Contentos-y-yo-También.

"Everybody happy," said the Consul, the certainty that he would drink a million tequilas between now and the end of his life stealing over him like a benison and postponing for the moment the necessity for the first one, "Including me."

A bell somewhere compounded sudden wild triphthongs.

They moved in the direction of the fiesta, their shadows falling across the square, bending upward on the door of the Todos-Contentos-y-yo-También, below which the bottom of a crutch had appeared.

They lingered curiously, noticing that the crutch rested for some time where it was, its owner having an argument at the door, or a last drink perhaps.

Presently, the crutch disappeared, as if it had been hoisted away. The door of Todos-Contentos-y-yo-También, through which they could see the bus driver and the *pelado* getting their drinks, was propped back, and they saw something emerge.

Bent double and groaning with the weight, an old, lame Indian was carrying out another Indian, yet older and more decrepit, on his back, by means of a strap clamped to his forehead. He carried the older man and his crutches —he carried both their burdens—

They all stood in the dusk watching the Indian as he disappeared with the old man around a bend in the road, shuffling through the gray-white dust in his poor sandals.

WILHELM

Gabrielle Roy

My first suitor came from Holland. He was called Wilhelm and his teeth were too regular; he was much older
than I; he had a long, sad face . . . at least thus it was
that others made me see him when they had taught me
to consider his defects. As for me, at first I found his
face thoughtful rather than long and peaked. I did not yet
know that his teeth—so straight and even—were false. I
thought I loved Wilhelm. Here was the first man who,
through me, could be made happy or unhappy; here was a
very serious matter.

I had met him at our friends' the O'Neills', who still
lived not far from us in their large gabled house on Rue
Desmeurons. Wilhelm was their boarder; for life is full
of strange things: thus this big, sad man was a chemist
in the employ of a small paint factory then operating in
our city, and—as I have said—lodged with equally uprooted people, the O'Neills, formerly of County Cork in
Ireland. A far journey to have come merely to behave, in
the end, like everyone else—earn your living, try to make
friends, learn our language, and then, in Wilhelm's case,
love someone who was not for him. Do adventures often
turn out so tritely? Obviously enough, though, in those
days I did not think so.

Evenings at the O'Neills' were musical. Kathleen played
"Mother Machree," while her mother, seated on a sofa,
wiped her eyes, trying the while to avert our attention,
to direct it away from herself, for she did not like people
to believe her so deeply stirred by Irish songs. Despite
the music, Elizabeth kept right on digging away at her
arithmetic; she still was utterly indifferent to men. But
Kathleen and I cared a great deal. We feared dreadfully

to be left on the shelf; we feared we should fail to be loved and to love with a great and absolutely unique passion.

When Mrs. O'Neill requested it of me—"to relieve the atmosphere," as she put it—I played Paderewski's "Minuet"; then Wilhelm would have us listen to Massenet on a violin of choice quality. Afterward he would show me in an album scenes of his country, as well as his father's house and the home of his uncle, his father's partner. I think he was anxious to convey to me that his family was better off than you might think if you judged by him— I mean by his having had to quit his native land and come live in our small city. Yet he need have had no fear that I should form an opinion on the basis of silly social appearances; I wanted to judge people in strict accordance with their noble personal qualities. Wilhelm would explain to me how Ruisdael had really most faithfully rendered the full, sad sky of the Low Countries; and he asked me whether I thought I should like Holland enough one day to visit it. Yes, I replied; I should much like to see the canals and the tulip fields.

Then he had had sent to me from Holland a box of chocolates, each one of which was a small vial containing a liqueur.

But one evening he had the ill-starred notion of accompanying me back home, as far as our front door, though it was only two steps away and darkness had not wholly fallen. He was chivalrous: he insisted that a man should not let a woman go home all alone, even if that woman only yesterday had still been playing with hoops or walking on stilts.

Alas! The moment his back was turned, Maman asked me about my young man. "Who is that great beanstalk?"

I told her it was Wilhelm of Holland, and all the rest of it: the box of chocolates, the tulip fields, the stirring sky of Wilhelm's country, the windmills. . . . Now all that was fine and honorable! But why, despite what I thought of appearances, did I believe myself obliged also to speak of the uncle and the father, partners in a small business which . . . which . . . made a lot of money?

My mother at once forbade me to return to the O'Neills, so long, said she, as I had not got over the idea of Wilhelm.

But Wilhelm was clever. One or two days each week he finished work early; on those days he waited for me at the convent door. He took over my great bundle of books—Lord, what homework the Sisters piled on us in those days!—my music sheets, my metronome, and he carried all these burdens to the corner of our street. There he would lower upon me his large and sad blue eyes and say to me, "When you are bigger, I'll take you to the opera, to the theater. . . ."

I still had two years of the convent ahead of me; the opera, the theater seemed desperately far away. Wilhelm would tell me that he longed to see me in an evening gown; that then he would at last remove from its moth-proof bag his dress clothes and that we should go in style to hear symphonic music.

My mother ultimately learned that Wilhelm had the effrontery to carry my books, and it annoyed her very much. She forbade me to see him.

"Still," said I to Maman, "I can hardly prevent his walking next to me along the pavement."

My mother cut through that problem. "If he takes the same sidewalk as you, mind you, cross right over to the other."

Now, she must have sent a message of rebuke to Wilhelm and told him, as she had me, precisely which sidewalk he should take, for I began seeing him only on the opposite side of the street, where he would stolidly await my passage. All the while I was going by, he held his hat in his hand. The other young girls must have been horribly envious of me; they laughed at Wilhelm's baring his head while I was passing. Yet I felt death in my soul at seeing Wilhelm so alone and exposed to ridicule. He was an immigrant, and Papa had told me a hundred times that you could not have too much sympathy, too much consideration for the uprooted, who have surely suffered enough from their expatriation without our adding to it through scorn or disdain. Why then had Papa so completely changed his views, and why was he more set even than Maman against Wilhelm of Holland? True enough, no one at home, since Georgianna's marriage, looked favorably upon love. Perhaps because as a whole we had already had too much to suffer from it. But I—presumably— I had not yet suffered enough at its hands. . . .

And then, as I have said, Wilhelm was clever. Maman had forbidden him to speak to me on the street, but she had forgotten letters. Wilhelm had made great progress in English. He sent me very beautiful epistles which began with: "My own beloved child . . ." or else "Sweet little maid. . . ." Not to be outdone, I replied: "My own dearest heart. . . ." One day my mother found in my room a scrawl on which I had been practicing my handwriting and in which I expressed to Wilhelm a passion that neither time nor cruel obstacles could bend. . . . Had my mother glanced into the volume of Tennyson lying open upon my table, she would have recognized the whole passage in question, but she was far too angry to listen to reason. I was enjoined from writing to Wilhelm, from reading his letters, if, by a miracle, one of them succeeded in penetrating the defenses thrown up by Maman; I was even enjoined from thinking of him. I was allowed only to pray for him, if I insisted upon it.

Until then I had thought that love should be open and clear, cherished by all and making peace between beings. Yet what was happening? Maman was turned into something like a spy, busy with poking about in my wastebasket; and I then thought that she was certainly the last person in the world to understand me! So that was what love accomplished! And where was that fine frankness between Maman and me! Does there always arise a bad period between a mother and her daughter? Is it love that brings it on? . . . And what, what is love? One's neighbor? Or some person rich, beguiling?

During this interval Wilhelm, unable to do anything else for me, sent me many gifts; and at the time I knew nothing of them, for the moment they arrived, Maman would return them to him: music scores, tulip bulbs from Amsterdam, a small collar of Bruges lace, more liqueur-filled chocolates.

The only means left to us by which to communicate was the telephone. Maman had not thought of that. Obviously she could not think of everything; love is so crafty! Then, too, during her loving days the telephone did not exist, and this, I imagine, was why Maman forgot to ban it for me. Wilhelm often called our number. If it was not I who answered, he hung up gently. And many a time did Maman then protest, "What's going on? . . . I shall write the company a letter; I'm constantly being bothered for nothing. At the other end I can barely hear a sort of sighing sound." Naturally she could not foresee how far the tenacity of a Wilhelm would extend.

But when it was I who answered, Wilhelm was scarcely better off. There could be between us no real conversation without its exposing us to the discovery of our secret and consequent prohibition of the telephone. Moreover, we neither of us had any taste for ruses; Gervais employed them when he had on the wire the darling of his heart, to whom he spoke as though she were another schoolboy. But Wilhèlm and I—without blaming Gervais, for love is love, and when it encounters obstacles, is even more worthy!—we strove to be noble in all things. Thus Wilhelm merely murmured to me, from afar, "Dear heart . . ." after which he remained silent. And I listened to his silence for a minute or two, blushing to the roots of my hair.

One day, though, he discovered an admirable way to make me understand his heart. As I was saying "Allo!" his voice begged me to hold the wire; then I made out something like the sound of a violin being tuned, then the opening bars of "Thaïs." Wilhelm played me the whole composition over the phone. Kathleen must have been accompanying him. I heard piano chords somewhere in the distance, and—I know not why—this put me out a trifle, perhaps at thinking that Kathleen was in on so lovely a secret. It was the first time, however, that Wilhelm put me out at all.

Our phone was attached to the wall at the end of a dark little hallway. At first no one was surprised at seeing me spend hours there, motionless and in the most complete silence. Only little by little did the people at home begin to notice that at the telephone I uttered no word. And from then on, when I went to listen to "Thaïs" the hall door would open slightly; someone hid there to spy on me, motioning the others to advance one by one and watch me. Gervais was the worst, and it was very mean on his part, for I had respected his secret. He manufactured reasons for making use of the hall; as he went by he tried to hear what I could be listening to. At first, however, I held the receiver firmly glued to my ear. Then I must already have begun to find "Thaïs" very long to hear through. One evening I allowed Gervais to listen for a moment to Wilhelm's music; perhaps I hoped that he would have enough enthusiasm to make me myself admire the composition. But Gervais choked with mirth; later on I saw him playing the fool in front of the others, at the far end of the living room, bowing an imaginary violin. Even Maman laughed a little, although she tried to remain angry. With a long, sad countenance which—I knew not how—he superimposed upon his own features, Gervais was giving a fairly good imitation of Wilhelm in caricature. I was a little tempted to laugh. For it is a fact that there is something quite comic in seeing a sad person play the violin.

When you consider it, it is astonishing that all of them together should not have thought much sooner of parting me from Wilhelm by the means they so successfully employed from that night forward.

All day long, when I went by, someone was whistling the melody of "Thaïs."

My brother grossly exaggerated the Dutchman's slightly solemn gait, his habit of keeping his eyes lifted aloft. They discovered in him the mien of a Protestant minister, dry—said they—and in the process of preparing a sermon. Maman added that the "Netherlander" had a face as thin as a knife blade. This was the way they now referred to him: the "Netherlander" or the "Hollander." My sister Odette—I should say Sister Edouard—who had been informed and was taking a hand in the matter, even though she had renounced the world, my pious Odette herself told me to forget the "foreigner" . . . that a foreigner is a foreigner. . . .

One evening as I listened to "Thaïs," I thought I must look silly, standing thus stock still, the receiver in my hand. I hung up before the end of the performance.

Thereafter, Wilhelm scarcely crossed my path again.

A year later, perhaps, we learned that he was returning to Holland.

My mother once more became the just and charitable pre-Wilhelm person I had loved so dearly. My father no longer harbored anything against Holland. Maman admitted that Mrs. O'Neill had told her concerning Wilhelm that he was the best man in the world, reliable, a worker, very gentle. . . . And Maman hoped that Wilhelm, in his own country, among his own people, would be loved . . . as, she said, he deserved to be.

UNEMPLOYED

Irving Layton

At that time I used to drop in each morning on the D'Alemberts. They always appeared glad to see me and would welcome me cordially.

"You are looking tired," Calan, the younger of the two sisters, murmurs over a bun she is eating. "As usual, you have gone to bed late and your jacket—ugh—it stinks something dreadful of tobacco." I readily forgave her this last thrust because of the charming way she had of squeezing her small pinkish nose as if to ward off further offense. And then taking my arm she led me forward to a chair and made me sit down.

But it was Mimi who came down to business with blunt precision. "Have you eaten?" Not waiting for an answer or only half listening to my stammered, ineffectual lies, she hastened to place a bowl of strong coffee and some buttered toast before me.

"There now, eat, you good-for-nothing," she clucked noisily.

The D'Alemberts kept a slightly discolored spoon especially for my use. It was an heirloom of the Directory and they knew the deep contentment it gave me to feel it between my thumb and forefinger. I would look up gratefully to Mimi whenever she placed it beside my plate, often losing myself in a reverie where silver spoons and tinkling delicate plates and joyful maidens danced an endless charade. "There's your spoon, *vieillard,* now do hurry up and eat."

Afterward I was escorted into the bedroom of Madame D'Alembert. She kept blinking at me from underneath her coverlet like a bright little animal, all the while speaking her meticulous Parisian French. Her overworked daughters took turns translating her words, yet they seemed powerless against the crystal jet of sound that bubbled out of her mouth and trembled in the air before cascading down the sides of her lace pillow. From time to time, a more than usually emphatic movement of her bonneted head punctuated her discourse. Then the cataract ceased and Mimi, smiling and embarrassed, indicated that her mother wished to dress. I was wheeled around and marched out of the room while another silver spray of sound rose and burst upon the air.

"*A bientôt, Monsieur Tennent.*"

"*A bientôt, Madame D'Alembert.*"

The living room was modestly furnished. An electric clock, the slender hand moving silently across its face, sat on a long, brown table. The clock was small and square, yet each time I saw it I was reminded of my landlady's horologe with its heavy, brassy notes striking out each splendid hour. Whenever it struck and I heard the booming, reverberating echoes—I was out of work and had nothing better to do—I would mutter to myself, "Nine . . . ten . . . eleven . . . cups of sand emptied down the winds of eternity." On the walls of the D'Alembert living room were various framed pictures taken from Greek mythology and *L'Illustration*. An enormous green vase contained in delicate basketing and gazed upon by silver peacocks, one on each side, ornamented the mantelpiece; and facing it on the wall opposite was a plate of the "Four Jolly Friars." A green oblong carpet covered the floor.

"Shall you read us something?" asked Calan, holding up a book to me. The two *minettes* were not exactly in love with their studies, but stories read or told to them they could listen to by the hour. I selected Gorki's beautiful legend, "The Fourth Nail," to read, and I can still remember their intent looks while Mimi would gasp and suck lusciously at an "Oh," puckering up her mouth if something sad or terrible happened.

"What a wonderful story," Mimi cried.

"And so beautifully told, too," commented Calan, on whom the somber biblical prose had made a profound impression. "But how can spirits make themselves heard?" Wherewith this disciple of Pragmatism seized her *Sta-Sta* and began cutting up a new dress for her.

"As for me I do not like it at all," I said drily. "It is fantastic, stupid, untrue."

"How can you say such things?" demanded Mimi angrily, who had not yet recovered from her immersion in Russian belles lettres. "It is you who are stupid."

And Calan shook her head over *Sta-Sta* and repeated slowly, "You are stupid. . . . Yes, you are ve-ry stupid."

It was evidently necessary to teach them a lesson. "Life," I began magnificently, "life is never like that. There is no single niche in it for beauty or truth, or suffering and endurance for the sake of either. And that is why tinkling legends are always conjugated in the past tense."

"You are always talking like that. By the way you speak no one would imagine there were ever any good people or good things to live for." The healthy color had left Mimi's face and her hand was clenched into a fist.

"All the same, life is not like that," I repeated fixedly. I envied and in turn was exasperated by her youthful self-assurance, her vigor, her strident optimism. An old smelly coat with which I had covered myself one bitterly cold night seemed to wave its sleeves mournfully at me. I wiped the vision away with a movement of my hand. "They will think me ungrateful if I continue like this," I reflected bitterly. So to change the subject, I said, "I have been to see my cousin."

"The rich one?" enquired Calan, who had put away her sewing and was now regarding an old atlas attentively.

I nodded. "It is altogether impossible to imagine what a gross and disgusting creature he is. An unclean beast, all flesh and perspiration and avarice. And his wife has too long shared the same room with him to be in any way his superior. Each morning they finger tenderly the pictures and marble statues they have bought at the auction sales and quarrel poisonously over their arrangement. 'This is the room for such and such a picture,' says his wife. 'No,' says her spouse, his artistic sensibilities profoundly outraged, 'the frame doesn't match the wallpaper in the least.' So they trip corpulently from wall to wall, stopping to finger, entreat, expostulate, and shout before every picture and engraving."

The two *minettes* burst out laughing. "But Paul, you must be exaggerating," cried Mimi, reveling in the vision of two slow bellies floating obesely before her eyes. In the midst of their mirthful protestations Madame D'Alembert had swept into the room and was bowing graciously to us in conscious imitation of the *haute noblesse*. So I rose from my comfortable armchair, bowed stiffly to her, and said the first complimentary thing that flew into my head.

She was not very pleased with my poor efforts at gallantry, or so pretended; but I remembered that on one occasion when I was indiscreet enough to compare her to a well-fed squirrel, she had been moved to remark:

"This is not at all flattering."

"No," I had countered hastily, my disinterested love of art making me reckless, "this is the truth, *la verité*."

"*Oui,* I love *la verité*."

But I saw the icy smile that accompanied her words and came to my own swift conclusions about her love of truth.

She took the other armchair and sat down opposite to me, her knees almost touching my own.

"Last night I went to see my cousin," I resumed. "You will not believe this, but whenever fruits are served he cuts them with his own penknife and offers a handsome slice to each of his guests."

"Oh," exclaimed Madame D'Alembert, making a small, black hole under her fattish nose, "and his wife . . . what does she do? Surely—"

"His wife," I answered with a serious air, "cuts the slices once again."

Small ripples of laughter raced up to her cheeks and lost themselves in the many furrows of her forehead. On her lower lip, savagely disfigured by gossip, appeared a white speck of saliva. With the forefinger of her right hand she pressed my knee.

"But you mustn't deal too harshly with them, my friend. They have tasted success late in life. Let them enjoy it in their own way."

"Success! Pooh! Do you call that success, Maman?" demanded Mimi, who was affirming or denying something violently. "That is what I call crawling on one's belly . . . with a grin on one's face, too."

Calan was busily counting the red spots of the British Empire. "Five . . . six. . . ." Finally she gave up. "Everything is so stupid," she commented sagely.

"No, my child, only people can be stupid," Madame

D'Alembert said primly, her manner conveying that she had uttered an epigram not unworthy of the great Voltaire himself.

I was thinking furiously, "She considers me a failure, a parasite. It is evident by the way she is looking at me." A gust of self-pity blew through the frayed edges of my soul. I shivered. "I have no right to an opinion on anything," I reflected. I hated the shiny, round, complacent face in front of me, streaked like an autumn apple which, now that Madame D'Alembert was smiling and showing her small white teeth, looked as if someone had taken a bite of it. Before I could begin the story of the torn overcoat, she had bounced out of the armchair and was commanding, while I dreaded the words she spoke:

"A table! A table!"

The family appeared to be regarding me attentively and I went hot and cold with embarrassment. *"Est-ce-que vous mangez avec nous?"* Even before Calan began translating her words to me I had already seized their meaning, and in my nervousness and confusion, stammered:

"No, really . . . really, you will not believe me . . . but I am not the least bit hungry. Maybe later," I said, trying to save myself that way.

"You must eat with us now," asserted Mimi forcefully.

"Father said you must take great care of yourself. Your X ray revealed clouded lungs, a weak heart, bad—"

I implored her not to go over again the melancholy catalogue of my ailments which Dr. D'Alembert seemingly had given to the family as a precious keepsake.

Madame D'Alembert placed before me a steaming dish of cooked ham, over which was piled a lavish heap of appetizing vegetables. The good smell rose to my nostrils and made me forget my self-reproaches, although it is true I almost choked on the first carrot and had to swallow a glass of water before my spasmodic coughing ceased. When I had cleaned my plate with a piece of soft bread, I grew bold enough to venture:

"Your mother does make excellent meals. I love the way she serves the cooked ham."

"There's bouillon today . . . with rice, you know," offered Calan.

"I believe your mother would make an excellent bouillon

out of anything," I said, and then added facetiously, "even out of black beetles."

We were always making witticisms like that at the time. One evening, for instance, when I had been invited to stay for supper and I had enquired whether they had enough to spare, Madame D'Alembert had replied with excellent spirit, "We can always scrape the dirt off the floor."

But I do not know what possessed me to blurt out now, "And if your mother threw herself in with the beetles, I should be unable to tell the difference."

Calan began rendering my words into remorseless French. Madame D'Alembert started as though she had been struck with a ruler, tightened her lips so that thin white lines covered them, and let drop her hand upon the table.

"*C'est sâle,*" she exclaimed. "*C'est dégoutant!*" I got up from my chair as if an enormous hand had dived through the ceiling and gripped me.

"Calan," I shouted excitedly, "you have mistranslated me! I didn't say that!" I turned to Madame D'Alembert. I was trembling visibly and was now shouting at the top of my voice, "I swear I didn't say that at all. Calan has made a stupid blunder."

It was Mimi who came to my rescue. "Yes . . . you said something entirely different. You said the beetles—"

Angry and humiliated as I was, I couldn't help smiling. I turned the evil jest so that Madame D'Alembert and the beetles weren't mentioned in the same sentence. Then my eyes slowly filled with tears.

The injured woman must have guessed my tortured feelings for she gave me a quick glance of sympathy. Mimi kept her gaze steadfastly on the tablecloth, seeking there the answer to my erratic behavior. Calan, however, sensed that a conspiracy had been hatched under her very eyes. She persisted valiantly in the strict observance of the truth:

"I tell you I didn't translate him falsely. I tell you, I didn't. He said—"

But nobody paid any attention to her.

Madame D'Alembert shook her head sadly. She thought of her own sorrows: of her unmanageable husband, of expensive chinaware, of kind people like herself, of the bitterness of growing old, and she began to weep softly.

"Why are you crying, Maman?" asked Calan, eyeing me as though I was in some way responsible for her mother's tears.

And Madame D'Alembert said quietly, "I am crying for the sorrows of humanity."

The daughters helped with the dishes and their rich voices blended in a tender French ballad above the running hot water and steam. I returned to the living room and lit a pipe, hoping to suck courage and faith through its stem—at least, forgetfulness. My dependence, my parasitism, ate like a crooked, rusty nail into my soul. How peaceful it was here. My mind went back to the day, almost two years ago, when my employer had called me into his office and handed me my last pay envelope.

Fate, it seemed, had seized me and placed me in a bottle and pasted a label on it, UNEMPLOYED. I began to stamp my feet impatiently, making all sorts of absurd gestures and shouting at the top of my voice. In vain! No one heard me. My friends fell away from me, or were themselves encased in bottles, pressing their noses against the glass and striking the same futile, ridiculous postures. Even when, seeing their senseless antics and guessing my own, I laughed out aloud, no one heard me. That depressed me most of all. Homunculi in bottles! All of us staring and grimacing at one another, our frantic capers moving the onlookers alternately to compassion and disgust. Only the D'Alemberts had remained steadfast in their friendship for me. My brother? Raoul was no doubt running his passengers up to the Laurentians, collecting his fee with a cool smirk and a bow. A year ago, penniless as myself, he had borne his martyrdom with befitting modesty. Now his soul was as slickly confidential as a billboard.

"You here again," he would say when he saw me coming up to him. My philosophy was well known to him by now. "A clever man," I had once declared in his presence, "does not have to work." He dropped a half-dollar piece into my palm and climbed into his car without looking at me. "Education is a great thing," he returned, as I stepped forward to thank him, "but keep away from me."

The remote past, secure and confident, took on warmth and color.

"What are you smiling at?" enquired Mimi as she came through the doorway. I thought she never looked more beautiful than now. Her hair was braided in two lovely coils around her head. Her wide-apart gray eyes, candid as a child's, now regarded me thoughtfully.

"I was thinking of the past," I said. "How fancy uses the excrement of life to fertilize beautiful visions."

She smiled and sat down beside me. For a few minutes neither of us spoke. A fly sailed into the room and settled itself before the clock as if to see how many happy summer hours remained.

Mimi edged over and took my hand in her own. She begged, "You'll came to Valcartier with us for the summer? Paul, you must. It won't hardly be an additional expense." The fly crawled diffidently on the brown table and then flew to Renoir's "Baigneuse," tactfully bringing her a precarious modesty. "You'll pay Maman whenever you can . . . whenever you have your first short story accepted."

I winced as she touched so carelessly this last, futile disguise.

"When we're in the country, I can get a job on a dairy farm," Mimi went on. "That'll pay for your keep."

I pressed her hand.

"Why don't you speak?" Mimi said.

"What's there to say?"

"Will you come?"

I was silent.

"You look worried. Is . . . is it that you feel you can't accept?"

"Quite the contrary," I said.

Mimi's piquant little face was turned upward to mine. I looked directly into her eyes.

"If I look worried, it's because I know I am quite capable of accepting."

Calan had overheard her sister's invitation and she now came bounding to us. "Oh, Paul, you will come with us to Val. It will be such fun and you will tell us ever so many delightful stories." Her eyes glistened with eagerness, my heart ached, and I wanted to kiss the naked, dimpled arms she held out to me.

But I answered softly, "No, my *minettes,* I must find something to work at." I lied bravely, "In fact, a certain man I know had promised me a job." A twinge of remaining conscience made me add, "At least, he only half promised me."

I looked at the clock and rose to my feet abruptly. It was nearly two.

"Need some matches," I mumbled. "I'll run down to the store and get them." At the door I shouted *au revoir* to Madame D'Alembert, who came toward us grimacing and wiping her hands on her checked apron.

"Bonjour, Paul. . . . *Demain?"*

I nodded my head ambiguously.

"You'll come tomorrow, won't you?" asked Mimi and Calan together.

"No," I smiled. "I'm never coming back. Good-bye, my *minettes."*

I didn't.

A TRIP FOR MRS. TAYLOR

Hugh Garner

Mrs. Taylor got out of bed at five o'clock that morning, an hour ahead of her usual time for getting up. She moved around her attic room with the stealth of a burglar, making herself her morning cup of tea on the hot plate, and dressing quietly so as not to disturb her landlady, Mrs. Connell, on the floor below.

She dressed her tiny self carefully, donning a clean white camisole and her black Sunday frock. After she had drunk her tea and eaten a slice of thinly margarined toast she washed her cup and saucer in some water she had drawn from the bathroom the evening before, and put them away on her "kitchen" shelf in the clothes closet. Then she tiptoed down the steep stairs to the bathroom and washed her face and hands—"a lick and a spit" as she called it.

When she returned to her room her seventy-six-year-old face shone with wrinkled cleanliness and the excitement of the day. She combed her thinning gray hair and did it up with pins into an unsevere bun at the back of her head. Then, half guiltily, she powdered her face and touched her cheeks with a rouge-tipped finger. Going over to her old trunk in the corner she extracted from its depths two pieces of jewelry wrapped in tissue paper. One of the pieces was a gold locket holding a faded photograph of her dead husband Bert, while the other was an old-fashioned gold chain bangle with a small lock shaped like a heart. She had lost the key to the bangle long ago, but it did not matter; her hands were now so thin that it slipped easily over her wrist.

When she had adjusted the jewelry she took her old black straw hat from its paper bag and put it on, primping a bit before the Woolworth mirror on the wall, smiling at herself and wishing that her false teeth were a little whiter.

All through her preparations she had been taking hurried glances at the alarm clock on the dresser, but now, when she was ready to go, she saw that she still had nearly two hours before train time. The train left at seven o'clock Standard Time, which was eight o'clock Daylight Saving, and here it was only a quarter to six. Still, it would take a half-hour to get downtown to the station, and she couldn't afford to be late on this day of days.

She unclasped her small cardboard suitcase and carefully checked its contents once again. There was a clean change of underwear, a towel and soap, some handkerchiefs, two pairs of black lisle stockings, Bert's picture in its frame, and one of the two boys in uniform, her blouse and blue serge skirt, and the red velvet dress that Mrs. Eisen had given her the year before. The dress didn't fit her, but she liked its rich color and the feeling of opulence it gave, just to possess it.

Picking up her heavy Bible from the top of the dresser, she said to herself, "I really should take it along, I guess. It'll weigh me down, but I couldn't go anywhere without it." Quickly making up her mind she placed the Bible in the suitcase and fastened the lid. Then she sat down on the edge of the bed and let the wonderful coming events of the day take over her thoughts.

The idea for the trip had come to her about a week before, on the day she had received her July old-age pension check. She had been down to the main post office, mailing a set of hand-crocheted runners to her daughter-in-law, Ruth, in Montreal when the idea struck her. Seeing all the holiday crowds hurrying into the maw of the station had prompted her to go in and inquire about train times.

The hurry and excitement of the place had brought back the nostalgic memories of those happier times when she and Bert and young Johnnie—yes, and young Bert, too, who was killed in Italy—had gone away sometimes in the summer. Their trips hadn't been long ones, and their destination was usually the home of her dead cousin Flora in Jamesville, but they had been filled with all the hustle and bustle of getting ready, packing salmon and peanut-butter sandwiches for their lunches, and making sure Bert had the tickets. There had been the warm picnicky feeling going to the station on the streetcar, trying to keep young Bert from kneeling on the seat and brushing his feet on the man beside him (she wiped away a vagrant tear at the memory) and the awareness that she *belonged* to the crowds around her.

That was the thing she had missed most during the past few years, the feeling of being one with those about her. The knowledge that she was old and ignored by younger people sometimes caused her to wish she were dead, but then appalled by the irreverence of such thoughts she would take refuge in her Bible, which was now her only solace.

Her loneliness and the striving to live on her old-age pension made mere existence a hardship. Mrs. Connell, her landlady, was a kindly soul, not much younger than herself, but she had no conception of what it was like to be cooped up month after month in a dreary little room, without even a radio to keep you company, without even a cat or a dog or a canary—nothing but the four walls, an electric plate, a bed, and a dresser.

Of course, she told herself, she could have gone to live with Johnnie and Ruth in Montreal, but she'd seen too much of that sort of thing in the past. When Johnnie had married down there after the war she had felt a sinking in the stomach at the thought that he, too, was leaving her. "Come on down there with me, Ma," he had said, but she had sensed the reluctance behind his words. "I'm not going to be a built-in baby sitter for my grandchildren," she had answered, trying to cover her sense of loss and disappointment under her bantering words. She was independent, a woman who had run her own home for years, and brought up her two boys on the skimpy and unreliable wages of a laborer husband. But sometimes her independence melted under her silent tears, and she wished that once, just once, somebody would need her again.

But today was not the time for such gloomy thoughts. She glanced at the clock and saw that it was after seven. She stood up, straightened her hat once more, and picking up the heavy suitcase, made her way from the room, closing the door silently behind her. She had no wish to waken Mrs. Connell and have to answer the surprised questions of that lady; this trip was going to be a secret one, known only to herself.

She hurried down the street through the cloying warmth of the summer morning as fast as the heavy bag would allow her. When she reached the streetcar stop she put the suitcase down on the sidewalk and searched in her purse for a car ticket. There was very little money left from her pension check, but by doing without a few things to eat over the past week she had managed to save the expenses for the trip.

When the streetcar came along she climbed aboard and sat down near the front of the car. She was aware of the stares from the men and girls who were going to work, and she felt important for the first time in months. There was something friendly in the glances they gave her, and perhaps even a slight envy that she should be going away while they could only look forward to another stifling day in their offices and factories.

The downtown streets at this hour of the day were strange to her, but there was a tired camaraderie among the people getting on and off the car which brought back memories she had almost forgotten; once again she saw herself as a young woman going to work as they were, stepping down from the open-sided cars they had in those days, proud of her narrow waist and new high-buttoned boots. She felt almost young again and smiled apologetically as a thin girl in slacks nearly tripped over her suitcase.

As they neared the station several people carrying pieces of luggage boarded the car, and Mrs. Taylor smiled at them as if they were partners in a conspiracy. Most of them smiled back at her, and she felt that the anticipation and preparation for a journey was only exceeded by its actual beginning.

When she alighted from the streetcar a young man in army uniform took her suitcase from her, and holding her by the arm, led her across the street.

"This is a heavy bag for you to be carrying," he said in a conversational tone.

"It is a little heavy," she answered, "but I haven't far to go."

"Everybody seems to be going away today," he said. "I guess I won't get a seat on the northbound train."

"That's a shame," Mrs. Taylor answered, trying to keep up with the soldier's long strides. "Are you on leave?"

"Sort of. I was down here on a forty-eight-hour pass from camp. I should have been back last night."

"I hope you don't get into trouble," she said. She felt suddenly sorry for the young man—only a boy really. She wanted to tell him that both her sons had been overseas during the war, and that young Bert had been killed. But then she thought he might think she was bragging, or trying to make him feel bad because he'd been too young to go.

As they entered the cathedrallike station concourse, she said to the young soldier, "I can manage now, thank you," and he stopped and placed the bag on the floor.

"If you're taking the northbound train I'll carry the suitcase to the gates for you," he offered.

"No. No, thank you. I'm taking the Montreal train," she answered.

"Well then, I'll have to leave you. Good-bye. Have a nice holiday," he said.

"Yes," she whispered, her voice cracking with emotion. As he walked away she shouted after him, "Good luck, son!" She watched him disappear into the crowd and felt a nameless dread for what might be before him. He was such a nice, polite young boy, but what was more he was the first person outside Mrs. Connell and the man at the grocery store that she had spoken to all week.

The man at the ticket window seemed surprised as she bought her ticket, but he stamped it on the back and handed it to her without a word. When she asked him where to get the Montreal train he pointed across the station to a queue of people lined up before a pair of gates, and she picked up her suitcase and made her way toward it.

The crowd was a good-natured one, as she had known it would be, and she spent several minutes taking stock of the other travelers. It was unbelievable that so many people had awakened this morning as she had done, with the idea of catching the same train. All night as she had tossed and turned in anticipation of the morning these other people had probably been doing the same thing, unknown to her. The knowledge that they all shared the same sense of immediacy seemed to bring them closer together, and they were united in their impatience to be going.

But Mrs. Taylor was not impatient. She knew the value

of time—she who had so little of it left—and this waiting
with the others in the crowded station was as exciting to
her as reaching the end of her trip—more so in fact.

She looked about her at the young people with their
overnight bags and their tennis rackets; at the older men
carrying haversacks and fishing rods, each looking a little
sheepish like boys caught playing hookey; the three girls
in the brand-new clothes whispering together ahead of her
in the line; the young couple with the baby in the go-cart
standing outside the queue, smiling at one another and
talking together in French; the two priests in white panama
hats who nodded solemnly and looked hot and cool at the
same time in their black alpaca jackets.

This was what she had looked forward to all week! It
was just as she had expected it to be, and she didn't care
if the gates never opened; the best part of any journey
was the waiting for the train.

There was the sound of a small scuffle behind her, and a
young woman's tired voice said, "Garry, stop that right
now!"

Mrs. Taylor turned and saw a slight dark girl wearing a
shabby suit trying vainly to hold a young baby in her arms
while she tugged at a little boy who was swinging on the
end of a harness. The boy was trying desperately to break
away.

"Here, young man, where do you think you're going!"
Mrs. Taylor said sternly, bending down and catching him
around the waist. The child stopped struggling and looked
at her in surprise.

"He's been a little devil all morning," his mother said.
"He knows I can't do much with him while I've got the
baby in my arms."

"Now you just stand still!" Mrs. Taylor warned, letting
him go and smiling at the young woman to show that she
did not mean to override her authority.

"He'll stop for you," the girl said. "At home he'll do
anything for his grandma, but when he knows I've got the
baby to look after, he takes advantage of it."

Mrs. Taylor nodded. "I know; I had two boys myself,"
she said. "Is the baby a boy, too?"

"Yes. Four months."

Mrs. Taylor reached over and pulled the light blanket

from the baby's face. "He's a big boy for four months, isn't he?" she asked.

She learned that the young woman's name was Rawlinson, and that she was on her way to New Brunswick to join her husband, who was in the Air Force. The girl's mother had wanted to come down to the station with her, but her arthritis had kept her at home. She also learned that the baby's name was Ian, and that his mother was twenty-two years old.

She in turn told the girl that she had lived alone since her oldest boy's marriage, and that Johnnie now lived with his wife and a young daughter in Montreal. In answer to the other's questions she also told the young woman that her husband and youngest son were dead, that she received the old-age pension, and that it wasn't enough in these days of high prices.

Mrs. Rawlinson said that a friend of her mother's went to the same church as Mrs. Taylor. Mrs. Taylor didn't recognize the woman's name, although she thought she knew who the girl meant: a stout woman with short-bobbed bluish hair who wore a Persian lamb coat in the winter.

She realized now that she had been starved for conversation, and she was so grateful for having met the young woman with the children.

"They should be opening the gates pretty soon," said the girl, looking at her wristwatch. "The train is due to leave in twenty minutes."

From the loudspeaker came the voice of the stationmaster announcing that the northbound train was due to leave. Mrs. Taylor thought about the nice young soldier who had overstayed his pass.

The little boy, Garry, indicated that he wanted to go to the toilet.

"Wait till we get on the train, dear," his mother pleaded desperately.

Mrs. Taylor said eagerly, "I'll hold the baby while you take him, if you like."

"Will you? Gee, that's swell!" the young woman exclaimed. She handed the baby over, and Mrs. Taylor cradled him in her arms, while the young mother and the little boy hurried away.

She pulled back the blanket once again from the baby's

face and saw that he was awake. She placed her finger on his chin and smiled at him, and he smiled back at her. The moment took her back more years than she cared to remember, back to a time when young Bert was the same age. She was filled with the remembered happiness of those days, and she thought, "I'd give up every minute more I have to live just to be young again and have my boys as babies for one more day." Then to hide the quick tears that were starting from her eyes she began talking to the baby in her arms, rocking back and forth on her heels in a gesture not practiced for years.

When the woman and the little boy returned she gave up the baby reluctantly. She and the young woman stood talking together like old friends, or like a mother and daughter-in-law. They discussed teething troubles, the housing shortage, and how hard it was to raise a family these days. They were so engrossed in their new-found friendship that they failed to notice when the man opened the gates.

The crowd began pushing them from behind, and Mrs. Taylor picked up her suitcase in one hand and grasped Garry's harness with the other. Then, followed by Mrs. Rawlinson and the baby, they climbed the set of iron stairs to the platform.

Mrs. Taylor's feet were aching after the long wait at the gates, but her face shone with happiness as she steered the small boy alongside the train. The boy's mother drew up to her, and they walked together to the day-coach steps where a trainman waited to help them aboard.

"You've got your hands full there, Granny," he said, picking up the little boy and depositing him in the vestibule of the car.

She was pleased that he mistook her for the children's grandmother, and she beamed at him, not attempting to correct his mistake.

Inside the coach she led the way to a pair of seats that faced each other at the end of the car, and dropped into one with a tired sigh. Then she held the baby while its mother took the harness off Garry and placed her small case and shopping bags on the luggage rack.

"Am I ever glad to get aboard!" Mrs. Rawlinson exclaimed. "I'd been dreading the wait at the station. Now I've only got to change trains in Montreal and I'll be all set."

"It's quite a job traveling with children," Mrs. Taylor sympathized. "Don't worry, I know. I've done enough of it in my day," she said with slight exaggeration.

Mrs. Rawlinson laid the baby on the seat beside her, before sitting back and relaxing against the cushions. The coach soon filled up, and several people eyed their double seat enviously. Mrs. Taylor was glad she had been able to get well up in the queue at the gates.

When the train started she moved over close to the window and pointed out to the little boy the buildings and streets they passed, and the tiny inconsequential people they were leaving behind them. Young Garry shouted excitedly, "Choo-choo!" at every engine they passed in the yards.

The city looked hot and uncomfortable in the morning sun, and Mrs. Taylor was surprised that all the little ant-like people didn't simply jump on a train and get away from it. It was remarkable that the ones she could see walking the streets were strangers to her now, as if there was no connection between them and the people on the train. They were a race apart; an earth-bound race separated from herself by movement and time, and the sense of adventure of her and her fellows.

She picked out landmarks as the train gathered speed; the streets she had lived on as a girl, now turned into industrial sites; the spinning mill where she had once worked; the soot-blackened park where she and Bert had walked so many years ago. . . .

"We won't be getting into Montreal until suppertime," Mrs. Rawlinson said from the opposite seat, intruding upon her memories.

"No."

"I'll bet you'll be glad to get there and see your grand-daughter."

Mrs. Taylor shook her head. "I'm not going to Montreal today," she said sadly. "I can't afford to go that far."

"But—but couldn't your son send you the fare?" asked the girl.

She had to protect Johnnie, who wasn't really mean, just forgetful. "Oh, he could, but I've never really cared to go that far," she lied.

"Well—well, where are you going then?" the young woman asked, her curiosity getting the best of her.

"Not very far. Just up the line a piece," Mrs. Taylor answered, smiling. "It's just a short trip."

The train seemed to flow across the underpasses marking the streets. Soon the industrial areas were left behind, and they began rushing through the residential districts.

Mrs. Taylor was enthralled with the sight of the rows of houses as seen from the rear; yards waving with drying clothes, and every house having an individuality of its own. She only recognized some of the familiar streets after the train had passed them, they looked so different when seen from her hurtling point of vantage.

In a few minutes the train began to slow down for an outlying station, and the conductor came along the car collecting tickets. When Mrs. Taylor handed him her small bit of pasteboard, he asked, "Are you getting off here, madam?"

"Yes, I am," Mrs. Taylor replied, coloring with embarrassment.

"Have you any luggage?"

She pointed to the suitcase at her feet, ashamed to face the stares of those who were watching her.

"Fine. I'll carry it off for you," the conductor said calmly, as if old ladies took ten-cent train rides every day of the week.

She stood up then and said good-bye to the little boy, letting her hand rest for a long minute on his tousled head. She warned him to be a good boy and do what his mother told him.

"You must think I'm crazy just coming this far," she said to Mrs. Rawlinson. "You see, I've wanted to take a trip for so long, and this was sort of—pretending."

The young woman shook the surprised look from her face. "No, I don't, Mrs. Taylor," she said. "I wish you were coming all the way. I don't know what I'd have ever done without you to help me with Garry."

"It was nice being able to help. You'll never know how much I enjoyed it," Mrs. Taylor answered, her face breaking into a shy smile. "Good-bye, dear, and God bless you. Have a nice journey."

"Good-bye," the young woman said. "Thanks! Thanks a lot!"

Mrs. Taylor stood on the station platform and waved at the young woman and her son, who waved back at her as the train began to move again. Then she picked up her bag and walked along the platform to the street.

When she boarded a streetcar the motorman looked down at her and said, "You look happy; you must have had a swell vacation."

She smiled at him. "I had a wonderful trip," she answered.

And it had been wonderful! While all the others in the train would get bored and tired after a few hours of travel, she could go back to her room and lie down on the bed, remembering only the excitement and thrill of going away, and the new friends she had made. It was wonderful, just wonderful, she said to herself. Perhaps next month, if she could afford it, she would take a trip to the suburbs on the Winnipeg train!

ANGUISH OF GOD

Yves Thériault

A spring morning is like that when it is born in the mist and then comes to full life.

It has shaken off the white everywhere and emerged in golds and greens and you have loved it very much, because it was bright and beautiful.

It was just such a one that marks the first moment of this story.

Everything speaks here of Angoisse-de-Dieu—of his right name, David Coudois—who is a blacksmith and who also thinks.

So the morning was drowned in mist so hard and white that you have to open your eyes wide to see where you are going.

Great, oppressive white with sounds within, the voices of the cows as they are being led to pasture and of the men leading the cows.

Same thing in the blacksmith's shop where it is traditionally dark, there are shreds of mist which have come in by the big door and which hang near the ceiling.

David wanted to take hold of one, see what it's made of. But he laughed as he tried and the Judith, his own Judith who is there, watched him do it and laughed also. Good springtime laughter, the rich sound feverish with memory and desires.

I'd like to get it.

So said the blacksmith.

Then no more. He did not say how the forge threw its fire which danced with long red tongues on the walls and that *la* Judith with her dark eyes and her soft bosom also, like the walls, had traces of fire playing on the pink of her skin. He did not say that he would have liked to catch

the fringe of the mist and to offer it to her as a crazy
jewel. That would have been words and even if a whole
poem haunted him inside, David could not say it. It beat
in him like a bellows and his heart which was going, too,
but that only made a glowing in his eyes and no other
words than:

"I'd like to get it."

"I'd really like for you to catch it."

And she also had confused images in her body as regards her heart and head. "Oh, look, I'd so much like to
have the mist. Catch it and make me a shawl to adorn my
neck. And then come closer, closer so that we touch." But
she, too, had simply said, "I'd really like for you to catch
it."

No, this morning in the low, rickety, ramshackle building, David and *la* Judith were thinking of things that they
could not say.

The point is that they do have the right to think of things
this way that would be guilty for others. *La* Judith is
David's and she's very much his. And in the semidarkness
of the shop they suddenly felt very close to each other.
Near each other within, far more than skin deep. The inside where ideas are made.

And David who thinks and who wants to understand
clearly all there is in life and in the world has great joy
from these thoughts.

Then he said:

"*La* Judith, how long have you been with me?"

"Two years."

She had answered with a smile, which had seemed like a
light in the dark nook.

"I'm very glad that you stay."

He had not said more this time than another. It was
what was not said that was great and beautiful and that
la Judith understood well, "Go. . . ." Then she came a
little closer, wishing that the distance, too, might not be
so long if David were feeling any tender thoughts.

But Daumier entered just then.

Daumier, the joker, who must not see David and *la*
Judith loving, since he would scoff at them in the hamlet
and make those laugh who find the frolics of others ridiculous.

Then the game is broken off and the shop becomes dirty and damp and not very beautiful.

It becomes once more a black hole lighted by the fire in the forge and clouded by the whitish-gray mist from outside.

Daumier has done that, and he said:

"My horse, *le* David, needs shoes."

And David goes to the horse while *la* Judith goes out and goes to the house.

And perhaps despite Daumier's arrival, the Judith and *le* David have loved each other well this morning and that it is going to tie them still more strongly for the coming year.

And if she is singing very low in a voice muffled by the mist, it's because she feels in her man things that make her dream beautifully.

Daumier in the shop speaks to make David reply, for the blacksmith had become silent and awkward since Daumier had entered and *la* Judith had left and since that something had cropped up.

David goes toward the forge, and reaching it, he turns toward Daumier.

"Do you believe in God, you?"

"Yes and no. I believe in him because they say so. If I did not believe it, and if there is one, it would be bad and I would sin. So I believe it. If there isn't one, I have all my trouble for nothing, and if there is one I gain on the exchange."

David remained dreamy, hammer in hand, for a moment reflecting carefully, then he turned toward the forge.

Since the year of the big crops, the last before the drought had interfered, David Coudois had had great doubts.

Not that he knew what caused the doubts, but it was like a disease.

He had said one time to the curé:

"I'm searching for God."

But that had been all. He had not been able to explain how and in what he was looking for God.

"I'm looking for God."

Inside him was a great muddy sea. You couldn't see inside; yet it's like waves are stirring.

Today the wave is strong; tomorrow it is still. But there

is always the movement and the denseness. It moves and you can't tell what it hides.

He was saying to himself, "Is there a God?"

And he begins again, "But where is he?"

And that kept up for many years.

And from time to time, he spoke of it to the people in the hamlet.

To Lorgneau he had said:

"I'm looking for God; I'd like to see how he is made."

Lorgneau, who believed nothing, had laughed.

And le Troublé, to whom David had spoken one day, because he had no person to speak to and because the wave was enormous and more muddy than ever, had shaken his head without a smile.

"God is a great fire far away, farther than the sun. When I sin it burns me in the guts. That's because it is fire, I tell you."

But David had not listened to him. "A big fire like your forge on market days. It is perhaps in this way that you have God in your hands."

David was lost in his confusion.

But if we are to speak of it, we must say that the hamlet knew of David's distress, and the mother Druseau, who knew how to put words together, had nicknamed him Angoisse-de-Dieu.

Ah, yes . . .

. . . she had said . . .

David Coudois, the man filled with the agony of God.

And it stuck.

They said "David" to him.

In front of him.

But behind, he had become Angoisse-de-Dieu.

When he had taken in *la* Judith, the name remained, but the doubt in David's insides blurred somewhat.

For a moment he believed that God was love like that he enjoyed with *la* Judith. But that wasn't so, for after a hard night, David still had the dark tide in his heart.

And as the months passed, the greater grew the tide.

One day le Troublé, who sometimes had the light of genius deep in his eyes, which made him feared by women, had said in the shop:

"David, you are very skillful with your hands; you make

great things with your hammer, anvil, and soft iron. If you are looking for God and don't find him, invent him."

Which had made David smile.

Even whole days at a time, each time that le Troublé's words returned, "Invent him, manufacture him, make God, become more than God himself since you will have made him."

And David would stop to think. God is mover since we move, and he is jointed since we move, and he thinks since we think and move.

But he found le Troublé's idea quite funny.

And this morning great sheets of slate had just been piled up in his mind. Like things that are built, they became an ordered pile. David had seen the shape of love close at hand.

He had wanted to seize a shred of mist and that had struck him. A shred of mist was love then? Trivial, fragile, colorless, lifeless but capable of muffling and covering so as to hinder seeing ordinary things as they are.

And if love had come so close to revealing itself, wouldn't it be that God also only waited the moment to reveal himself?

"Eh, Daumier, God for you is what?"

Daumier thought carefully.

"It's something way up high that has no form, but that is very great and very powerful and that is going to punish us if we do bad deeds."

"But you don't see him in your idea."

"Yes, he is very great, I think, and very long with huge arms which can crush everything. If he gets angry, we will die as in the flood."

"I myself see him in a different way. It seems to me that it's all wheels and levers and that it's going all the time and if it gets angry it's going to burst and is going to perish."

Daumier wondered why there was such a flash in the depth of David's eyes. He saw it when David threw the glowing shoe on the ground which he should have put on the horse's hoof.

"I'm going to make your God for you . . . with my hands. I won't look for him any more. I'll have him and he'll be my own work."

Daumier wanted to know:

"My horse, you are going to shoe him?"

For David was already searching in the bottom of a big drawer trying to find something.

"Your horse? Take him to the big village. I'm not going to shoe him."

And from that day on he spent his every day making God.

He no longer went out, and the shop door stayed shut.

David Coudois, called Angoisse-de-Dieu, was making the God he had looked for. Only Judith saw him every evening when he returned to the house weary from the task that was wasting him. He had locked the main door and kept himself closed in the shop, refusing to open it to everyone, even to le Troublé.

And within it, the clear sounds of the anvil could be heard and the roaring of the forge.

In the hamlet they said that David was making God, and all shook their heads and looked at one another without saying what they thought.

Then one day, David rushed out and began to shout as he went along the three streets.

"I've made God! I've made God! I've invented him. Come and see him."

They went, and on the floor, there was David Coudois's God, which looked like a very complicated machine with its wheels and levers and which was polished and dark and full of the golden-brown gleams of well-oiled metal.

They were all there, and David made a quick move and set a wheel in motion.

But nothing happened. Then he looked around him and saw the mocking faces—four deep—which encircled the machine and filled the shop. There were even some children perched on the bellows of the forge.

David tried again. . . . Nothing.

And again. . . . Still nothing.

Then he wanted to smash the whole machine and shouted as he was struggling. But it was very plain that he had gone crazy, and he was taken away so that he might be shut up in the city.

In the deserted shop, Judith remained alone, resigned because she had for several weeks feared that *le* David might become mad and she had let him go his way.

They will cure him maybe in the city?

She stood in front of the machine and at first had stroked it because it was the dream of *le* David, whom she loved and it was precious.

Then the idea came to her that the machine was the reason that *le* David had become mad; so she spat in it and said:

"Damned machine!"

And the machine began to move and one of the levers wanted to snatch hold of Judith, and Judith ran outside shouting:

"God is real, David's God is real, David is not mad!"

And as she ran shouting, she heard a loud noise, and turning round she saw that David's shop was on fire and was going up into the air.

They did not believe her in the hamlet.

The shop had burned by itself. Someone had been negligent, and the fire had taken hold.

La Judith really cried for a long time, then she went away and they did not see her again.

THE HOUSE ON
THE ESPLANADE

Anne Hébert

Stephanie de Bichette was a curious little creature with frail limbs that seemed badly put together. Only her starched collarette kept her head from falling over on her shoulder; it was too heavy for her long, slender neck. If the head of Stephanie de Bichette looked so heavy, it was because all the pomp of her aristocratic ancestors was symbolized in her coiffure, a high up-swept style, with padded curls arranged in rows on her narrow cranium, an architectural achievement in symmetrical silvery blobs.

Mademoiselle de Bichette had passed, without transition period, without adolescence, from the short frocks of her childhood to this everlasting ash-gray dress, trimmed at neck and wrists with a swirl of lilac braiding. She owned two parasols with carved ivory handles—one lilac and the other ash-gray. When she went out driving in the carriage she chose her parasol according to the weather, and everyone in the little town could tell the weather by the color of Mademoiselle de Bichette's parasol. The lilac one appeared on days of brilliant sunshine, the ash-gray one whenever it was slightly cloudy. In winter, and when it rained, Stephanie simply never went out at all.

I have spoken at length about her parasols because they were the outward and visible signs of a well-regulated life, a perfect edifice of regularity. Unchanging routine surrounded and supported this innocent old creature. The slightest crack in this extraordinary construction, the least change in this stern program would have been enough to make Mademoiselle de Bichette seriously ill.

Fortunately, she had never had to change her maid. Geraldine served and cared for her mistress with every evidence of complete respect for tradition. The whole life of

Stephanie de Bichette was a tradition, or rather a series of traditions, for apart from the tradition of the well-known parasols and the complicated coiffure, there was the ritual of getting up, of going to bed, of lace making, of meal times, and so on.

Stephanie Hortense Sophie de Bichette lived facing the Esplanade, in a gray stone house dating back to the days of the French occupation. You know the sort of house that implies—a tall, narrow edifice with a pointed roof and several rows of high windows, where the ones at the top look no bigger than swallows' nests, a house with two or three large attics that most old maids would have delighted in. But, believe it or not, Mademoiselle de Bichette never climbed up to her attics to sentimentalize over souvenirs, to caress treasured old belongings, or to plan meticulous orgies of housecleaning amid the smell of yellowing paper and musty air that even the best-kept attics seem to possess.

No, she occupied the very heart of the house, scarcely one room on each floor. On the fourth story, only Geraldine's room remained open, among the rooms of all the former servants. It was part of the family tradition to close off rooms that were no longer used. One after another, bedroom after bedroom had been condemned: the room where the little brothers had died of scarlet fever, when Stephanie was only ten years old; the bedroom of their mother, who had passed away soon after her two children; the room of Irénée, the elder brother who had been killed in an accident, out hunting; the room of the elder sister, Desneiges, who had entered the Ursuline convent; then the bedroom of Monsieur de Bichette, the father, who had succumbed to a long illness; to say nothing of the room belonging to Charles, the only surviving brother, which had been closed ever since his marriage.

The ritual was always the same: once the occupant of the room had departed for the cemetery, the convent, or the adventure of matrimony, Geraldine would tidy everything away, carefully leaving each piece of furniture exactly in place; then she would draw the shutters, put dust covers on the armchairs, and lock the door for good. No one ever set foot in that room again. One more member of the family was finally disposed of.

Geraldine took a distinct pleasure in this solemn, unvarying rite, just as a gravedigger may take pride in a neat row of graves, with well-kept mounds and smoothly raked grass above them. Sometimes she remembered that one day she would have to close Mademoiselle Stephanie's room, too, and live on for a while, the only living creature among all the dead. She looked forward to that moment, not with horror, but with pleasant anticipation, as a rest and a reward. After so many years of housework in that great house, all its rooms would be fixed at last in order, for all eternity. Mildew and dust could take possession then; Geraldine would have no more cleaning to do then. The rooms of the dead are not "done up."

This was not the calculation of a lazy woman. Geraldine dreamed of the last door closed and the last key turned in the lock just as the harvester dreams of the last sheaf of corn, or the needlewoman of the last stitch in her embroidery. It would be the crowning achievement of her long life, the goal of her destiny.

It was strange that the old servant reckoned two living people among the dead: Mademoiselle Desneiges, the nun, and Monsieur Charles, a married man and the father of a family. They had both left the family roof, and that was enough for Geraldine to class them as nonexistent. The heavy door of the cloister had closed forever on one, while Charles, by marrying a common little seamstress from the Lower Town, had so grieved his father that the old house and all it contained had been left to Stephanie. Charles came to see his sister every evening, but Geraldine never spoke a word to him. For her, Stephanie was the whole of the de Bichette family.

On the third floor, all the bedrooms were closed, with the exception of Mademoiselle de Bichette's. On the second, only the small blue boudoir lived on, a life of dimness and disuse. On the first floor, an immense drawing room stretched from front to back, cluttered with furniture of different periods, each piece bristling with fussy, elaborate knickknacks. The ground-floor doors were always open, with high, carved portals to the vestibule, the parlor, the dining room. In the basement was the old-fashioned kitchen, uncomfortable and always damp. Geraldine was the cook as well as the maid-of-all-work, but was never addressed as such.

If her mistress lived by tradition until it became a religion, Geraldine, too, had her tradition, the collecting of bright-colored buttons. Her black skirt and her white apron never changed, but she used her imagination in trimming her blouses. Red buttons sparkled on blue blouses, yellow ones on green, and so on, not to mention buttons in gold and silver and crystal. In the attic, she had discovered great chests of ancient garments which she stripped, shamelessly, of their trimmings. Apart from this innocent craze for buttons, the big woman with the ruddy complexion made no objection to touring the wine cellar every evening before going to bed, as the last of her duties, conscientiously and even devotedly performed. But where she excelled was in the observance of tradition where her mistress was concerned.

Every morning, at seven o'clock in summer and eight in winter, she climbed the three flights of stairs and knocked at the bedroom door. . . . Two taps, two firm, decided taps, no more, no less. This was the signal for the ceremonial to begin.

Geraldine opened the bed curtains, then the window curtains, and finally the shutters. Her aging mistress preferred to sleep in complete darkness, requiring several thicknesses of material and polished wood between herself and the wicked witchcraft of the night. She was afraid of the first rays of sunlight as well, not knowing what to do about them, since they might easily wake you long before the proper time for getting up.

Then Geraldine would return to the passage to fetch a kind of wagon equipped with everything Stephanie might need for the first few hours of the day. Two white pills in a glass of water, coffee and toast, toothbrush and toothpowder, a copper bathtub, white towels, white starched underwear. Also a feather duster, a broom, a dustpan—all that she used for tidying up the room. This wagon was as wide as a single bed, four feet wide, with three shelves. Geraldine had made it herself out of old packing cases.

When Stephanie's breakfast was finished, the maid would bathe, dress, and powder her mistress, then do her hair. Stephanie allowed her to do everything, silent, inert, trusting. After that, there was sometimes a moment of painful indecision, an anguished knot in the brain of Mademoiselle de Bichette, when Geraldine leaned over to look out of the window, examining the sky and frowning as she declared:

"I really don't know what sort of weather we're going to have today."

Then the old lady would stare at her maid with such forlorn eyes that Geraldine would say hurriedly:

"It's going to rain. You're not going to be able to go out this morning. I'll let the coachman know."

Stephanie would grow calm again after that, but she would not be entirely herself until Geraldine had settled her carefully in the blue drawing room, on her high-backed chair of finely carved wood, near the window, her half-finished lace on her knee and her crochet hook in her hand. Only then would the idea take firm root in her brain:

"It's going to rain. I can't go out. . . . All I have to do is to handle this hook and this thread as my mother taught me to do when I was seven years old. . . . If it had been a fine day, it would have been different, I would have gone out in the carriage. There are only two realities in the world . . . only two realities I can rely on . . . and I close my eyes, deep inside them: the reality of going out in the carriage, the reality of making my lace. . . . How lost and strange I am when Geraldine cannot tell what the weather is going to do, and I am left in suspense with no solid ground beneath my feet. . . . It just wracks my brain! Oh! Not to have to think about it, to let myself be carried away by one or the other of these, my only two sure and certain realities—going out for a drive or sitting here, making my lace. . . ."

Even if the day turned out fine in the end, Geraldine never said so. It would have been too much of a shock for her mistress. Imagine what confusion in such a patterned existence if someone had suddenly announced a change, after she had firmly established herself for the day in the reality of lace making, and dared to tell her she had taken the wrong road? She could never again have believed in any reality at all.

Since her childhood, Mademoiselle de Bichette had been making lace doilies of different sizes, which Geraldine used in many different ways. These doilies flowed from her fingers at the steady rate of four per week, small pieces of white lace that resembled each other like peas in a pod. They were everywhere in the house—five or six on the piano, seven or eight on all the tables, as many as ten on every armchair, one or two on all the smaller chairs. Every knickknack rested on a piece of delicate openwork, so that the furniture all seemed powdered with snow-flakes, enlarged as if under a microscope.

In winter, and in summer, on the days when Geraldine had decided the weather was not fit for going out, Mademoiselle de Bichette would crochet all the morning, in her blue boudoir, sitting up so straight and still that she scarcely seemed real, her feet resting on a stool covered by something that was strangely like the work the old lady held in her hands.

At five minutes to twelve, Geraldine would announce:

"Mademoiselle Stephanie's luncheon is served."

At the mention of her name, the old lady would rise at once; the ritual phrase had touched a switch somewhere within her, so that without effort, without thinking, without even understanding, she would put herself slowly and ceremoniously in motion, descend the staircase, and take her place at the table.

If Stephanie did go out, she invariably returned home at a quarter to twelve, so she had ample time to receive the announcement that luncheon was served with the necessary calm.

The outings of Mademoiselle de Bichette were governed by just as incredible a routine. She came out on the sidewalk with tiny steps, her frail little body bending under the weight of that enormous pile of scaffolded curls. Geraldine helped her mistress into the carriage, the coachman whipped up his horse, and the victoria started on its slow, quiet drive, invariably the same, through the streets of the little town. The horse knew the road by heart, so the coachman seized the opportunity for a short nap, his cap pulled down over his eyes, his legs stretched out, his hands folded on his stomach. He always woke up in time, as if by magic, when the drive came to an end, crying out and stretching himself, with a jolly air of surprise:

"Well, well, mamzelle, here we are back again!"

Just as if the old fellow, when he went to sleep as the drive started, had not been quite sure he would come back when he awoke, or if his return would be to the country of the living!

Mademoiselle de Bichette would disappear into the

house, on Geraldine's arm; the coachman would unharness the horse and put the carriage away; and it was all over. With regret, the townsfolk watched the disintegration of this strange conveyance, like a ghostly apparition cutting through the clear morning light . . . the ancient nag, pulling an antique carriage, with a sleepy coachman and a tiny figure like a mummy, swathed in ash-gray and lilac.

After luncheon, Geraldine would lead her mistress into the long drawing room on the first floor, where, without ever laying her crochet aside, Stephanie would receive a few callers, and the maid would serve dandelion wine and madeleines.

The old lady never left her chair, forcing herself to hold her head high, though her neck felt as if it were breaking under the weight of her monumental coiffure. Sometimes, this constant, painful effort was betrayed by a twitch of the lips, the only change of expression that callers could ever distinguish upon that small, powdered face. Then Stephanie would ask, "How is Madame your mother?" in a voice so white and colorless that it might have come from one of the closed rooms, where, according to the gossips of the town, some of the original inhabitants still lived on.

This phrase of Stephanie's had to do for greeting, for farewell, for conversation; indeed, it had to do for everything, for the wine was sour and the madeleines stale and hard as stones. The callers were all so aged and unsteady that the most utter stranger would have had the tact never to ask that preposterous question, but Mademoiselle de Bichette knew no other formula, and in any case, she attached no importance whatever to the words she was saying. If she finished a lace doily while her callers were present, she simply let it fall at her feet, like a pebble into a pool, and began another identical piece of lace. The visiting ladies never stayed very long, and Stephanie seemed to notice their departure as little as she did their presence.

At a quarter past six, Geraldine would announce that Monsieur Charles was waiting below. The program of the day was ticking on like the mechanism of a good Swiss watch, and the invisible wheels of Mademoiselle de Bichette responded perfectly, warning the limbs of this strange little creature that they must immediately convey her to the ground floor.

Her brother would kiss her brow and smile, rubbing

his stubby-fingered hands together and remarking:

"Um-phm! It feels good in the house."

Then he would hang his overcoat up on a hall stand, while Geraldine followed his every movement with her look of triumphant disdain. With her arms crossed upon her swelling chest, she doubtless thought she looked like the statue of the Commendatore, bound on revenge. She would cast a glance of scorn on the threadbare coat, as if to say:

"Well, what did you expect? Monsieur Charles would get married to a chit of a girl from the Lower Town, so naturally his father cut him off, and I locked up his room as if he were dead. If Mademoiselle Stephanie wants him here every evening, it's her own business, but *I'm* going to let him know that I'm *glad* he was thrown out, if I *am* only the servant. I know he's poor, and that's his punishment for disobeying his father. He comes here because there isn't enough to eat at home. So he gobbles up our dinners and carries away on his nasty skin a bit of the warmth from our fires. . . . The good-for-nothing!"

If it were true that Charles had only one decent meal a day, it was astonishing that he was not at all thin. He was even fat, very fat, flabby and yellow-complexioned, with a bald head and a shiny face, colorless lips and almost colorless eyes. Geraldine said he had eyes like a codfish and his clothes always smelled of stale grease. Apart from that, she could not forgive a de Bichette for forgetting his table manners.

"To think that his slut of a wife has made him lose all he ever learned in decent society. . . . You wouldn't believe it possible," she would grumble to herself.

As dinnertime drew near, Charles became more and more noisily jolly. He never stopped rubbing his hands together; he got up, sat down, got up again, went from window to door and back a dozen times, while Stephanie's eyes ignored him. Then the brother and sister took their places, one at each end of the long table in the dining room. There was no gas chandelier in this room, so it seemed even longer and darker, lit only by two tall candles in silver candlesticks. The corners of the room disappeared into the dimness, and the shadows of the brother and sister danced like black flames on the curiously carved oak paneling of the walls.

Every evening, the atmosphere of this dining room seemed more impressive to Charles. Perhaps he felt unseen forms hiding in the darkness, invisible spectators of this singular repast; perhaps he feared to find the ghosts that haunted the bedrooms above, to see them take their places at the huge dining table, where an old creature presided, small as a cat, white as the table linen, who seemed already to be living in the uneasy world of phantoms.

As soon as Stephanie's brother had swallowed a few mouthfuls of soup, his good humor fell away, lifeless, utterly destroyed. When he entered the house, the smell of cooking would stimulate him, would intoxicate him with its marvelous promise, but now that the promise was kept, the man became gloomy again. Through his own bitter thoughts, he stared at the lace cloth, the heavy silverware, the fine china, and at this sister of his, who was still alive, in spite of her look of belonging to some other world. What mysterious thread was keeping Stephanie here on earth? To look at her, you would have thought the slightest breath might carry her away, yet there she was, still alive.

Geraldine came and went around the table and her sharp eyes seemed to plumb the very depths of the man's thoughts. The brother sat there, knowing himself watched and understood, telling himself, in his embarrassment, that his sister would have joined her ancestors long ago had it not been for this fiendish servant, who by some diabolical process had contrived to keep the dying thing alive in her father's mansion, simply in order to enjoy as long as possible the spectacle of his own failure. In what dread no-man's-land of the spirit had the old witch made a pact with Monsieur de Bichette—and with Satan himself? Geraldine had inherited all the father's anger against his son; and faithful to that anger as if to a sacred promise, she was constantly reminding Charles of the curse that lay heavy upon him. At that moment he raised his head, resenting the eyes he felt fixed upon his every movement, but Geraldine was no longer there. Charles could hear the tinkle of her keys, in the passage between the staircase and the kitchen. He shuddered, for he knew very well which keys she carried at her waist. No cupboard, no inhabited room possessed a key. It chilled his heart strangely to know that the key of his room was there, along with those of the rooms of the dead. It scared him. Then he took hold of himself again and muttered:

"This damned house! . . . Enough to drive a man crazy to sit here night after night with two cracked old fools of women. . . . The wine must have gone to my head."

But Stephanie had just got up from the table, and Charles followed her as usual.

The evening began like all the rest. Stephanie took up her lace again, while her brother walked to and fro in the long drawing room, his hands behind his back.

And so, night after night, in complete silence, without a single word exchanged between brother and sister, the time passed until the old clock chimed ten. Then Charles, having laid up a store of warmth for the night, kissed his sister's brow, slipped on his overcoat, and with his hands in his pockets, made for Ireland Street, walking slowly along, like an idle fellow accustomed to musing as he walked.

The man followed his shadow as it flickered on the walls. The same thoughts were turning and twisting in his brain; he was used to them, as a man gets used to animals he tends every day. He knew them too well to be surprised by them; he had stopped looking at them straight in the face; they passed to and fro behind his pale eyes without ever changing his passive stare.

As he came near his own home, Charles thought of his wife. He was going back to her, in no hurry, but with a certain feeling of security, as if to a piece of property he knew belonged to him.

Suddenly, he noticed that he was nearly there. Two low houses, identical twins in misery and poverty, stood waiting for him, their tumbledown gray stoops jutting out to meet the sidewalk. He rented rooms on the second floor of one of these houses.

He climbed the stairs, lit a candle and went into the bedroom. A hoarse, veiled voice, a well-known voice, that could still charm him in spite of himself, said wearily:

"That you Charles?"

He set the candle on the night table. The woman shaded her eyes with her hand. He sat down on the foot of the bed.

"How's your sister?"

"Just the same."

This question, this reply, as on every other night, fell heavily into a dull silence. Beneath the words was stirring in the shadows the real meaning, unexpressed:

"Do you think your sister will last much longer?"

" 'Fraid so. . . . She's still hanging on. . . ."

At that moment, in the house on the Esplanade, Stephanie de Bichette was crossing her tiny cold hands on her breast and abandoning to the great empty gulf of night the small emptiness that was herself, ridiculous as an old fashion plate and dry as a pressed fig.

And Geraldine lay awake, dreaming that death had closed the last door in the old house.

LOVE IN THE PARK

William C. McConnell

He could never conceive of the Park not being there,
never having existed, with its shards of grass, too long
by necessity in the small stream which ran through its center, and the evergreen hedge trees which looked clipped
but really grew that way with time, as if the monstrous
gods tired of licking their bases and really slirruped at their
peaks. The Park must, at one time, of course, have not
been there, for the city was not old, perhaps one hundred
years, and even sixty years ago away out here on the
edge of the beach and crowding suburbs there had been a
real creek where the stream now was, and evergreens so
high and thick that many an oxen team had been hullooed
and chivied and goaded before they were skidded away to
the first mill on the inlet.

He had often thought of the Park always being there,
from the time he was a boy and his wizened nurse, whom
everyone but himself called Panky, let him roll on the un-
dulating bank which led to the stream, while she read *The
Woman's Companion,* or some sort of companion which
was its predecessor, for of course he wasn't able to read
even titles in that long ago time. He called Panky a stink
when she cut his visit short to walk further to the beach,
but to her face, particularly when she let him nestle
against the ratty fur neckpiece which garroted her neck,
he called her Gray Anne—why, God alone knew in retrospect, for it sounded even then like one of the makes of
English biscuits his mother placed so much credence in
as nourishment between meals, or even a heavy butterfat-
yielding cow, though Panky, of course, had no milk in her
or to her or even a suggestion of lactation when she seldom
smiled. In fact, she was a woman of so little emotions

and those so thoroughly diced and shredded into her imagined duties that one could almost call her a person of
curried emotion, except there was no real seasoning, not
even anger, for she didn't shout or grow cross but merely
snapped. Yet, whatever her nature or lack of it, she did
introduce him to the Park, and its small three acres, seeming huge then, had since been vested with the oblique-rayed
charm of childhood discovery. So much so that in later
years on repeated walking through it and over it and
around it and by it his senses simply refused to believe
that it was encompassed by backs of three-story wooden
homes of Victoria's reign and a strong batter might easily
hit any of its boundaries if the batting of baseballs in its
center were allowed by the always elderly caretaker.

Now, of course, the houses were old and leaned on their
acquired wooden fire escapes with which authorities de-
creed their senility as rooming houses must be fortified if
thirty instead of eight or ten persons were to be rent-coz-
ened in each. His home had been of stone for most of its
way up three storys. Yet it, too, had changed, even though
not backing on the Park, as there were red-paint-covered
varicoses of never-used stairs from its height over the
beach almost to the ground. He seldom walked by it, even
though he often visited the Park, yet when he did his
mouth would tighten a little wryly at the wooden strip-
tease. The city hall bylawed that stairs, even firestairs never
used, should almost but never quite touch the ground
which afforded safety.

For some never-ascertained reason—certainly not aesthetic—none of the houses could be called a home (just as
he couldn't call his deserted house by the beach *home,* or
for that matter call the place he now lived in a home, or
any place which didn't have his anxious long-dead mother,
his sporadically absent father and Panky-the-stink and himself and his brother and perhaps some dog he vaguely remembered as Sport, a half-dozen toys the sight of which
would now sprout either tears or a yawn of boredom or
even both, and finally the self of him which had long
since died far more successfully than mother, father,
Panky, brother, Sport, and toys).

Perhaps, he thought, as he scuffed the autumn turf, that
is why he couldn't conceive the Park as never having been
there. Not because it physically remained while the others

had moldered as fast or faster than the beach leaves sticking to his wet soles. Nor even that its sides and size refused to shrink as he grew older and less magical and less real. But (and here he was only pondering, with no real outcome to lure him on, or even fantasy to bewilder and bewitch) because it was here he first loved, loved first, loved often, and loved always and where he never failed to return. The Park wasn't approximate, or time-filled, as everything else was, even the pulsing race of physical love itself, but actual and equating. The very placing of each and every house which surrounded it on all but two sides proved this, for they all looked wrong and the Park was exactly right.

This was true when the weeping willows, hedge pines, bush maples, and mountain ash were tiny, probably newly planted, for then they were monstrous to his three, four, then five and six feet. His growth didn't match theirs, but it was so commensurate that when he died he knew for certain if he were laid in their middle boughs as the Indians buried their dead, he would be lifted gently and inexorably to the clouds and beyond, for it would be commensurate then. It was not that he felt communion with the Park—that, in his nature, was impossible—but it was the place of love and rightness, and unlike the surrounding houses, would never need props to make it bear age.

It had had its dangers. Once, when he lingered too long with his romping and Panky (as the others insisted on calling her with callous disregard for associations) had left him without a call, the spring evening had suddenly wavered into near darkness, and the smoke from dozens of garden fires curled and blued into the quiet air, so that with a little effort, he knew he would be able to roll uphill, even up-air, much more smoothly than down. When he leaped across the brook and toiled up the green slope to where Panky was sitting, a huge man stepped from behind a monkey tree and said:

"Wait!"

The voice was neither cold nor warm, loud nor soft, commanding nor entreating, but an empty sound inviting him to step into it and rattle around and make its sides echo for the first time of his experience.

He would have obeyed, but Panky suddenly appeared and shrieked at him to hurry and the man disappeared around the monkey tree without another word. Panky had chewed the man's presence to pieces all the way home, filling him so full of terror that even now he himself couldn't approach children, even one he knew (except of course his own, and even with him it was always a cautious process) unless there was first a litany of court formalities which killed all interest in himself and the approached and turned their freckles gray.

Again, when he was almost in his teens, he was walking after parking his bicycle at the entrance, when he saw Belknapp, the wheezing dandruffian neighborhood cop, creeping about the far hedging, uniformed knees almost touching the grass in his obvious anxiety to stifle his own presence, then suddenly pounce like a scrofulous cat and pull a shamed struggling couple from a niche and shake them with glee so that their loosened clothing fell from their white terrified shanks. This time he was old enough, however, to respond. With Belknapp's cycle held by his right hand, he careened past the night-stalker and on, right to the footpath of the beach with the unmajestical law heaving in pursuit, where he sent the bicycle sideways into deep tidewater and cursed because he was too thin and little to hurl its owner, too.

Over the stream which ran through the Park, not too far from the covey of vine maples which hid the sun, no matter how hot the summer day, there was a log bridge so hugely hewn that it might have served for a niagara underneath, yet instead the stream merely widened and quietened and formed a large pool where he and the others when he was growing swore there were trout. There might have been, for then, even as now, it was clear, with a sand bottom and enough gnats and bluebottles stitching the air just above its surface to feed a thousand fish. If you trotted over the bridge there was a slight rumble, as the planks were always giving nonuniformly with age, and replacements only muted the sound for a while till they, themselves, gained character and sedate looseness. It was perpetually cool under the bridge and it was pleasant, no matter what your age, to sit there, chew the tender stalks of stray grass, and see the Rubenslike hams of the summer-dressed housewives out for a stroll before their husbands came home.

The Park never prompted chance matings, for it was too

formal and chastely dressed with underbrush. Yet it was a place for lovers, and even he had loved there, under the sympathetic scorn of a cheese moon and with the white beginning of hoar frost on the close-clipped grass. He had loved by walking slowly over the brittle stubble of grass, touching her arm, her fingers, suddenly clutching her when passing a benign bare tree trunk, only to have the magic swilled down the drain when she whispered:

"No, no. Let's go home."

And her voice, till then compared to the stream, was neither loud nor soft, cold nor warm, commanding nor entreating, but an empty sound inviting him to step into it and rattle around and make its sides echo, with the difference that the long-forgotten man belonged to the Park and she didn't for she wished them somewhere else.

It had been many months before he knew that hand gropings, like word gropings, were not love, any more than acres and trees with interspersed shrubs could ever duplicate the Park. For fortunately, they returned many times, and it was he who was at fault in trying to mesmerize the shadings of feeling which must grow and never become detached. They wandered each evening for many months through and along the chance walks. It was autumn and the huge seas only a block away in their casting in of spindrift and roar, though muted, still caused the air about them to smell strongly of salt, and each tree trunk, seemingly secure, tremored from the blows in its upper branches, trying to warn the two below of the violence elsewhere.

When he left for war they met for the last time in five years. He remembered his own false puckishness as he kicked snow, crystal by crystal it seemed, for it was so cold, about her protected ankles, and talked vaguely and wildly of how she must retrace every step each evening and recount in her daily letters how many steps she paced for him, a promise she did not make but which he imposed. This night it was his voice which was the empty sound, his invitation to treat him like an empty gourd and shake him hard, while she was dreamy and tactile and seemingly too engrossed by their trysting place to let him matter whatever he intended to do.

Each day she wrote and for many months there was always a reply. The seasons in their minutest changes were transmuted for him although he was five thousand miles away where climate dropped its seasons like badly handled stage curtains—so sudden they shocked changelessness from its seat and galled one into age. And unlike him, she always walked alone.

Away, some alchemy worked a change in him. Blood, strange bruising images, hills instead of mountains and sand dunes where there should have been a sea, all gnarled and twisted so that he never walked alone, or talked alone, or bedded alone, or talked or walked or bedded at all but crowded in with a thousand others a frenetic activity that was neither life nor death and frosted every root of existence till one became a sad-gay corpse giving out and receiving death and life with drugged abandon.

And although his letters stopped, and long after hers did, too, almost stopping with an audible sigh, she still walked daily to the Park, rescued shoaled boats in the stream, talked gravely and low with neighbors, hoped and sustained by what it had meant to him, till it grew the same for her, and gave the strength which caused her certainly not to forget, but to grow and supplant till there was another walking the self-same paths, learning slowly the identical mysteries (which wondrously never changed) till he, too, was accepted.

This, the first one learned when he returned. Learned, not from her, for they never spoke, though they nodded solemnly each day when they met. He learned from the shrubs, the changing sky, the moist descent of rain when everyone who walked but he carried an umbrella or at least a hat. Yet he was happy as he limped along, his shattered left leg adding a new sound to the packed clay walk— happy to know his earliest knowledge of the Park always being there and always holding his love inviolate was now confirmed, and to see there are two grave children, shy at his uneven talk, glancing up and into him.

UNCLE T

Brian Moore

Vincent Bishop, standing at his hotel room window saw in momentary reflection from the windowpane a nervous young man with dark eyes and undisciplined black hair. Above Times Square the sky hemorrhaged in an advertising glare. His reflection dissolved. He turned away.

"Are you nearly ready, Barbara?" he called.

She was in the bathroom putting polish on her nails. His uncle was due any minute. Maybe he should have bought a bottle to offer his uncle a drink before they started off? The half-dozen roses he had chosen for his aunt—maybe he should have taken them out of the box and let them stand in water for a while? Were half a dozen roses enough?

"Barbara, do you think I should run down to the lobby and get a box of chocolates?"

She did not hear him. Her and her nails. If this was the way she kept him waiting on the second day of their honeymoon, what faced him in the years to come? What would his uncle think of her? Or of him? How could he tell? He had never met his uncle. This morning, as soon as he and his bride checked into the hotel after the flight from Toronto, his uncle had been on the phone to invite them to dinner at his apartment. He was coming now to pick them up. He sounded very kind, but what could you tell from a voice on the phone?

Of course there was his letter. That was the important thing.

Grenville Press
182 West 15th St.
New York, N.Y. 10011

Dear Vincent,
    I am delighted to hear that you are planning to

get married and that you are contemplating a honey-moon trip to New York. Both Bernadette and I offer our heartiest congratulations to you and our best wishes to your fiancée. Needless to say, we are look-ing forward to meeting you at last, but unfortunately, I cannot offer to put you up, as ours is a very small apartment. However, don't worry, I will find you a hotel room.

I was most interested to read that you do not want to return to Ireland when your exchange teaching year in Canada is completed. I can well see the prob-lems of going home with a new bride who is neither Irish nor Catholic and not likely to enjoy the atmos-phere there at all. Now, as you also mention that you are fed up with teaching and would like to find something else, let me make you a proposal. How would you consider joining me here at Grenville Press? I'm sure that a young man with your background would be ideal for the editorial side of the business. As you know, Bernadette and I have no children and we consider you very much a member of our family. I might add that since I bought out old Grenville's widow last year, I am now the proprietor of this firm.

Anyway, since you are coming to visit us in New York, we can talk about this in more detail. In the meantime, let me say that although we know each other only from letters, I have long thought that you —a rebel, a wanderer and a lover of literature—must be very much like me when I was your age. I look forward to our meeting. Till then,

Affectionately,
Uncle T

Uncle T. Three years ago, in Ireland, Vincent sat in his bedroom sending letters over all the world's oceans, messages in bottles, appeals for rescue. *I am twenty-two years old and have just completed an Honors English Lan-guage and Literature degree at the Queen's University of Belfast. I am anxious to live abroad.* Resident clerk in the Shan States, shipping aide in Takoradi, plantation overseer in British Guiana—any job, anywhere, which would exor-cise the future then facing him: a secondary school in an

Ulster town, forty lumps of boys waiting at forty desks, rain on the windowpanes, two local cinemas, a dance on Saturday nights.

Back with the foreign postmarks, the form replies, the we-regret-to-inform-you's came a letter signed "Uncle T." A letter in answer to Vincent's veiled appeal to a never-seen uncle who was now, Vincent's mother said, a partner in a New York publishing firm. The letter contained a fifty-dollar money order. The writer regretted that he could not suggest any job at that time, but hoped that, relations established, he and Vincent would keep in touch.

They kept in touch. Even for a young iconoclast there was comfort in a precedent. And what better precedent than Uncle Turlough Carnahan, who, like himself, had published poems in undergraduate magazines, who had once formed a university socialist club, and who (again, like Vincent) had left his parents' house forever after a bitter anticlerical dispute? Vincent wanted to escape from Ireland. Uncle Turlough lived in America. Vincent dreamed of some sort of literary career. Uncle Turlough, by all accounts, had achieved it. Was it any wonder then that this relative was the one Vincent boasted of to his bride?

"Well, will I pass muster for the great man?" Barbara asked, coming from the bathroom, her nail polish still wet, her hands extended before her like a temple dancer's. She was small and fair and neat; her girlish dresses drew attention to her breasts and legs. They had met three months ago when she began to teach modern dance at the Toronto high school where Vincent was spending his exchange year. Since then, she and he had rarely been separated; yet they were strangers still, unsure of each other, too anxious to please.

"Pass muster?" he said. "You'll do more than that." He bent to kiss her ear as the room telephone growled twice.

"That must be him, Vincent."

"Hello," said the telephone voice. "Are you decent? Can I come up for a moment?"

"Of course."

The phone went dead. "He's on his way up," Vincent told her.

"Oh Vincent, I'm so nervous."

How could she be? What was Uncle Turlough to her, who three months ago had never even heard his name? Whereas he, for how many years had he dreamed that one day his uncle might beckon him into his literary world he dreamed of? How would she understand his panic now as he waited at the door of their room, remembering the slight, dark youth he had seen so often in his mother's photograph album, wondering how the person who knocked lightly on the door would differ from that youth. Of course, those photographs would be thirty-five years old. Uncle Turlough must be almost sixty.

He opened the door.

"Vincent, how are you? Welcome to New York." The stranger shook hands, then moved past Vincent. "And this must be Barbara. How are you, my dear? Why, you're even more lovely than he said you were. Welcome, welcome."

On the telephone Vincent had noticed it but had not been sure. Now, he was. The stranger's voice had no trace of his own harsh Ulster burr, but was soft, broguey, nasal, like the voice of an American imitating an Irish accent. Confidential and cozy, it told Barbara, "Do you know, it's an extraordinary thing, my dear, but this husband of yours is the spitting image of me when I was his age. Look at us together. Don't you still see a resemblance?"

What resemblance? Vincent thought, but hoped Barbara would have the sense to pretend.

"Oh, yes," she said, "of course, I see it."

The stranger bobbed his head in acknowledgment, and as he did Vincent noticed his hair, black and shiny as a crow's wing, unexpected as the chocolate-brown overcoat and blood-colored shoes. Resemblance?

"Do you have a couple of glasses, by any chance?" the stranger said, unbuttoning his overcoat to reveal a rumpled gray suit, too tight at the middle button. From his jacket pocket he took a pint bottle of whiskey and broke the seal. "Bernadette won't be expecting us for a while," he said. "I left the office early. I thought we might have one for the road here, before we start."

Obediently, Barbara went into the bathroom, returning with two water glasses. "I'd better phone for ice," she said.

"Don't bother," the stranger said. "Just run the cold tap awhile. There's no sense letting them rob you blind with their room service."

He poured two large whiskies and presented them to his guests. "I don't need a glass," he said, raising the pint to his lips. "It's bottles up for me." Silent, they watched, their own drinks untasted. Then Barbara took the two glasses of neat whiskey and went to run the cold tap, as ordered. If it were one of her relatives, Vincent thought, there'd be no surprise, the uncle would be just as advertised, solid, Canadian, safe; he would be the man he said he was and not—what? Oh, Uncle, what uneasy eyes you have! What ruddy cheeks you have, Uncle dear!

"And how's your mother keeping?" the stranger asked.

"She's well."

"Dear little Eileen. Many is the time I've wanted to go home and see her and my other brothers and sisters and all the rest of the Carnahan clan. Maybe I will, some day. Maybe I will."

He recorked the pint and put it on their dressing table. "I'll just leave this here in case you youngsters need a little refreshment when you get home tonight. After all, it's your honeymoon." He winked at Barbara, who was coming out of the bathroom, a wink at once collusive and apologetic. "Although you know, Barbara, my old mother used to say you should never give an Irishman the choice between a girl and the bottle. Because it's a proven fact that most of them will prefer the bottle. Am I right, Vince?" He punched Vincent's shoulder in uncertain good-fellowship. "Now, finish up that sup of drink and we'll be on our way."

Obediently, they drank their whiskies. Obediently they got their coats and followed him to the elevator. At the lobby entrance the hotel doorman approached, asking if they wanted a cab. The stranger shook his head. "You two wait here," he said, and ran a block down the street to find a cab himself.

"*Well*," Barbara said.

"Well, what?"

She made a face. "I do not like thee, Uncle T, the reason why is plain to see."

"What are you talking about?"

"Just look at him, Vincent. His hair, for one thing."

'What about it?"

"Lovely head of hair," she said. "It's dyed."

"Oh, come off it."

"It's d-y-e-d," she said. "And I'll bet that's not the only phony thing about him."

"Now wait a minute. What do you mean?"

"Darling," she said, "if he's a publisher, I'm Mrs. Roosevelt."

"Now give the man a chance, will you? Why jump to conclusions?"

She did not answer, for at that moment, a cab drew up in full view of the doorman and the stranger leaned out, beckoning them to come. In shame, they passed the doorman's contempt. *Give the man a chance. . . .* But as the taxi rushed them onto the bright carnival rink of Times Square, Vincent heard his father's dry, diagnostic voice: "If your mother's family have a weakness, it's that never in my life have I known any of them to spoil a good story for the sake of the truth." Upgrading their relations, exaggerating their triumphs, hiding their shortcomings under a bluster of palaver—wasn't that what his father thought of the Carnahan clan? Even his mother, hadn't she a touch of it? When twenty-five exchange teachers had been picked to go out to Canada, hadn't she told all her friends the story as though her son were the only one chosen? And this stranger was his mother's brother. Could those letters about Grenville Press be Carnahan exaggeration? No, of course no. *Give the man a chance.*

"Your wife's an American, isn't she, Mr. Carnahan?" Barbara asked.

"Yes, Bernadette was born right here in New York City, although she's of good Irish stock. Where do your people come from, my dear?"

"My grandparents came from England," Barbara said.

"Both sides?"

"Both sides."

And wasn't there a certain Anglo-Saxon attitude in the way she said that? But the stranger did not seem to notice. On and on he went, telling about the Tenderloin district, pointing out the Flatiron building, keeping the small talk afloat as though to distract his listeners from the true facts of the journey. For their taxi was moving from bad to worse, entering streets that Vincent would not have dreamed of in his afternoon of sightseeing along the elegance of Fifth Avenue, streets of houses whose front entrances looked like rear exits, of stale little basement shops left over from an older New York, of signs which proposed *Keys Made, Rooms to Let, Shoes Repaired.* A group of sallow-skinned men played pitchpenny on the pavement. The taxi stopped.

"Here we are," the broguey voice said. "It's very convenient, you know, because it's right downtown."

They skirted the pitchpenny players, entered the apartment building, and climbed two narrow flights of stairs, their guide hurrying ahead of them to press a buzzer outside one of the corridor doors. He rang twice, and as on a signal, a woman opened the door, drawing a mauve woolen stole tight about her bosom as she met the corridor draft. To Vincent's surprise, she was in her late thirties, a brassy blonde, blown stout, wearing a gray sateen dress one size too small for her, moving her weight uncomfortably on tiny ankles and feet. "Bernadette," the stranger said. And kissed her cheek.

Those heads together, kissing, made Vincent think of their mutual hairdressing problems. Did they dye each other's? Awkwardly, he offered his gift of flowers.

"Oh, roses! Aren't they lovely! Thank you, Vincent. Aren't you the perfect gentleman! Barbara, dear, do you want to come with me and freshen up a little? Turlough, take their coats, will you?"

The sight of their overcoats disappearing into a closet reminded Vincent that the evening was a sentence still to be served. If only he had come alone to New York, if only he hadn't told Barbara that this job would be the end of their worries about what to do when his exchange year was over. If only—he thought of his father's remark —yes, if only he hadn't behaved like a Carnahan. And now, in confirmation of his mother's blood, the first thing he noticed in the living room was a familiar face in a familiar oval frame. Dyed hair or not, publisher or not, this stranger was his kinsman. The photograph was of Vincent's maternal grandmother.

The living room was strangely bare, its furniture worn and discolored, as though his uncle and aunt had several small children and had long ago given up the struggle with appearances. Yet the letter said there were no children. He looked at the bookcase near what must be his uncle's easy chair. Shakespeare, and some poetry, second-hand copies of Goethe, Swift, Dante, Dickens, Flaubert. All were dusty as though they had not been disturbed since the flat was first moved into. By a small table near the reading lamp were several well-used copies of *The Saturday Evening Post*.

"Glass of sherry?" his uncle said, coming in with a tray on which were four glasses, none of them used. But the newly broken tinfoil seal of the sherry bottle lay beside them and the sherry bottle had already been depleted. Dark, uneasy eyes saw Vincent notice the diminished bottle level, skittered nervously toward the door as Aunt Bernadette reappeared with Barbara. Everyone sat down. Sherry was poured. The verbal gropings began. Aunt Bernadette brought out her wedding present (an ugly salad bowl) and was duly thanked for it. She asked about the wedding. Had they had a big reception? Had they sent photographs to Vincent's mother? How was his mother keeping, by the way?

"She's in great form, from the letters she sends," Vincent said.

"And your Dad, how is he? Turlough tells me you and your Dad didn't always hit it off too well. I hope you made it up with him before you came out here?"

Made it up? He had gone back to Drumconer Avenue the week before he sailed as an exchange teacher. His mother received him, talked to him for a long while, then asked him to wait. He sat alone in the drawing room, listening for his father's step. He heard his father leave the surgery and go along the hall. His father did not come up. He went out of the drawing room and looked over the banister. His father was at the front door, putting on his hat and coat. "Father?" he said. "Father? . . ."

His father did not look up. "I have to go out on a sick call," his father said.

"But couldn't you spare a minute? Or could I come with you?"

His father did not answer. His father reached down into the monk's bench for his consulting bag. His father's attitude had not changed since that day two years before when he looked up from the breakfast table, the newspaper shaking in his fingers. "So this is your damn socialism, is it? Have you seen the paper? My son up on a platform at the university, helping a couple of Protestants to run down his religion and his country. My son! Oh, haven't I reared a right pup. You're going to apologize, do you hear? You're going to sit down this minute and write a public apology and send it out to this newspaper. Do you hear me? This minute!"

Vincent refused. His sister wept: she said his conduct had broken their mother's heart. His mother packed a suitcase and went on a pilgrimage to Lough Derg, walking in her bare feet over the stones of that penitential island, praying God to give her son back the gift of faith. But despite his father's rage, his sister's tears, his mother's penance, he could not recant. Oh, yes, he loved them, he loved them all. But fourteen and eight made twenty-two, eight years of hypocrisy, of going to Mass and the sacraments for their sake. He tried to tell the truth in that university debate. The truth troubled him. But his father belonged to a generation who had had their troubles; they had no time for any others. And so after a month of his father's silent anger, Vincent left home to become a schoolmaster in a provincial town. And two years later when he returned, hoping to see his father, his father reached down into the monk's bench in the hall, picked up his consulting bag and opened the front door, leaving his plea unanswered. What answer had he wanted, he wondered? Forgiveness? Or merely some sign that they still were kin? They knew, both he and his father, that if he crossed the Atlantic he might never return. But his father had to go out on a sick call. His father walked down the path, opened the garden gate, did not look back. Went down the avenue, turned the corner, no look back.

And now, remembering this, what should he say to his uncle's wife? What should he answer this strange woman who asked if he had "made it up"?

"Ah, your father always was stubborn," Uncle Turlough said, seeing his hesitation. "I remember well. He and I were schoolmates. . . ."

"Stubborn?" Aunt Bernadette said. "But isn't it children that are stubborn when they go against their own parents? Don't be putting excuses into the boy's head, Turlough. You've no right. Look what happened with your own father. When you heard he was dead you sat in this room and wept." She turned to Vincent. "Too late to make it up then," she said. "Too late."

Her face was very close. Her flabby, powdered cheeks were pitted and spongy as angel food cake. Yet a few years ago she must have been pretty enough to make an old fool dye his hair. A few years ago, before the fat, before the coarseness, before the skin began to sag as though the body had sprung a slow leak. An old man marries a pretty face and ends up in a room with a monster. Strange monster, what right have you to reproach me with my father? He turned from her, determined to ignore her.

She would not be ignored. "Oh, I know you think it's none of my business," she said. "But Turlough tells me you're just like he was when he first came out here. So, I'm warning you, Vincent. Don't make his mistake."

"Now Bernadette, now dear," Uncle Turlough said. "You're confusing two different cases entirely."

"Am I? You never went home because you were too stubborn to go back on all your boasting. You were even ashamed of me."

"Now, that's not true, sweetheart. . . ."

"It is true." She turned to Barbara. "He's always complaining that I don't have his education. Well, I don't, but is that my fault? Oh, let me tell you, dear, your troubles are only starting when you marry into this Carnahan clan."

"I can't believe I'll have any trouble," Barbara said, smiling.

"Do you mean because you're better educated than me?"

"I didn't mean that at all, Mrs. Carnahan."

"Oh yes, you did. But don't forget you're a Protestant. Show me the mixed marriage that doesn't have its troubles. You'll have your share of tears."

"Drinks? Drinks, anyone?" Uncle Turlough said in a hoarse voice. "Barbara, a little more? Vincent, can I top that up for you? Bernadette? Anyone? . . ."

No one answered him. Barbara sat stiff in her chair, her eyes fixed on the lamp across the room. Aunt Bernadette, her neck red beneath the powder line, looked at Barbara in open dislike.

"Charity," Uncle Turlough said, pouring himself the drink that no one else wanted. "Charity for the other person's point of view, that's what counts. Don't try to make everyone else the same as you, that's the thing I've learned as I get older. . . . Vincent, maybe you'd like to switch to a shot of whiskey?"

Maybe he would. Getting drunk might be the only way to survive this evening. So Vincent said yes, aware of Barbara's sudden disapproval, watching her gather up her handbag as though she were preparing to walk out on him. In that moment he felt her Protestant prejudice against all the things which the words "Irish Catholic" must bring into her mind: vulgarity, backwardness, bigotry, drunkenness. But the litanies of love he had recited to her these past three months, didn't they count for anything? Didn't she know very well that he was no longer a Catholic, that it was not his fault that he had been born Irish, that he could hardly be held responsible for relatives he had never laid eyes on? If her lovemaking last night meant anything more than animal desire, wouldn't she be suffering with him now, not sitting in judgment on him as though he had tricked her?

Still, he had tricked her, hadn't he? Tricked her by boasting of his publisher uncle, tricked her by holding out New York as bait, knowing how bored she was with Toronto. Yes, he had. She knew it and she would make him pay for it. She stirred in her chair, turned toward his uncle, and in a disarmingly innocent voice, asked the question Vincent had feared all evening. "By the way, Mr. Carnahan, we've been wondering what sort of books you publish. Is it mostly fiction, or nonfiction?"

Aunt Bernadette looked at her husband. "Fiction?"

"What about the dinner, dear?" Uncle Turlough asked. "Isn't it nearly ready?"

"I'll go and see."

In the silence which followed Aunt Bernadette's departure, Uncle Turlough poured himself another sherry. "Well . . ." he said. "Well, I thought Vincent and I would talk business tomorrow at the office. Tonight, let's just enjoy ourselves, eh?"

"Oh, I wasn't thinking of it in that sense," Barbara said. "I was just wondering if perhaps I've read some of your authors?"

"Authors?" Dark, uneasy eyes appealed to Vincent, found no support, fixed their gaze on a neutral corner. "We—ah—we don't do any fiction, my dear. Not that I wouldn't be happy to, mind you. But you see—perhaps I've never explained this properly in my letters—we're in a more specialized field."

"Oh, really?"

Vincent stared at her, willing her to look at him. Drop it, can't you? But she had no mercy. "Well," she said, "what sort of books do you do, then?"

"Books? Not too many books, I'm afraid. You see we're not what you might call book publishers. We do a few directories. And we do brochures and booklets and pamphlets—that sort of work."

"Directories?"

"Well, for instance, we do a dental directory that's a very profitable line. We try to get out a new edition every five years. You'd be surprised how many dentists can afford to shell out five dollars for a nicely got-up book that has their name in it."

"Dinner's ready," said Aunt Bernadette.

Dinner. The fusty dining room was crowded with heavy walnut furniture which, by the awkwardness of its presence, announced that their hosts did not often eat there. There was, however, a bottle of wine, and the main dish of roast beef and baked potatoes was good and plentiful. A plated silver candlestick with three candles lit. An Irish linen tablecloth still glistening new, its folds heavily creased from years of lying in a gift box, proclaimed that in honor of Vincent and his bride Aunt Bernadette had set out her best. But Barbara did not relent; the questions continued. Behind his uncle's apologetic smiles, behind the evasions, the unwillingness to be specific, Barbara laid the imposture bare; Grenville Press, those boastful letters notwithstanding, was in reality a hole-and-corner print shop whose main activity consisted in cooking up lists of names in the manner of a spurious *Who's Who*. There was, Uncle Turlough admitted, a great deal of work in canvassing people to get them to buy the books and brochures in which their names would be included, a great deal of "sounding out groups in specialized fields to see if the response merits publication."

"And what exactly did you have in mind for Vincent in all this?" Barbara asked.

"Well. . . ." His uncle's dark eyes sought out Aunt Bernadette, who sat silent, eating with a concentration which showed plainly how she had come to lose her looks. "Well, I thought he might take Miss Henshaw's place. Eh, Bernadette?"

Aunt Bernadette nodded, still chewing.

"As a matter of fact, Vincent, the week you wrote to me saying you wanted to stay, that was the week we found out Miss Henshaw had cancer of the bowel. She was our editor, my right arm, and old Grenville's before me. Wonderful woman, she could turn out anything you wanted, from a seed catalogue to a school prospectus. She was a great loss, but"—he smiled painfully at Vincent— "if it had to happen, then what better time than now, which it gives me a chance to offer you a good job with the firm. Which you'll accept, I hope."

Barbara was waiting. He must speak. "Well," he said, "of course my teaching year isn't over yet. I haven't really made up my mind."

"But you're fed up with teaching, your letter said."

"Yes."

"And you have to find some sort of job here, don't you?"

"Yes."

"And you wrote that you'd like to live in New York, didn't you?"

"Yes."

"Well, then?"

Vincent did not answer. "I think Vincent was under the impression that you were a book publisher," Barbara said.

"Book publisher? Book publisher. I see. So you thought we were something on the order of Scribner's, did you? Something in that class. Ah, I'm afraid that's not the case, although who knows, great trees from little acorns, as the saying goes. Well, maybe it's my fault. Maybe I made the firm sound a little more important than it really is. But that's only human, isn't it? Isn't it, Vincent?"

Vincent nodded, his eyes on the tablecloth. Aunt Bernadette, speaking for the first time since she had started eating, announced that she would serve coffee in the front room.

"Coffee, yes," Uncle Turlough said, lurching to his feet, tossing his napkin on the table. "Coffee it is. And we'll have a spot of brandy in your honor, children. Come along, Barbara, let me take you in."

Coffee was poured. Aunt Bernadette took her cup and

retired to the kitchen, refusing Barbara's halfhearted offer to help with the dishes. Uncle Turlough handed brandies around, then moved uncertainly into the center of the room, his own glass held aloft.

"A toast," he said. "I mean, I want to tell you both how happy I am that you're here at last. I want to tell you how much tonight means to me. You see, Vincent, you're the first relative I've laid eyes on since the day I left Ireland. Yes, this is a great occasion. As you know, I've no children of my own and reading Vincent's letters was like living my own life over again. Funny, isn't it, how you and I have done so many of the same things? Yes. . . . So, *Cead Mile Failte* to you and to this lovely bride of yours, and may this night be the beginning of your long and happy memories of New York."

Vincent raised his glass but Barbara put hers down. "I'm superstitious," she said, smiling. "I never like to drink to something before we've really made our minds up."

"Well then, let's say, here's hoping," his uncle said. "Here's hoping you'll like it enough to stay. Eh, Vincent?"

"Here's hoping," Vincent said, smiling in embarrassment. He and his uncle drank, Barbara did not pick up her glass. His uncle noticed that.

"As for the money," his uncle said. "I think I'll be able to start you on more than you're earning as a schoolmaster." He turned to Barbara, empty glass in his hand, in an attitude which reminded Vincent of a beggar asking alms. "And you know, Barbara," he said, "if it's moving to a new place that worries you, Bernadette and I will do all we can to help you get settled."

"It's not the moving that worries me," she said.

"Then what is it, my dear?"

"Well, if you must know," she said, "I'm worried about the job and whether it's what Vincent wants."

Said, her sentence hung in the air like smoke after a bullet. His uncle turned toward Vincent, waiting, his puffy face curiously immobile, his dark eyes stilled at last. In the kitchen Aunt Bernadette could be heard turning on taps, stacking dinner dishes. No one spoke, and after a few moments his uncle pulled out his handkerchief and coughed into it. Coughed and coughed, bending almost double while Vincent watched, heartsick, waiting for the paroxysm to wear itself out, watching as his uncle straightened up again, handkerchief still shielding his mouth, eyes staring at them in bloodshot, watery contrition. "Yes . . . well, of course, that's for you and Vincent to decide," his uncle said. "Excuse me—this cough. Sorry. Anyway, it's my fault, talking business to a young couple on their honeymoon. *Mea culpa.* Now, let's talk about something else. How was your trip?"

"Very tiring," Barbara said. "I don't know about Vincent, but I feel quite exhausted."

"Sorry to hear that," his uncle said. "If you're tired we mustn't keep you too late. But it's still the shank of the evening, after all. Would you like another cup of coffee?"

"No, thank you."

Again there was silence. "Vincent tells me you teach modern dance," his uncle began. "I'm a great admirer of Katherine Dunham. Have you ever seen her troupe?"

"Yes."

"And Martha Graham's 'Letter to the World,' " his uncle continued. "Yes, I used to go to a lot of ballet once upon a time." He smiled at her as he spoke, smiled as though pleading for her friendship. But Barbara did not return his smile and so, rejected, he reached unsteadily for the bottle and poured himself another brandy. Vincent tried to speak; in that moment he felt embarrassed for this man who had written a letter, booked a hotel room, bought a festive meal, made a speech of welcome, and who, his illusion of family feeling destroyed, sat silent, half drunk, his smile rejected. Vincent talked. He talked of the Abbey Theatre, of the plays he had seen in Toronto. For a few minutes, he and his uncle stumbled over broken rocks of conversation, recalling the sights and spectacles of former days. But a conversation with no dark corners could no longer be sustained. The talk died. Aunt Bernadette came back into the room to collect the coffee cups. Barbara gathered up her handbag.

"It's been a lovely evening, Mrs. Carnahan," she said, "and a wonderful dinner. But I'm afraid you must excuse me. I'm awfully tired from the plane trip. We had to be up so early this morning."

Aunt Bernadette bent down, put the coffee pot on her tray, stacked the saucers, heaped the cups on top.

"Leave those dishes, won't you dear?" Uncle Turlough said. "What's it matter?"

"I just want to put them in the sink."

"But Barbara's leaving, dear."

"I won't be a minute." She picked up the tray, went out of the room, and again they heard the rush of water taps in the kitchen.

"Bernadette won't be a minute," Uncle Turlough said. "She . . . she likes to get the dishes done in one washing. I'll just go and hurry her up. Sit down for a second, Barbara, I'll be back in a moment."

He went out.

"My God, Barbara, it's not ten o'clock yet. You could have been a bit more polite to them."

"I didn't feel like it," she said. "I'm sick. Why didn't you have the guts to tell him? You'd be insane to take that job. *Insane*. Why didn't you speak up?"

"Shh! They'll hear you."

"Well, what do I care? Do you think I want to spend our honeymoon being shown around by him and that floozy of his? My God, Vincent—"

But at that moment the sound of unmistakably quarrel-some voices reached them from the kitchen. "I don't care," Aunt Bernadette's voice said. "Let them go."

"Ah now, wait a minute, sweetheart—"

"Oh, shut up! I know you. It's your own fault. It's an old story, making yourself out to be something you never were."

"Shh!" his uncle's voice pleaded. Mumbling, indistinct, the argument died to whispers. A door shut. Uncle Turlough came from the kitchen, his face again fixed in its apologetic smile.

"We really must go," Barbara said, standing up.

"Oh? Well then, I'll just run down and find a taxi for you. Just a minute, I won't be long. Bernadette? . . . Bernadette, will you get the children's coats?"

In answer the water taps roared again in the kitchen.

"Won't be long," Uncle Turlough said, opening the apartment door. "Vincent, get yourself a drink."

The front door shut. Vincent stood up and walked toward the brandy bottle. He had drunk too much. He felt slow, uncoordinated, dull.

"Vincent, you're not going to have another drink!"

"I am."

"I'm getting my coat then. Where is it?"

"In the closet in the hall."

He heard her leave the room. He picked up the bottle. Perhaps in twenty years his face would bloat and blotch as his uncle's had. Drink, that was an Irish weakness. Self-deceit, that was an Irish weakness. He drank the brandy. He stared at the bookshelves with their dusty, unused books. Drunkenly, he turned to face their Carnahan grandmother on the mantelpiece. Never give an Irishman the choice between a girl and the bottle, she had said. Most of them will prefer the bottle.

The front door opened and he heard his uncle call, "Barbara, let me help you with that coat. And is this Vincent's coat? I have a cab waiting downstairs. Where's Vincent?"

His uncle came in, his step unsteady, his face still fixed in that apologetic smile which was, wasn't it, the very mirror of the man? "Here's your coat, Vincent lad. And wait till I get your aunt. Bernadette? Bernadette?"

He went out again and Vincent heard him go into the kitchen. A moment later, the front door shut. Vincent ran out to the hall. She was gone. Furious at her, he opened the front door to call her back, but as he did, his uncle returned from the kitchen. "Oh, there you are," his uncle said. "Bernadette asked me to say goodnight for her, she has a touch of migraine." He held out a clumsy parcel. "Your wedding present," he said. "I wrapped it up for you. Now, what about a nightcap? One for the road. Where's Barbara?"

"I asked her to go down and hold the cab."

His lie, complementing his uncle's, their mutual shame as they stood face to face, each seeking to atone for his wife's rudeness, each hoping to preserve the fiction of family unity . . . Oh God, Vincent thought, we are alike. Quickly, he opened the front door. "No thanks," he said. "Goodnight, and thank you for a very nice evening. Don't bother to come down, please."

"No bother at all. But are you sure now, you wouldn't stay a wee while? You could send Barbara home if she's tired and then we could sit down over a glass, just the two of us."

"I'm afraid I'd better go. Barbara is waiting, you see."

"I see," his uncle said. "Yes, of course. All right, I'll come down and say goodnight to her."

"Please, it's not necessary."

"No bother," his uncle said, following him out, pursuing him down two flights of stairs, coming with him into the street. The taxi waited, its bright ceiling light showing Barbara huddled in the far corner of the back seat. She did not appear to see them, and Vincent, afraid that she would refuse to say good-bye, hurried ahead of his uncle and pulled open the taxi door. "Say góod-bye to him, will you?" he whispered.

"Where is he?" She looked past him, peering into the darkness of the shabby street. But his uncle had stopped about twelve feet from the taxi. She waved to him and he raised his hand and waved back. "Goodnight, my dear," he called. "Have a good rest."

"Goodnight, Mr. Carnahan. And thank you." She smiled at him and leaned back in her seat. For her it was over; she wanted to go back to the hotel, to escape forever from these people she despised. "Come on," she said. "Get in."

But as she spoke, Vincent heard a low voice behind him. "Vincent? Vincent?"

Father? he had called. Father? But his father had not looked back. His father had walked down the path, opened the gate, no look back. Went down the avenue, turned the corner, no look back.

He turned back. There, half drunk on the pavement stood a fat old man with dyed hair. Where was the boy who once wrote poems, the young iconoclast who once spoke out against the priests? What had done this to him? Was it drink, or exile, or this marriage to a woman twenty years his junior? Or had that boy never been? What did this old man want of him now, Vincent wondered? Forgiveness? Or merely some sign that they still were kin?

"Vincent," his uncle said. "I'll see you tomorrow, won't I?"

"Yes."

"And Vincent? It's a good job, on my word of honor it is. I hope you'll take it, Vincent."

"Well, I must think about it, Uncle Turlough."

"Of course, of course. And Vincent? Bernadette, ah, you shouldn't mind her. Some days she's not herself. I'm sorry you didn't enjoy yourself this evening."

"But we did. We had a very good time."

"Thanks, Vince, thanks for saying that. Now, I don't

want to keep you but I wish we'd had more time to talk. I know you don't like the looks of the job. I think you don't like the looks of me, either. Well, I can't say I blame you, no, I can't say I blame you one bit. But, Vincent?"

"Yes, Uncle Turlough?"

"I was counting on your coming in with me. I had great hopes of passing on the business—but, never mind, if you don't want the job you don't want it and there's no use talking. Go on back now. You're on your honeymoon, you have better things to do than sit around at night with the likes of me. So off with you, lad, and good luck to you."

"Goodnight, Uncle Turlough."

As he shook hands with his uncle, Vincent looked at the taxi. There she sat, her pretty face averted in contempt. Was that all last night's lovemaking had meant to her? Didn't she know it was for both their sakes that he had come here this evening, that unless he could find something to do on this side of the water, she would be condemned to a life of drizzling boredom as a schoolteacher's wife in an Irish country town?

He leaned into the taxi. "Barbara, let's not go just yet."

"I'm tired," she said. "I'm leaving."

He fumbled in his trouser pocket. "Here's your fare then." He pushed the money at her and shut the taxi door. The taxi moved away from the curb. He watched; she did not look back.

"What's the matter, Vincent?"

He turned, his face forming an apologetic smile, his dark, uneasy eyes searching his kinsman's face. "I've changed my mind," he said. "Maybe I'll have one for the road, after all."

"I knew it, I knew it," said his spitting image.

ACCEPTANCE OF
THEIR WAYS

Mavis Gallant

Prodded by a remark from Mrs. Freeport, Lily Littel got up and fetched the plate of cheese. It was in her to say, "Go get it yourself," but a reputation for coolness held her still. Only the paucity of her income, at which *The Sunday Express* horoscope jeered with its smart talk of pleasure and gain, kept her at Mrs. Freeport's, on the Italian side of the frontier. The coarse and grubby gaiety of the French Riviera would have suited her better, and was not far away; unfortunately it came high. At Mrs. Freeport's, which was cheaper, there was a whiff of infirm nicety to be breathed, a suggestion of regularly aired decay; weakly, because it was respectable, Lily craved that, too. "We seem to have finished with the pudding," said Mrs. Freeport once again, as though she hadn't noticed that Lily was on her feet.

Lily was not Mrs. Freeport's servant, she was her paying guest, but it was a distinction her hostess rarely observed. In imagination, Lily became a punishing statue and raised a heavy marble arm; but then she remembered that this was the New Year. The next day, or the day after that, her dividends would arrive. That meant she could disappear, emerging as a gay holiday Lily up in Nice. Then, Lily thought, turning away from the table, then watch the old tiger! For Mrs. Freeport couldn't live without Lily, not more than a day. She could not stand Italy without the sound of an English voice in the house. In the hush of the dead season, Mrs. Freeport preferred Lily's ironed-out Bayswater to no English at all.

In the time it took her to pick up the cheese and face the table again, Lily had added to her expression a permanent-looking smile. Her eyes, which were a washy blue, were tolerably kind when she was plotting mischief. The week in Nice, desired, became a necessity; Mrs. Freeport needed a scare. She would fear, and then believe, that her most docile boarder, her most pliant errand girl, had gone forever. Stealing into Lily's darkened room, she would count the dresses with trembling hands. She would touch Lily's red with the white dots, her white with the poppies, her green wool with the scarf of mink tails. Mrs. Freeport would also discover—if she carried her snooping that far—the tooled-leather box with Lily's daisy-shaped earrings, and the brooch in which a mother-of-pearl pigeon sat on a nest made of Lily's own hair. But Mrs. Freeport would not find the diary, in which Lily had recorded her opinion of so many interesting things, nor would she come upon a single empty bottle. Lily kept her drinking to Nice, where, anonymous in a large hotel, friendly and lavish in a bar, she let herself drown. "Your visits to your sister seem to do you so much good," was Mrs. Freeport's unvarying comment when Lily returned from these excursions, which always followed the arrival of her income. "But you spend far too much money on your sister. You are much too kind." But Lily had no regrets. Illiberal by circumstance, grudging only because she imitated the behavior of other women, she became, drunk, an old forgotten Lily-girl, tender and warm, able to shed a happy tear and open a closed fist. She had been cold sober since September.

"Well, there you are," she said, and slapped down the plate of cheese. There was another person at the table, a Mrs. Garnett, who was returning to England the next day. Lily's manner toward the two women combined bullying with servility. Mrs. Freeport, large, in brown chiffon, wearing a hat with a water lily upon it to cover her thinning hair, liked to feel served. Lily had been a paid companion once; she had never seen a paradox in the joining of those two words. She simply looked on Mrs. Freeport and Mrs. Garnett as more of that race of ailing, peevish elderly children whose fancies and delusions must be humored by the sane.

Mrs. Freeport pursed her lips in acknowledgment of the cheese. Mrs. Garnett, who was reading a book, did nothing at all. Mrs. Garnett had been with them four months. Her blued curls, her laugh, her moist baby's

mouth, had the effect on Lily of a stone in the shoe. Mrs.
Garnett's husband, dead but often mentioned, had evidently
liked them saucy and dim in the brain. Now that William
Henry was no longer there to protect his wife, she was the
victim of the effects of her worrying beauty—a torment
to shoe clerks and bus conductors. Italians were dreadful;
Mrs. Garnett hardly dared put her wee nose outside the
house. "You are a little monkey, Edith!" Mrs. Freeport
would sometimes say, bringing her head upward with a
jerk, waking out of a sweet dream in time to applaud.
Mrs. Garnett would go on telling how she had been jostled
on the pavement or offended on a bus. And Lily Littel,
who knew—but truly knew—about being followed and
hounded and pleaded with, brought down her thick eyelids
and smiled. Talk leads to overconfidence and errors. Lily
had guided her life to this quiet shore by knowing when
to open her mouth and when to keep it closed.

Mrs. Freeport was not deluded but simply poor. Thirteen
years of pension keeping on a tawdry stretch of Mediter-
ranean coast had done nothing to improve her fortunes and
had probably diminished them. Sentiment kept her near
Bordighera, where someone precious to her had been buried
in the Protestant part of the cemetery. In Lily's opinion,
Mrs. Freeport ought to have cleared out long ago, cutting
her losses, leaving the servants out of pocket and the grocer
unpaid. Lily looked soft; she was round and pink and
yellow-haired. The imitation pearls screwed on to her
doughy little ears seemed to devour the flesh. But Lily
could have bitten a real pearl in two and enjoyed the
pieces. Her nature was generous, but an admiration for
superior women had led her to cherish herself. An excellent cook, she had dreamed of being a poisoner, but decided to leave that for the loonies; it was no real way to
get on. She had a moral program of a sort—thought it
wicked to set a poor table, until she learned that the sort
of woman she yearned to become was often picky. After
that she tried to put it out of her mind. At Mrs. Freeport's
she was enrolled in a useful school, for the creed of the
house was this: It is pointless to think about anything so
temporary as food; coffee grounds can be used many
times, and moldy bread, revived in the oven, mashed
with raisins and milk, makes a delicious pudding. If Lily
had settled for this bleached existence, it was explained

by a sentence scrawled over a page of her locked diary:
"I live with gentlewomen now." And there was a finality
about the statement that implied acceptance of their ways.

Lily removed the fly netting from the cheese. There was
her bit left over from luncheon. It was the end of a portion
of Dutch so dry it had split. Mrs. Freeport would have
the cream cheese, possibly still highly pleasing under its
coat of pale fur, while Mrs. Garnett, who was a yoghurt
fancier, would require none at all.

"Cheese, Edith," said Mrs. Freeport loudly; and little
Mrs. Garnett blinked her doll eyes and smiled: "No,
thank you." Let others thicken their figures and damage
their souls.

The cheese was pushed along to Mrs. Freeport, then
back to Lily, passing twice under Mrs. Garnett's nose.
She did not look up again. She was moving her lips over
a particularly absorbing passage in her book. For the last
four months, she had been reading the same volume, which
was called *Optimism Unlimited*. So as not to stain the
pretty dust jacket, she had covered it with brown paper,
but now even that was becoming soiled. When Mrs. Freeport asked what the book was about, Mrs. Garnett smiled
a timid apology and said, "I'm *afraid* it is philosophy." It
was, indeed, a new philosophy, counseling restrain in all
things, but recommending smiles. Four months of smiles
and restraint had left Mrs. Garnett hungry, and to mark
her last evening at Mrs. Freeport's, she had asked for an
Italian meal. Mrs. Freeport thought it extravagant—after
all, they were still digesting an English Christmas. But little
Edith was so sweet when she begged, putting her head to
one side, wrinkling her face, that Mrs. Freeport, muttering
about monkeys, had given in. The dinner was prepared and
served, and Mrs. Garnett, suddenly remembering about
restraint, brought her book to the table and decided not
to eat a thing.

It seemed that the late William Henry had found this
capriciousness adorable, but Mrs. Freeport's eyes were
stones. Lily supposed this was how murders came about—
not the hasty, soon-regretted sort but the plan that is sown
from an insult, a slight, and comes to flower at temperate
speed. Mrs. Garnett deserved a reprimand. Lily saw her,
without any emotion, doubled in two and shoved in a sack.
But did Mrs. Freeport like her friend enough to bother

teaching her lessons? Castigation, to Lily, suggested love.
Mrs. Garnett and Mrs. Freeport were old friends, and
vaguely related. Mrs. Garnett had been coming to Mrs.
Freeport's every winter for years, but she left unfinished
letters lying about, from which Lily—a great reader—
could learn that dear Vanessa was becoming meaner and
queerer by the minute. Thinking of Mrs. Freeport as "dear
Vanessa" took flexibility, but Lily had that. She was not
"Miss" and not "Littel"; she was, or rather had been, a
Mrs. Cliff Littel, who had taken advantage of the disorders
of war to get rid of Cliff. He vanished, and his memory
grew smaller and faded from the sky. In the bright new
day strolled Miss Lily Littel, ready for anything. Then a
lonely, fretful widow had taken a fancy to her and, as
soon as travel was possible, had taken Lily abroad. There
followed eight glorious years of trains and bars and dis-
creet afternoon gambling, of eating éclairs in English-style
tearooms, and discovering cafés where bacon and eggs
were fried. Oh, the discovery of that sign in Monte Carlo:
Every Friday Sausages and Mashed! That was the joy of
being in foreign lands. One hot afternoon, Lily's employer,
hooked by Lily into her stays not an hour before, dropped
dead in a cinema lobby in Rome. Her will revealed she
had provided for "Miss Littel," for a fox terrier, and for
an invalid niece. The provision for the niece prevented the
family from coming down on Lily's head; all the same,
Lily kept out of England. She had not inspired the death
of her employer, but she had nightmares for some time
after, as though she had taken the wish for the deed. Her
letters were so ambiguous that there was talk in England
of an inquest. Lily accompanied the coffin as far as the
frontier, for a letter of instructions specified cremation,
which Lily understood could take place only in France.
The coffin was held up rather a long time at customs,
documents went back and forth, and in the end the relatives were glad to hear the last of it. Shortly after that,
the fox terrier died, and Lily appropriated his share,
feeling that she deserved it. Her employer had been living
on overdrafts; there was next to nothing for the dog, companion, or niece. Lily stopped having nightmares. She
continued to live abroad.

With delicate nibbles, eyes down, Lily ate her cheese.
Glancing sideways, she noticed that Mrs. Garnett had

closed the book. She wanted to annoy; she had planned
the whole business of the Italian meal, had thought it out
beforehand. Their manners were still strange to Lily, although she was a quick pupil. Why not clear the air, have
it out? Once again she wondered what the two friends meant
to each other. "Like" and "hate" were possibilities she
had nearly forgotten when she stopped being Mrs. Cliff
and became this curious, two-faced Lily Littel.

Mrs. Freeport's pebbly stare was focused on her friend's
jar of yoghurt. "Sugar?" she cried, giving the cracked basin
a shove along the table. Mrs. Garnett pulled it toward her
defiantly. She spoke in a soft martyred voice, as though
Lily weren't there. She said that it was her last evening and
it no longer mattered. Mrs. Freeport had made a charge
for extra sugar—yes, she had seen it on her bill. Mrs.
Garnett asked only to pay and go. She was never coming
again.

"I look upon you as essentially greedy." Mrs. Freeport
leaned forward, enunciating with care. "You pretend to
eat nothing, but I cannot look at a dish after you have
served yourself. The *wreck* of the lettuce. The *destruction*
of the pudding."

A bottle of wine, adrift and forgotten, stood by Lily's
plate. She had not seen it until now. Mrs. Garnett, who
was fearless, covered her yoghurt thickly with sugar.

"Like most people who pretend to eat like birds, you
manage to keep your strength up," Mrs. Freeport said.
"That sugar is the equivalent of a banquet, and you also
eat between meals. Your drawers are stuffed with biscuits,
and cheese, and chocolate, and heaven knows what."

"Dear Vanessa," Mrs. Garnett said.

"People who make a pretense of eating nothing always
stuff furtively," said Mrs. Freeport smoothly. "Secret eating is exactly the same as secret drinking."

Lily's years abroad had immunized her to the conversation of gentlewomen, their absorption with money, their
deliberate over- or underfeeding, their sudden animal
quarrels. She wondered if there remained a great deal
more to learn before she could wear their castoff manners
as her own. At the reference to secret drinking she looked
calm and melancholy. Mrs. Garnett said, "That is most
unkind." The yoghurt remained uneaten. Lily sighed, and
wondered what would happen if she picked her teeth.

"My change man stopped by today," said Mrs. Garnett, all at once smiling and widening her eyes. How Lily admired that shift of territory—that carrying of banners to another field. She had not learned everything yet. "I *wish* you could have seen his face when he heard I was leaving! There was really no need for his coming, because I'd been in to his office only the week before, and changed all the money I need, and we'd had a lovely chat."

"The odious little merchant in the bright-yellow automobile?" asked Mrs. Freeport.

Mrs. Garnett, who often took up farfetched and untenable arguments, said, "William Henry wanted me to be happy."

"Edith!"

Lily hooked her middle finger around the bottle of wine and pulled it gently toward her. The day after tomorrow was years away. But she did not take her eyes from Mrs. Freeport, whose blazing eyes perfectly matched the small sapphires hanging from her ears. Lily could have matched the expression if she had cared to, but she hadn't arrived at the sapphires yet. Addressing herself, Lily said, "Thanks," softly, and upended the bottle.

"I meant it in a general way," said Mrs. Garnett. "William Henry wanted me to be happy. It was nearly the last thing he said."

"At the time of William Henry's death, he was unable to say anything," said Mrs. Freeport. "William Henry was my first cousin. Don't use him as a platform for your escapades."

Lily took a sip from her glass. Shock! It hadn't been watered—probably in honor of Mrs. Garnett's last meal. But it was sour, thick, and full of silt. "I have always thought a little sugar would improve it," said Lily chattily, but nobody heard.

Mrs. Freeport suddenly conceded that William Henry might have wanted his future widow to be happy. "It was because he spoiled you," she said. "You were vain and silly when he married you, and he made you conceited and foolish. I don't wonder poor William Henry went off his head."

"Off his head?" Mrs. Garnett looked at Lily; calm, courteous Miss Littel was giving herself wine. "We might have general conversation," said Mrs. Garnett, with a significant twitch of face. "Miss Littel has hardly said a word."

"Why?" shouted Mrs. Freeport, throwing her table napkin down. "The meal is over. You refused it. There is no need for conversation of any kind."

She was marvelous, blazing, with that water lily on her head. Ah, Lily thought, but you should have seen me, in the old days. How I could let fly . . . poor old Cliff.

They moved in single file down the passage and into the sitting room, where, for reasons of economy, the hanging luster contained one bulb. Lily and Mrs. Freeport settled down directly under it, on a sofa; each had her own newspaper to read, tucked down the side of the cushions. Mrs. Garnett walked about the room. "To think that I shall never see this room again," she said.

"I should hope not," said Mrs. Freeport. She held the paper before her face, but as far as Lily could tell she was not reading it.

"The trouble is"—for Mrs. Garnett could never help giving herself away—"I don't know where to *go* in the autumn."

"Ask your change man."

"Egypt," said Mrs. Garnett, still walking about. "I had friends who went to Egypt every winter for years and years, and now they have nowhere to go, either."

"Let them stay home," said Mrs. Freeport. "I am trying to read."

"If Egypt continues to carry on, I'm sure I don't know where we shall all be," said Lily. Neither lady took the slightest notice.

"They were perfectly charming people," said Mrs. Garnett, in a complaining way.

"Why don't you do the *Times* crossword, Edith?" Mrs. Freeport asked.

From behind them Mrs. Garnett said, "You know that I can't, and you said that only to make me feel small. But William Henry did it until the very end, which proves, I think, that he was not o.h.h. By o.h.h. I mean *off his head*."

The break in her voice was scarcely more than a quaver, but to the two women on the sofa it was a signal, and they got to their feet. By the time they reached her, Mrs. Garnett was sitting on the floor in hysterics. They helped her up, as they had often done before. She tried to scratch their faces and said they would be sorry when she died.

Between them, they got her to bed. "Where is her hot-water bottle?" said Mrs. Freeport. "No, not that one. She must have her own—the bottle with the bunny head."

"My yoghurt," said Mrs. Garnett, sobbing. Without her makeup she looked shrunken, as though padding had been removed from her skin.

"Fetch the yoghurt," Mrs. Freeport commanded. She stood over the old friend while she ate the yoghurt, one tiny spoonful at a time. "Now go to sleep," she said.

In the morning, Mrs. Garnett was taken by taxi to the early train. She seemed entirely composed and carried her book. Mrs. Freeport hoped that her journey would be comfortable. She and Lily watched the taxi until it was out of sight on the road, and then, in the bare wintry gardens, Mrs. Freeport wept into her hands.

"I've said good-bye to her," she said at last, blowing her nose. "It is the last good-bye. I shall never see her again. I was so horrid to her. And she is so tiny and frail. She might die. I'm convinced of it. She won't survive the summer."

"She has survived every other," said Lily reasonably.

"Next year she must have the large room with the balcony. I don't know what I was thinking, not to have given it to her. We must begin planning now for next year. She will want a good reading light. Her eyes are so bad. And, you know, we should have chopped her vegetables. She doesn't chew. I'm sure that's at the bottom of the yoghurt affair."

"I'm off to Nice tomorrow," said Lily, the stray. "My sister is expecting me."

"You are so devoted," said Mrs. Freeport, looking wildly for her handkerchief, which had fallen on the gravel path. Her hat was askew. The house was empty. "So devoted . . . I suppose that one day you will want to live in Nice, to be near her. I suppose that day will come."

Instead of answering, Lily set Mrs. Freeport's water lily straight, which was familiar of her; but they were both in such a state, for different reasons, that neither of them thought it strange.

REQUIEM FOR BIBUL

Jack Ludwig

Once upon a time—if we counted time not by calendars but by assimilated history and scientific change I'd be tempted to say four of five thousand years ago: before total war and all-out war, before death camps, Nagasaki, before fusion and fission, jets, moon shots, cosmonauts, Luniks in orbit, before antibiotics, polio vaccine, open-heart surgery, before TV, carburetors and other wonders of automation, before dead-faced hoods on motorcycles, dead-faced beatniks on maldecycles—once upon *that* kind of time lived a boy and his horse.

The year was 1939. This is no pastoral tale. The boy and the horse are both dead.

Twenty years late, counting time by the calendar, I write you of this boy Bibul and his horse Malkeh, of Bibul's ambition and his sad, sad end. In time-sorrowed perspective I record for you the imprint Bibul left on my mind and feeling—his ticlike blink, his coal-black hair in bangs over his forehead, his emery-cloth shaver's shadow, his ink-stained mouth, his immutable clothes that wouldn't conform to style or the seasons: always black denim Relief-style pants whitened by wear and washing, always a brown pebbled cardigan coiled at the wrists and elbows with unraveled wool, always a leather cap with bent visor, split seams, matching the color and texture of Bibul's hair. And old ruined Malkeh, scorned before lamented, making her daily round under Bibul's urging, dragging his creak of a fruit-peddler's wagon through Winnipeg's "island" slum north of the Canadian Pacific Railway Yards.

Bibul peddled while my time burned: in 1939 all of us high-school boys, owlish with sixteen- and seventeen-year-old speculation, almost missed seeing this Bibul foxy with world-weary finagling. We were out to save the world, Bibul a buck. Hip deep in reality, trying to beat tricky suppliers, weasely competitors, haggling customers, Bibul couldn't believe in us vaguesters. Peddling had forced him to see, hear, and judge everything. By his practical measure we were simply unreal. We'd speculate; Bibul would respond with *yeh-yeh*—the Yiddish double affirmative that makes a negative. He didn't have to say a word, or raise a sceptical eyebrow, or even frown with that tic. His smell alone argued a reality out of reach of our politely neutral Lux, Lifebuoy, Vitalis middle-class sweetness: "effluvium Bibul" we called that mixture of squashed berries, bad turnips, dank pine apple crates, straw, chickens, sad old horsey Malkeh. Bibul had a grand gesture to sweep away our irrelevance, a sudden movement of the hand like a farmwife's throwing feed to chickens, his nose sniffing disgust, his sour mouth giving out a squelching sound, *aaaa.* Sometimes he sounded like a goat, other times a baby lamb —just *aaaa,* but enough to murder our pushy pretentions.

We were a roomful of competitive sharks—math sharks, physics sharks, English, Latin, history sharks—secretly, often openly, sure we surpassed our teachers in brain and know-how. Joyfully arrogant we shook off the restricting label of high-school student, considering ourselves pros—mathematicians, scientists, writers, artists. In our own minds we had already graduated from the university, had passed through Toronto or Oxford, were entangled in public controversies with the great names in our respective fields, ending right but humble, modestly triumphant. But where was Bibul in this league? As loud as we pros hollered Bibul heard nothing. He only yawned, slouched, even snoozed, gave out with that killing *yeh-yeh,* poked his grayish nose into his peddler's notebook red with reality's ooze of tomato.

"Bibul," we'd say in the break between classes, "do semantics mean nothing to your knucklehead? An intellectual revolution's coming. You've got to stand up and be counted. What'll it be? Are you *for* Count Korzybski or against him?"

"Aaaa," *aa*ed Bibul, and his chicken-feeding motion sent us back to ivory towers.

"You' nuddin' bud gids," he'd say haughtily whenever we disturbed his audit of fruit-and-vegetable reality. "A 'ell of a lod you guys know aboud live."

Though we jeered and mocked, treated him like a clown, he was one of us, so how could we disown him? Kings of St. John's High, lording it from our third-floor eminence over the giants and dwarfs living the underground life in the school's basement ascreech with whirling lathes and milling machines, or those second-floor, salt-of-the-earth commercial students dedicated to bookkeeping, typing, the sensible life, we of course wanted to pass our nobility on to Bibul. We ran the yearbook and could have established him there, but on the "island" English ran a poor second to Ukranian, Polish, German, or in his case, Hebrew. We could have made him captain of the debating team, but peddling wrecked that; wrought up he stammered, angry he slobbered—no way to win arguments. Being a businessman, like his breed he had no time for politics; being tone-deaf he was a flop at glee-club tryouts. At sports he was dreadful. He couldn't swim a stroke, or skate, was flubby-knuckled at baseball, slashingly pigeon-toed at soccer, truly kamikaze going over a hurdle. And women? He had no time for them in his practical life; his old mare Malkeh and the ladies who haggled with him were the only females Bibul knew.

In recognition of his memo-book involvement we made Bibul our room treasurer.

After classes we theoreticians sprawled on the school green and took pleasure from long-limbed, heavy-thighed, large-breasted girls thwarting an educator's pious wish that the serge tunic neutralize the female form. Bibul was never with us. At the closing bell he'd run off to his horse and wagon, set to run the gauntlet of his customers (*shnorrers*, pigs, he called them); and early on a morning, when we theoreticians-turned-lovers, weary after a long night of girl-gaming, sat in Street Railway waiting houses knocking ourselves out over a noisy reading of Panurge's adventure with the Lady of Paris, Bibul, up and dressed since 4:00 A.M., struggled at the Fruit Row for bruised fruit and battered vegetables in competition with wizened peddlers and their muscular sons.

Lost in abstraction—and me, I thought little of Bibul in those days. He was a clown. A mark. A butt. The peddling was part of the sad, desperate struggle for money every family in the Depression knew. Bibul was the eldest of four children, his widowed ma supporting them on what she could make out of a tiny grocery store, doing the best she could, the dear lady, known throughout the "island" as "The Golden Thumb" and "The Adder," the latter reference ambiguous, meaning either snakes or computation, Bibul's ma being famous for a mathematical theorem that said $5 + 6 = 12$ or 13, whichever was higher.

Not till the year of our graduation did I discover why Bibul peddled with such dedication, why he rode out like a teen-age Don Quixote to do battle with those abusive, haggling, thieving *shnorrers*.

And what a riding-out that was! His paintless wagon listed like a sinking ship, sounded like resinless fiddles in the hands of apes, each wheel a circle successfully squared. Bibul sat on a tatter of leatherette bulging at the ends like a horsehair cream puff over his wilted greens and culled fruit Bibul's faultless-in-his-favor scales made judgment, his battered tin scoop more dented than a tin BB target. And what was more fitting than a nag like Malkeh to drag that crumbling wagon on its progress?

As grim as Don Quixote's Rosinante would look next to elegant Pegasus, that's how Malkeh would have looked next to Rosinante; she was U-shaped in side view, as if permanently crippled by the world's fattest knight luggging the world's heaviest armor. She sagged like a collapsed sofa with stuffing hanging low. She was bare as buffed mohair, her shoulders tanned from the rub of reins, her color an unbelievable combination of rust, maroon, purple, bronze, found elsewhere only in ancient sun-drenched velvets. Her tail was a Gibson Girl's worn discarded feather boa, its fly-discouraging movements ritualistic, perfunctory, more to let flies know that Malkeh wasn't dead than that she was alive. Her legs, like a badly carpentered table, were of assorted lengths, which made Malkeh move by shuffling off like a pair of aged soft-shoe dancers in a final farewell. Her hooves were fringed with fuzzy hairs like a frayed fiddle bow abandoned to rain and sun, her horseshoes dime thin, rusty as the metal hinges on her wagon's tailgate. To encourage Malkeh to see, Bibul covered her almost-blind eyes with a pair of snappy black racing-horse blinkers trimmed with shiny silver rivets, a touch to her decor like a monocle in the eye of a Bowery bum.

Out of compassion, out of loyalty to this wreck of a horse, Bibul let his wagon go to ruin: wood could be camouflaged with paint or varnish but where was covering to hide or revive sad old mortal Malkeh?

One day I came to school early, and saw her.

She was the horse version of the "Dying Gaul." On Bibul's "island" Malkeh suffered no invidious comparisons, but on a main thoroughfare like St. John's High's Salter Street, Malkeh was exposed to the cruelty of horse hierarchy, and her submarginal subproletariat hide was bared. High-stepping, glossy-flanked, curried and combed T. Eaton Company horses, middle-class cousins of aristocratic thoroughbreds seen only on race tracks, veered their rumps sharply as they passed, hooves steel-ringing, traces white as snow. Their tails were prinked out with red ribbon, their wagons chariots sparkling in red, white, gold against blue-blackness that could mean only good taste. These bourgeois horses had the true bourgeois comforts—warm blankets, stables with hay wall to wall, feed bags that offered privacy and nourishment. Their drivers looked like sea captains—neat contrasts to a slop like Bibul. And their commercial feed was gastronomical compared with the bad lettuce, wilted carrot tops, shriveled beets Bibul shoved at Malkeh in a ripped old postman's pouch.

Malkeh took their snubs without flinching. It was part of the class struggle. What hurt was the heavy, powerful working-class Percherons and their stinking garbage scows when they avoided kinship with Malkeh, acting like a guest at a high-toned party ignoring a waiter who's a close relative.

Pity old Malkeh's vengeful heart; the only pleasure she got from her enforced station on Salter Street came from knowing flies used her as an aerodrome from which to launch vicious attacks on the elegant department-store horses passing.

I saw her. The principal, too, saw her, slouched with resignation, a "Don't" in an SPCA exhibit, her right foreleg flatteringly fettered by a cracked curling stone to give Malkeh the impression she had the vim and youth to turn runaway horse. Malkeh died a long time ago, but years before she did the principal had her one visit gnomically memorialized and graven in metal; early next morning, where Malkeh had stood, this marker went up: *No Parking at Any Time.*

Bibul never again brought her to school.

Which is not to say that life on the "island" was without its grim side; what accounted for an almost-blind horse wearing blinkers? *Shnorrers!* Those women with bare feet stuck hurriedly into their husbands' outsized felt slippers, their hair uncombed, faces unmade, women in nightgowns at four on a sunshiny afternoon, hands clenching pennies and silver Bibul had to charm away from them with hard-sell and soft-soap. Singly they waited, in concert plotted, en masse moved in on him. Their purpose was simple—*get much, pay little.* To the victor went Bibul's spoiled spoils.

"Giddy ahb, Malgeh," Bibul would holler from his high seat on the wagon, and his cry sounded to a *shnorrer's* ears like a warring clarion.

Into the lists Malkeh dragged the keening wagon, onto the "island" in ruins like a medieval town (Canadian history is short, but our buildings add spice by getting older faster). Foundationless hovels kids might have built out of assorted-sized decks of cards sagged, leaned at crazy-house angles to astound Pisa. Gates tipsy as Malkeh's wagon swung on one hinge from a last lost post; dry, cracking wood fences leaned in surrender toward the ground, begging like old men in sight of a grave to be allowed to fall the rest of the way; windows were tarpaper-patched, like pirates' eyes, ominous as the blackness left in the streets by uninsured fires.

Behind every window or screen opaque with dust, behind every door splintered from kids' kicking waited the *shnorrers,* trying to make Bibul anxious, make him sweat a little, a cinch for persistent hagglers.

"Ebbles, ebbles, den boundz f'a quadder," Bibul shouted.

Crafty with stealth the *shnorrers* didn't bite.

Unflustered, unfooled, Bibul took advantage of the phony war, biting off the only three unspotted cherries in his entire stock while Malkeh dragged the exposed tin rims of the wagon wheels into the frost heaves and back-lane crevices. That cramped stinking back lane was mutually agreeable as a Compleat Battlefield—for Bibul because the solid pall of chicken droppings and horse dung was fine camouflage for the imperfections Time and Decay wrought his produce, for the *shnorrers* because the narrow quarters made tampering with the scale easier, detection harder, filching a hot possibility.

"Whoa beg, whoa der, Malgeh," Bibul ordered, oblivious of the spying women.

There, among rusted bedsprings hung up like huge harps, torn mattresses resembling giant wads of steel wool, in a boneyard of Model T's, Malkeh and the wagon rested. Dogs scooted in darts of nervous yapping, cats hissed down from rust-streaked corrugated rooftops, pigeons wheeled high above Bibul's untroubled head, returning to perch on overhanging eaves like fans anxious to get close to a scene of scuffle.

The *shnorrers* tried to read Bibul's face: the text was that Sphinxlike tic of a blink. Stalling, he made entries into that memo book, peeled an orange, scratched himself with casual but maddening thoroughness.

The *shnorrers'* united front crumbled. A foot slipped out from behind a door. Then a head.

"What you gonna cheat me on t'day, Bibul?" rasped out of an impatient throat.

The war was on! Horseflies, the Depression having made pickings so sparse they dropped their high standards and declared Malkeh a host, left the depressing fare of uncovered garbage cans (each lid long ago commandeered to be target in the minor-league jousts of the *shnorrers'* unknightly kids), and hiding behind the *shnorrers* sneaking up to do Bibul battle, launched assault on old Malkeh's flat weak flanks.

The siege began swiftly, deftly: a red-haired old woman flipped two-cent oranges into the one-cent bins, her other hand pointing up at the sky to make Bibul raise his eyes and predict weather.

Her accomplice brought Bibul back to reality, picking the bargains up before they'd even stopped rolling.

"Boyaboy Bibul, you god good tings in y'usually stinkin' stock. Look here, Mrs. Gilfix, at such oranges."

Bibul's ticlike blink snapped like a camera shutter on their mischief.

"Give over here dem oniges," he reproved them. "*Yoysher,* show a liddle resdraind," and the sad old innocents watched the two-cent numbers fall back into the two-cent bins.

On the other side of the wagon a pair of raspberry hands crushed away at lettuce greens.

"Hom much off f'damaged goods?" the criminal hollered, wiping lettuce juice on her gaping nightgown.

But the red-haired old woman hadn't given up on oranges.

"Black head means black heart, robber," she cried out. "Perls, d'fruit man who has a white head and eight kids and supports two unmarried sisters in Russia, from *him* I get fresher cheaper by two coppers—ha come, ha? Ha come?"

"My oniges are Sundgizd, Blue Gooze," Bibul, a sucker for brand names, came back huffily. "Berls' oniges grow on ebble drees."

One man's quarrel is another woman's smoke screen. The *shnorrers* moved in, squeezing the fruit, poking, tapping, complaining with shrieks and curses that sent the pigeon-hearted pigeons high off their perches. Like a bucket brigade the ladies passed fruit up and down the length of the wagon, each nose an inspector, those with teeth taking their duties more seriously, tasters whose opinions Bibul could live without.

"*Shnorrers,* dad youz are," he hollered, holding up a nipped apple, a chewed-up orange. "You god no gare vor my brovids?"

"Look how he's independent," mocked the red-haired one, lunging fruitless after a fistful of cherries. "Look how he holds hisself big! His fadder's a doctor, maybe? Or the mayor?"

Bibul was a lone guard defending his fortress from desperate pillagers; ubiquitous as Churchill, many-handed as Shiva, he had to be compassionate as Schweitzer. Though *I* didn't know what Bibul's dedication to peddling was all about, the *shnorrers* did: Bibul was saving up to become a Rabbi. Bibul immersed himself in the practical, pedestrian, material life because of a Great Cause—the Yeshiva in New York, eventual immersion in a spiritual life dedicated to comfort suffering mankind.

How the *shnorrers* used that Great Cause in their war with Bibul! It was all double; in sincerity they poured out their hearts to him—an educated boy, soon to be a Rabbi, maybe he'd understand their side—the husband who had taken off and never come back, the bad-hearted rich relatives, the ungrateful kids, the treacherous friends, root, trunk, branch of a Jewish Seven Deadly Sins. They dizzied him with complicated stories, unsettled his strong stomach with demonstrations of human frailty—missing teeth, crossed eyes, wens, tumors, needed operations.

As a bonus to sincerity they hoped the tales would divert Bibul long enough for their aprons to fill with filched fruit.

Crying real tears Bibul would free an apricot from a fist already stained with cherry.

"A religious you call yourself?" the caught thief howled. "God should strike me dead if I stole ever in my life one thing!"

Glancing up at the sky she moved closer to the other ladies; who knew what kind of pull with God a boy-study-ing-to-be-a-Rabbi had?

"Bibul, sveedhard," cooed one Mrs. Itzcher, blemished but bleached, "give off ten cents a dozen by oranges and Tillie'll show plenty appreciation."

Bibul used his chicken-feed gesture to ward off temptation.

The *shnorrers* prayed God to give Bibul good enough ears to hear their laments but to compensate with a little dimming of the eyes so he wouldn't catch them stealing. When they lost they cursed in tones loud enough to be heard above the world's fishwifery in action.

No wonder Bibul considered us sharks irrelevant. After those *shnorrers* poured it on what was left to be said?

"My brudder's second wibe's kid wid da hump in back, Rabbi Bibul, has already her third miscarriage."

In the midst of haggle they rained down proofs of suffering and absurdity—banged heads, cut knees, singed eyelashes, hands caught in wringers, slippery floors, broken steps, toppling ladders. The compensation they asked was meager: pity, a buy on a busted watermelon.

When we sharks, hot for culture, cool for Schoenberg, long on judgments, short on facts, turned our abstract expressions Bibul's way how else could he respond but with that *aaaa?* What did our books and ideas have to compete with a *shnorrer's* lament? Now when I think of that *aaaa* I translate it: "When I was a child I spake as a child . . ." (may Bibul forgive me for quoting St. Paul). *Aaaa* said "Vanity of vanities, all is vanity," in explanation of the term for Mammon so that the rest would be with Abraham, Isaac, and Jacob. *Aaaa* said "To everything there is a season, and a time to every purpose under the heaven."

On St. John's High School's Graduation Day Bibul was already at least half a Rabbi. The cardigan was gone, so too the denims and the black leather cap. He wore a fancy blue serge suit so new it still smelled of smoke. His sideburns were growing religiously into side curls, his emery-cloth shadow was now a beardlike reality. But it was Bibul's eyes I remember, excited, gay, snapping under that tic. He looked incredibly happy.

"Bibul," I said seriously, "you look beautiful in that suit!"

"Damorra, Joe," he said low and secretive, "damorra I go d'Noo Yorick an' d'Yeshiva."

I talked to him without clowning. He told me what he wanted, explained the peddling.

"Bibul," I said as we were walking out to our waiting parents, "doesn't the idea of a city the size of New York scare you? You'll be strange. Winnipeg's a village—"

"Wadz t'be asgared?" Bibul said with that wave of his hand. "Beoble iz beoble. I zeen all ginds aready."

He told me he'd sold Malkeh to Perls, the peddler. His mother walked proudly toward Bibul as we reached the street.

"Bibul," I shouted as parents came between us, "you'll be a terrific Rabbi! Good luck!"

He gave that chicken-feed flourish, but with new style, and with modesty.

"Aaaa," I heard above the shouting congratulations of parents, the last time I heard or saw Bibul.

That fall we sharks entered the university, and Canada the war. Winnipeg was transformed, full of aircrew trainees from places I knew about before only through postage stamps, men with yellow skins, red, brown, black, Maori tribesmen from New Zealand, bushmen from Australia, strange-sounding South Africans, carved-faced Indians thronging the streets and beer parlors. But far off in New York, Bibul, who had known war with the *shnorrers,* paid little attention to this latest struggle. He studied Torah and Talmud. He made his spending money selling fruit to Lower East Side *shnorrers* at the Essex Street Market.

Bibul's old Winnipeg customers haggled half-heartedly with old man Perls and old horse Malkeh, the one mercifully deaf, the other nearly blind. The Depression seemed over; money came easier.

Once in a long while I checked in at Bibul's mother's store, and gleaning news of Bibul, let her weigh me up a light pound of corned beef. She wore her hair Buster Brown, carried a huge buxom body on little feet in gray-white tennis shoes.

She shoved a letter at me.

"Look how a educated boy writes!" she said, pugnaciously proud. "Who but a Rabbi could understand such words?"

She pulled it back before I could answer.

"See him only, just look," she pushed a picture at my eyes.

Bibul huddled against a bare Williamsburg wall grinning the same grin as the three other Bibuls in the picture, all of them bearded and wild as Russians, in black beaver hats bought with money they had earned tutoring the Americanized grandchildren of rich Chassidim.

"Some boy, my Bibul," his mother called to me as I was leaving.

Winter passed and the war grew grimmer. Spring was beautiful, the war more dreadful. Summer was hot, particularly in New York, where Bibul divided his time between the Yeshiva and Essex Street's *shnorrers*. For days the temperature was in the high nineties. Bibul had never known such heat. He couldn't study, sleep, sell. In desperation he took himself one evening to the "Y," forgetting in the heat that he'd never learned to swim.

An attendant, going off duty, warned Bibul away, told him not to enter the pool. Who can be blind to Bibul's response?

"Aaaa," and that gesture.

He drowned.

His *shnorrers* on the "island," being told, wept and lamented. We sharks, even in the midst of war's casualties, were moved and stricken. Bibul was the first of us to die.

I cannot find Bibul's like in Winnipeg today.

Somebody waved a T-square wand over the old "island," bringing in the ninety-degree angle unknown in Bibul's far-off day. Progress pretends Bibul's "island" never really existed; the lanes are paved, the rotten wood of wall and fence has been sloshed over with paint. A few sneaky signs of the old world are around: a clothesline pole, exhausted from long years of soggy fleece-lined underwear to support, seems ready to give up the ghost; an outside staircase, impermanent as a hangman's scaffold, mocks the fire commission that asked for greater safety and got greater danger.

Malkeh is dead. The wagon is all bits and crumble. Motorized peddlers in trucks like Brink's Cars zoom through the reformed "island" late at night with the remnants of produce picked over by ringed and braceleted hands on the day route—River Heights, Silver Heights, Garden City, places of Togetherness, Betterness, Spotlessness, the polite answers Comfort has given to the sad old questions of Civilization.

"Apples, apples, two pounds for a quarter," the peddlers call, but not too loudly, and the women once poor enough to be *shnorrers* (few are still alive), the women who have replaced the departed *shnorrers* in remodeled, rebuilt houses, look over the fruit and vegetables (ironically like Bibul's old rejects and reduced-to-clears because of prior though elegant pawing), buy a little, haggle not at all, or withdraw with a snub at peddling, a bow in favor of the superior refrigeration of supermarkets.

Through the streets where old Malkeh drew that creaking wagon, urged on by leather-capped Bibul, chrome-trimmed cars speed in unending gaggle, their sport-capped, stylishly hatted drivers in control of power the equivalent of four hundred un-Malkeh horses. The mayor tells Winnipeggers to "Think Big," bid for the Pan-American Games, hang out more flags and buntings. Slums like Bibul's "island" and the City Hall are fortunately doomed; Winnipeg is obviously a better place to live in.

Who doesn't welcome prosperity?

But the fact remains: I cannot find Bibul's like in Winnipeg today.

And that is why here and now, in this, his and my city, I write you this requiem for Bibul, for his face, for his Great Cause, his tic, his wave, his *aaaa*. In love and the joy of remembering I sing you this Bibul and all that's past and passing but not to come.

When the City Hall is torn down they will build Winnipeg a new one; but where, O where shall we find more Bibuls?

A GOURDFUL OF GLORY

Margaret Laurence

You could walk through the entire market and look at every stall, but never would you see calabashes and earthen pots any better than those sold by Mammii Ama. She was honest—true as God, she really was. You might claim that there were as many honest traders here as there were elephants, and Mammii Ama would understand your meaning, and laugh, and agree with you. But she would let you know she was the one old cow-elephant that never yet died off.

She was a petty trader. A few market women grew rich, and became queen mammies, but Mammii Ama was not one of these. She got by. She lived. Nobody ever got the better of her, but she wasn't one to cheat her customers. She handled good stock. She wasn't like some of those shifty mammies who bought cheap and sold at the regular price the gourd with the faint seam of a crack right in the bottom where you wouldn't notice it until the soup began to leak out. She never sold flawed pots and bowls, either, a bit damaged in the firing so that they broke if you laughed in the same room with them. Such a trick was not Mammii Ama's way. The odd cull, maybe, she would admit. A few could always slip into a lot. You know how it is. A trader woman has to live, after all.

The cockerels, piercing the dawn gray with shrill and scarlet voices, awoke no earlier than Mammii Ama. Expertly, she bunched her fish-patterned cloth around her, bound on a headscarf of green and glossy artificial silk, and was ready for the day. She puffed the charcoal embers into flame, plonked on the tin kettle, brewed tea, and ate some cold boiled yam.

Comfort was still lying curled up on the straw mat.

One always hated to waken a sleeping child. Mammii Ama gently shook her granddaughter, and Comfort sat up, dazed, like a parrot with all its feathers ruffled. She was soon dressed; not yet five years old, she wore only a shame-cloth, a mere flutter of red and beaded rag around her middle and between her legs.

Then they were off. Wait—a last thought. Did Adua sleep peacefully? Was she covered? If you sweated, sleeping, you got a chill in your belly and you had pain passing water forevermore. Quiet as a watchnight, Mammii Ama padded across the hut to the iron cot where her snoring daughter lay. Adua was properly covered—the blanket was drawn up to her neck, and all you could see of her was her head with its wiry hair that she was always straightening with hot pull irons, and her face, breathing softly and brown under its matting of white powder from the night before. Mammii Ama did not understand why her daughter daubed herself with talcum until she looked like a fetish priestess in a funeral parade. Many things about Adua were difficult to comprehend. The high-heeled shoes, for instance, which hurt and were all but impossible to walk on. Teeter this way, lurch that—a fine business. The woman's anklebones would snap one of these days—but try to tell her. And the palaver about the name —a lunacy. Adua called herself Marcella, and insisted that everyone else do the same. It was not like the grand-daughter's name, Comfort—a decent name. A mission name, true, but it had lived here a long time, until it seemed to have been African always. But Marcella— whoever heard of such a name? Mammii Ama couldn't bring herself to speak it. She called her daughter "moon woman" or "choice of kings," and Adua, who was—you had to admit it—very vain, liked to hear those names as she preened herself.

Still, she was a good daughter. She brought home money —worked all night for it. A club girl, she was, at the Weekend in Wyoming, and Mammii Ama loved her more dearly than life, and felt for her a shy and surprised pride, for the daughter was certainly a beauty, not a cow-elephant like her mother.

Mammii Ama looked once more on the powdered and sleeping face, then she was gone, shutting quietly behind her the packing-case door of the mud-brick shanty.

Mammii Ama took the child's hand while they clambered onto the crowded bus. She paid her fare, and the bus, with a rumble like the belly of a giant, jolted off down the road and into the city.

The market was already filling with sellers. The best hunter got an early start, Mammii Ama would say. You'd never catch a fat cutting-grass by sleeping late. As she spread out her wares in front of her stall, Mammii Ama sang. She sang in pidgin, so that every passerby, whatever his language, would understand.

> *Mammii Ama sell all fine pit,*
> *Oh, oh, Mammii Ama.*
> *She no t'ief you, she no make palavah,*
> *Oh, oh Mammii Ama . . .*

And the girl child, squatting in dust as she arranged just so the stacks of brown earthen bowls, the big-bellied black cooking pots, added to the refrain her high and not-quite-true-pitched voice.

> *Oh, oh, Mammii Ama . . .*

Everywhere there were voices, and sweet singing bodies. Everywhere the market women's laughter, coarse and warm as the touch of a tongue. It was still early, and the morning cooks had not yet arrived to buy vegetables and meat for the Europeans.

Moki was already perched atop his firewood. He wiped the rheum from his eyes with an end of his dirty turban. He was old, and his eyes ran mucus, especially in the morning. He was not a Muslim, but his nephew, who died of a worm in the guts, had been one, so Moki always wore a turban in memory of him. No one knew where Moki came from. He didn't know himself. He knew the name of his village, but not the country where it was, and he knew the names of his people's gods. He had come here who knows how long ago, with a Hausa caravan, and had somehow lost the trader who hired him to carry headload. Now he sold pieces of firewood, which he gathered each evening in the bush.

"Morny, Mistah Moki! I greet you!" Mammii Ama called, and the old man fake-bowed to her as though she were a queen mother.

On the other side, a Hausa man was hanging up his white and black wool mats and huge pointed hats and long embroidered robes which only men tall as the Hausas could wear. Sabina, the cloth seller, snapped at a small boy who pissed beside her stall, complaining that he was spraying her second-best bolts, draped outside to catch the eye. The small boy's mother threw a coconut husk which caught him on the ear, and he ran off, leaking and howling.

T'reepenny, who looked more ancient than the gods, creaked and trembled. up to Mammii Ama's stall. Her hands, bony as tree roots and frail as grass, lugged along the bucket of gourd spoons, half of them broken. She had no stall. She had no money to rent one, so Mammii Ama allowed her to sit beside the calabash-and-pot stall with her bucket. She said only one word, ever. Maybe she knew only one. "T'reepenny," she would quiver and quaver. "T'reepenny, t'reepenny," over and over like a brain-fever bird, as she held up the gourd spoons for all to admire. She was pleased if she got one penny. Only from white women, rich and gullible, had she ever received as much as three.

With the wares arranged, Mammii Ama was light in heart. Now she began to recall last night's rally. She had gone with the others in the Association of Market Women. They all wore new cloth, in the party's colors, red and white and green. What a thing it had been! Her well-fleshed hips remembered their jigglings and marvelous convolutions in the parade. Her shoulders and hearty arms remembered the touch of others' arms and shoulders as the market women marched. Four abreast, they entered the meeting place like a charging army, like an army with spears of fire, with rifles fashioned of power and glory. And they all shouted together—loud as a thousand lorry horns, loud as the sea—"Free-Dom!"

And he had been there, the lovely boy they loved so well, the Show-Boy. He spoke to them of the day that was coming, the day of freedom. And they shouted with one voice, and they cheered with one voice. They were his women, his mothers and his brides.

"Hey, you, Sabina!" Mammii Ama shouted. "Were you at the rally?"

"Naturally," the shriek came back. "Didn't you see me, Mammii Ama? I was at the back, in between Mercy Mensah and that old Togo woman, whatever her name is."

"I was at the front," Mammii Ama said loudly, but with modesty.

"I was there, too," Moki chipped in.

Everyone laughed.

"Wha-at? I never knew you were a market woman, Moki," Mammii Ama bellowed.

"When you get to my age, it's all the same," Moki replied evenly. "Man—woman—what does it matter? We all eat. We all die."

An outburst of chitter-chatter:

"Don't tell me that story, Moki!"

"Maybe it's an old muzzle loader, but I'll bet it still fires!" And so on.

"What did you think of it, Sabina, the rally?" Mammii Ama continued, when the gust of ribaldry faded.

Sabina shrugged. She was thin, and her mouth always turned down, as though she had just swallowed a piece of rotten fish.

"Well, it's a lot of talk, if you ask me," she said. "Free-Dom. Independence. All right—the white men go. So, then? We'll still be haggling over tuppence at our stalls, my friends."

Mammii Ama jumped to her feet and shook her head and both fists at Sabina.

"Ei! Somebody here is like a crocodile! Yes, somebody acts like the crocodile who crawls in the mud of the river. He lives in the river mud—and he thinks the whole world is only river mud. Oh, blind! Blind!"

She appealed to the others.

"Free-Dom—it's like the sun," she cried. "You have to crawl out of the river and mud or you can't see it."

Moki muttered and went on cleaning his eyes. Old T'reepenny nodded her head. She agreed in this way with everything Mammii Ama said. She didn't understand, but she agreed. Whatever Mammii Ama said must be right. The Hausa man stared—he spoke no Ga.

Sabina went on shrugging, and Mammii Ama grew so

furious she rushed over to Sabina's stall and burst into fresh argument. She grew inspired. She no longer cared about Sabina. Around her, the market women gathered. They cried, "Ha—ei!" when she paused for breath. They swayed and chanted to the rhythm of Mammii Ama.

"Go call all de market woman!" Mammii Ama cried, this time in pidgin, to captivate a wider audience. "Tell dem say 'Free-Dom'! Go call all de market woman—say, you no go sell befoah five minute. You sell Free-Dom dis time. What dis t'ing, what dis Free-Dom? He be strong, he be fine too much. Ju-ju man he no got such t'ing, such power word. Dis Free-Dom he be sun t'ing, same sun he be shine. Hey, you market woman, you say, 'Money sweet—I be poor woman, nothing with, on'y one penny. I no 'gree dis Free-Dom, I no be fit for chop him.' Oh—oh—I t'ink you be bush woman, no got sense. I no 'gree for you. I tell you, dis Free-Dom he be sweet sweet t'ing. You wait small, you see I tell you true. Market woman all day be queen mammy den."

Moki stopped his eye wiping and waved a piece of firewood, roaring encouragement to his friend Mammii Ama. The Hausa man uttered somber cries in his own tongue— "Allah knows it! Has not the Prophet himself said the same? It will be shown at the Last Day!" T'reepenny, carried away by excitement, grasped a gourd spoon in either hand and executed a sort of dance, back bent and stiff-kneed, all by herself, until her unsteady breath gave out and she sank down beside her bucket once more, chirping her mournful word.

Sabina, feeling herself outnumbered, began to weep, begging them all not to forget her unfortunate past. If she seemed sour, she sobbed, they knew why.

Mammii Ama immediately grew sympathetic. She broke off and put an arm around Sabina's shoulder. A terrible thing it must have been, she agreed. Enough to mark a person for life.

Sabina had once had a wealthy lover—well, not wealthy, perhaps, but certainly nicely fixed. A clerk, he was, a man in a government office. He always seemed healthy, Sabina used to say. He seemed so strong, so full of life, so full of love. How that man would do it! Again and again— why, half a dozen times in a single night, that was nothing to him, Sabina said, simply nothing.

Then one night, his heart swelled and burst, and he died, just like that. He was with Sabina at the time. They had gone to sleep, still together. At least, she had gone to sleep. A little later, feeling cramped and trying to turn, she had wakened to find a dead man there. Dead as a gutted fish, and his eyes wide open. Sabina got a baby that night, it turned out, and she went round saying her child had been given her by a dead man. She was sure of it. She screeched and cried. A child begotten by a corpse—who could stand the thought? No one was surprised when the baby was born dead.

The women clucked softly. Mammii Ama, ashamed of her attack, soothed and soothed in her full mother-voice.

"There, my red lily. Cry, then. It is nothing. I am a fool. I have a head like a calabash, empty."

Into the hush-hushing throng of women ran Comfort. Her face was frightened and excited.

"Mammii Ama! Mammii Ama! A white woman has come to your stall!"

And Mammii Ama looked amazed, dumbfounded, only partly in mockery of the child. Hastily she hitched her cloth up around her, and flew back.

"Ei—what a madness!"

She went running along like a girl, like a young girl at her first outdooring. She carried her weight lightly, and her breasts bounced as she bounded over gutter and path, over smoldering charcoal burner, over the sleeping babies with blackflies at their nostrils' edge.

"Who is the young virgin fleeing from her seducer?" Moki shouted, as she approached. "Oh, oh, Mammii Ama!"

The white woman was thin and tall. She had very little flesh on her, just yellow hide over bones, and her eyes were such a pale blue they seemed not to be there at all—only the jelly of the eyeball, nothing to see with. She was holding a brown earthen bowl in her hands.

Mammii Ama regained her breath.

"Madam, I greet you," she said with hoarse cheerfulness.

The white woman smiled uncertainly and looked over her shoulder. Mammii Ama looked, too, and it was Ampadu standing there.

Ampadu was a clerk. He had a good job. One heard he had influence. He was a really educated man—he knew not only reading and writing, but also the work of account books and typewriters. Mammii Ama, who could neither read nor write, and who kept her accounts in her head with never a mistake in twenty-four years, was greatly impressed with Ampadu's power over words and numbers. She did not tell him so—in fact, she constantly made fun of him. They were distantly related, and Ampadu, who understood her unexpressed pride in this relationship, took her jibes in an easy-natured way.

She clapped him on the shoulder. He was neatly dressed in a white shirt and gray flannel trousers. How prosperous he looked. And his rimmed spectacles, how well they suited him.

"Ampadu! I greet you!" she cried in Ga. "How are you, great government man? Do they still say your pen is more active than your love-branch? Hey—you, Moki! Did you know this? When the old chief's young wife wanted a lover, she sent for Ampadu's pen!"

The clerk laughed, but not wholeheartedly. He patted his stomach in embarrassment. Mammii Ama, realizing Ampadu was accompanying the white woman, began to roll her eyes and pretended to stagger.

"What's this, Ampadu? What's this? What's all this about?"

Ampadu held up his hand, like a policeman stopping a lorry.

"She wants to see the market," he hissed. "She's the wife of my new boss. Mammii Ama, please be sensible, I implore you. She wants to buy a calabash, God knows why."

The white woman was growing impatient.

"Ampadu—ask her what she'll take for this bowl, please."

"Ten shilling," Mammii Ama replied without hesitation.

"Ten shillings!" the white woman cried, and even Ampadu looked stunned.

Mammii Ama seized the bowl from her hands.

"See, madam—dis one, he be fine too much. No be bad one. Look—put you fingah heah—you feel? All fine—nevah broke, dis one. Ten shilling, madam."

"How much is the usual price?" the white woman asked Ampadu.

Ampadu scuffed his shoes in the dust. Mammii Ama

felt quite sorry for him, but she had to try hard not to laugh.

"Usual price?" Ampadu appeared to search his memory. "Let me see, what is the usual price? I am sorry, madam— I am afraid I don't really know. My wife, you see, buys all the cooking pots—"

"Ten shilling!" shouted Mammii Ama in a huge voice. "All time, meka price he be ten shilling! I tell you true, madam. I no t'ief you."

"Five shillings," the white woman offered.

"Nine shilling sixpence—for you."

They settled at length on six shillings, to Mammii Ama's well-disguised delight. The white woman then bought a black cooking pot and two calabashes. Mammii Ama was amazed. What could such a woman want with cooking pots and calabashes? Were Europeans living like poor Africans all of a sudden? Mammii Ama felt excited and confused. The order of things was turning upside down, but pleasurably, in a way that provided food for speculation and gossip.

When the white woman was gone, they all discussed it. Who could understand such a thing? Mammii Ama, dusting and rearranging her stock of pots and bowls, began one of her speeches.

"Hey! Stranger woman, listen to me! Do you feed your man from a calabash you bought in the market? Does your man eat from a bowl made of river clay? Ei! The gourd-vine dances—he shakes his leaves with laughter. Ei! The river fish drown in their laughter. Your own dishes—are they not white as a silver shilling? They are white as the egret's feathers when he sleeps in the baobab tree. If the fine vessels displease you, give them to my granddaughter. Yes! Give them to Comfort, the lovely and dear one—"

Mammii Ama turned the last bit into a song, and sang it all day. Some of the others joined the refrain, varying it from time to time for amusement.

> *Yes! Give them to the woodseller,*
> *Give them to Moki, the lovely one . . .*

Mammii Ama added a stanza in pidgin, so everyone around would know she was no longer cross at Sabina.

Meka you dash dem for Sabina,
She fine too much, same been-to gal,
She like all fine t'ing . . .

A week later, the white woman returned, this time alone. Mammii Ama greeted her like an old friend. The white woman bought a gourd spoon from T'reepenny, and haggled with Mammii Ama over the price of another bowl. Finally, Mammii Ama could restrain her curiosity no longer.

"Madam—why you buy African pot?"

The white woman smiled.

"I want to use them for ashtrays."

"Ashtray! For dem cig'rette?" Mammii Ama could not believe her ears. "You no got fine one, madam?"

"Oh—I have lots of others," the woman said, "but I like these. They're so beautifully shaped."

Mammii Ama could not credit it.

"An' dem calabash? Madam chop *fu-fu* now?"

"I use the shallow ones to put groundnuts in," the woman explained. "For small chop with drinks. The big ones I'm using for plants."

"Free-Dom time, meka all African get dem fine dish," Mammii Ama mused. "I look-a dem na Kingsway store. Fine dish, shine too much."

She stopped herself. It would not do, for business, to admit she would like to use fine white dishes. She even felt a little guilty at the thought. Were not her calabashes and bowls the best in the market? But still—

The white woman was looking at her oddly.

"You don't mean to tell me that you think you'll all be given—what did you say?—shiny dishes when Independence comes?"

Mammii Ama did not know whether she believed it or not. But she grew stubborn.

"I tell you true!" Speaking the words, she became immediately convinced of their absolute truth. "Market woman, all dey be same queen mammy den."

"Is that what freedom means to you?" the woman asked.

Mammii Ama felt somehow that she was being attacked at her very roots.

"What dis t'ing, what dis Free-Dom? You no savvy

Free-Dom palavah, madam. He be strong, dis Free-Dom, he be power word."

"You're free now," the woman said. "We give you justice. I'll wager you won't have it then."

The woman did not speak pidgin. Mammii Ama could not follow every word, but she detected the meaning. The white woman was against Free-Dom. Mammii Ama was not surprised, of course. Nor was she angry. What else would you expect of Europeans? When she spoke, it was not to the white woman. It was to the market, to the city, to every village quiet in the heat of the sun.

She spread her arms wide, as though she would embrace the whole land. She felt the same as she had once long ago, when she went to meet her young man in the grove. She was all tenderness and longing; she was an opening moon flower, filled with the seeds of life everlasting.

"Dis Free-Dom he be sun t'ing," she cried. "Same sun, he be shine. I no 'gree for Eur'pean. I 'gree for Free-Dom."

The woman looked thoughtful.

"Your leader seems popular among the market women."

"Ha—aah! He fine too much. He savvy all t'ing. He no forget we. Market woman all day come queen mammy. All—all—"

She stuttered and stopped. The Free-Dom speech seemed to have lost something of its former grandeur. Now, Mammii Ama's words would not rise to her heights. Earthbound, she grasped for the golden lightning with which to illumine the sky. She found it.

"Dat time, you t'ink we pay wen we deah go for bus?" she cried. "We no pay! At all! Nevah one penny."

The white woman still peered. Then she laughed, a dry sound, like Moki breaking firewood.

"You really think the buses will be free after Independence?"

"I hear so," Mammii Ama said truthfully. Then, feeling her faith not stated with sufficient strength: "Be so! Meka come Free-Dom nevah one penny for we. We go for bus free, free, free!"

Her words had the desired effect. The white woman was staring at her, certainly, staring with wide eyes. But in her face was an expression Mammii Ama did not understand. Who was this stranger, and why did she come here with her strange laughter and strange words and a strange look on her skull-face? Why didn't she go away?

Mammii Ama frowned. Then she heaved her shoulders in a vast shrug and turned back to her stall.

"Hey, you, Comfort! Hasn't the village woman come yet with the new calabashes?"

Soon, with the white woman gone, everything was in order, everything was itself once more, known and familiar.

> *Mammii Ama sell all fine pot,*
> *Oh, oh, Mammii Ama!*
> *She no t'ief you, she no make palavah,*
> *Oh, oh, Mammii Ama!*

The white woman did not come again for a long time, and Mammii Ama forgot about her. Things weren't going so well. Both Adua and the child got sick—skin burning all over, belly distended. Mammii Ama went to a dealer in charms. Then she went to a dealer in roots and herbs. She spent, altogether, six pounds four shillings and ninepence. But it did no good. Adua wouldn't drink the brew the herb dealer concocted, nor would she allow Mammii Ama to give it to the child. When the fetish priest came to the shanty, Adua lay with her head covered by the blanket, not wanting to see him, but afraid to send him away. Then Adua insisted that Mammii Ama take Comfort to the hospital to see the doctor. Mammii Ama was very much opposed to the idea, but one did not dare argue with a sick person. She took the child. They waited three days before they could see the doctor, and Mammii Ama was in a panic, thinking of her empty market stall, and no money coming in. She had a little money saved, but it was almost gone now. Finally, the doctor gave Comfort a bottle of medicine, and Mammii Ama, when they arrived home gave some of it to Adua as well. Slowly, the sickness went away, withdrawing a speck of its poison at a time. Adua went back to work, but Comfort was still too weak to help in the market.

That was always the way—sometimes you had luck: you were well; the coins in the wooden box grew; you bought a little meat, a little fish, a bowl of lamb's blood for the stew. Then—bam! Fever came, or somebody robbed you, or nobody needed pots and calabashes that month. And you were back where you started, eating only *garri* and lucky to have anything. You got by somehow. If you couldn't live, you died, and that was that.

But then a great thing happened. Not in the ordinary run of exciting things, like Moki killing a small python, or Sabina getting pregnant again, this time by a live man. No—nothing like that at all. This was a great thing, the greatest of all great things.

Independence.

The time came. Everyone was surprised when the time actually came, although they'd been expecting it for so long. It was like a gift—a piece of gold that somebody dashed you for nothing.

Mammii Ama was so excited she could hardly breathe. The night before the Day, everyone gathered at the Parliament building, everyone who could dance or walk or totter, even old T'reepenny, who nearly got broken like a twig by the crowd, until Mammii Ama staunchly elbowed a path for her. And there at midnight, the white man's flag came down, and the new flag went up—so bright, and the black star so strong and shining, the new flag of the new land. And the people cried with one voice, "Now—now we are Free!"

The Day—who could describe it? Commoners and princes, all together. The priest-kings of the Ga people, walking stately and slowly. The red and gold umbrellas of the proud Akan chiefs, and their golden regalia carried aloft by the soul bearers, sword bearers, spokesmen, guards. From the northern desert, the hawk-faced chiefs in tent-like robes. The shouting young men, the girls in new cloth, the noise and the dancing, the high-life music, the soldiers in their scarlet jackets. The drums beating and beating for evermore. The feasting. The palm wine, everybody happy. Free-Dom.

Mammii Ama sang and shouted until her voice croaked like a tree toad's. She drank palm wine. She danced like a young girl. Everybody was young. Everybody's soul was just born this minute. A day to tell your grandchildren and their children. "Free-Dom shone, silver as stars—oh, golden as sun. The day was here. We saw it. We sang it and shouted."

The day, of course, like any other day, had to finish sometime. Mammii Ama, exhausted, found her way home through the still-echoing streets. Then she slept.

The next morning Mammii Ama did not rise quite so early. The tea and boiled yam tasted raw in her mouth. She swallowed her cold bile and marched out.

Only when the bus drew to a stop did she remember. She climbed on, cheerful now, full of proud expectancy. She was about to push her way through the standing people near the door, when the driver touched her arm.

"Hey—you! You no pay yet."

She looked at him shrewdly.

"Wey you say? You t'ief me? I no pay now."

"So? Why you no pay?"

Mammii Ama folded her arms and regarded him calmly.

"Free-Dom time, meka not one penny for we. I hear it."

The driver sighed heavily.

"De t'ing wey you hear, he no be so," he said crossly. "Meka you pay you fare. Now—one time!"

Some of the other passengers were laughing. Mammii Ama scarcely heard them. Her eyes were fixed on the driver. He was not deceiving her—she could read it in his tired, exasperated face.

Without a word, she took out the coin and dropped it in the metal farebox.

That day the white woman visited the market again. Mammii Ama, piling bowls in neat stacks, looked up and saw her standing there. The white woman held up a calabash and asked how much.

"Twelve shilling," Mammii Ama said abruptly, certain that would be enough to send the woman away.

To her utter astonishment, however, the woman paid without a murmur. As Mammii Ama reached out and took the money, she realized that the calabash was only an excuse.

"How were your Independence celebrations?" the white woman smiled. "Did you have a good time?"

Mammii Ama nodded but she did not speak.

"Oh, by the way—" the white woman said in a soft voice. "How did you get on with the bus this morning?"

Mammii Ama stared mutely. She, the speech maker, was bereft of speech. She was more helpless than T'ree-penny. She did not have even one word. She could feel her body trembling. The fat on her arms danced by itself, but not in joy. The drummer in her heart was beating a frenzy. Her heart hurt so much she thought she would fall down there in the dust, while the yellow skull of the woman looked and tittered.

Then, mercifully, the word was revealed to her. She had her power once more. Her drumming heart told her what to do. Snake-swift, Mammii Ama snatched back the calabash, at the same time thrusting the coins into the woman's hand.

"You no go buy from Mammii Ama! You go somewhere. You no come heah. I no need for you money."

She felt a terrible pang as she realized what had happened. She had parted with twelve shillings. She must be going mad. But she would not turn back now. She took another belligerent step, and the yellow menacing skull retreated a little more. She spoke clearly, slowly, emphasizing each word.

"I no pay bus dis time," she said. "Bus—he—be—free! You hear? Free!"

Inspired, Mammii Ama lifted the gourd vessel high above her head, and it seemed to her that she held not a brittle brown calabash but the world. She held the world in her strong and comforting hands.

"Free-Dom he come," she cried, half in exultation, half in longing. "Free-Dom be heah now, dis minute!"

The sun rolled like an eye in its giant socket. The lightning swords of fire danced in the sky.

She became calm. She knew what was what. She knew some things would happen, and others—for no reason apparent to her—would not. And yet, there was a truth in her words, more true than reality. Setting down the calabash, she readjusted her fish-patterned cloth above her breasts. She looked disinterestedly at her former customer. The white woman was only a woman—only a bony and curious woman, not the threatening skull shape at all.

She watched the white woman go, and then she turned back to her stall. She picked up the calabash and set it with the rest. An ordinary calabash, nothing in it. Where was the glory she had so certainly known only a moment before? Spilled out now, evaporated, gone. The clank of the coin in the fare box echoed again in her head, drowning the heart's drums. She felt weary and spent as she

began stacking the earthen pots once more. A poor lot—
she would be lucky to get ninepence apiece. They seemed
heavy to her now—her arms were weighted down with
them. It would continue so, every day while her life
lasted. Soon she would be an old woman. Was death a
feast day, that one should have nothing else to look forward
to?

Then a voice, hoarse as a raven's, began to sing. It was
Moki, the wood seller, and as he sang he beat out the
rhythm with one of his gnarled sticks. Nearby, others took
up the song. Sabina, singing, wrapped her cover cloth
more tightly and swaggered a little in front of her stall so
they could see her belly was beginning to swell with the
new, good child. The Hausa man donned one of his gilt-
beaded hats and waggled his head in mock solemnity.
Ancient T'reepenny shuffled in her solitary dance.

Mammii Ama, looking from one to the other, understood their gift and laughed her old enduring laughter and
sang with them.

> *Mammii Ama sell all fine pot,*
> *Oh, oh, Mammii Ama . . .*

She was herself again, known and familiar. And yet—
there was something more, something that had not been
before. She tried to think what it was, but it eluded her.
She could feel it though. So that the others might know,
too, she added to her old chant a verse no one had ever
heard her sing before.

> *Mammii Ama, she no come rich.*
> *Ha—ei! Be so. On'y one penny.*
> *She nevah be shame, she no fear for nothing.*
> *D' time wey come now, like queen she shine.*

And they caught the rhythm, and the faith, and the
new words. Mammii Ama straightened her plump shoulders. Like a royal palm she stood, rooted in magnificence,
spreading her arms like fronds, to shelter the generations.

THREE HALVES
OF A HOUSE

Hugh Hood

East of Kingston the islands—more than eleven hundred of them—begin to sprout in and all around the ship channel, choking and diverting the immense river for forty amazing miles, eastward past Gananoque, almost down to Stoverville. But a third of the continent leans pushing behind the lakes and the river, the pulse, circulation, artery, and heart, all in one flowing geographical fact, of half the North Americans, the flow we live by all that long way from Minnesota to the Gulf.

Saint Lawrence's Gulf, martyr roasted on a gridiron, Breton saint, legend imported by the French to name the life's current of a hundred million industrious shore dwellers, drinking the water, lighting their houses by it, floating on it in numberless craft. "Seas of Sweet Water," the Indians called the lakes, and to the east the marvelous Saint Lawrence with the weight of the American Northeast inclining to the Gulf.

So the channel must be cut, though the islands press against the current in resistance, cut sometimes through needles' eyes and wearing deep, deep, through solid pressed ancient rock a hundred and fifty feet down, two hundred, icy cold ten feet below the surface. A holidaying swimmer floats up half frozen in the narrow channel from a shallow drive of the current, lucky to catch an exposed tree root at the edge of a corroded island and haul himself ashore, the water sliding and driving beneath him two hundred feet down to the anonymous rock.

Try to swim upstream, brother, at Flowerlea! And feel yourself carried backward through your best stroke, feel yourself whipped out of yourself as the river pulls at your thighs, hauling you down away eastward as though you

were falling helpless down a chute. Then grab at the skeletal
roots, hang on, swing in the water and ride an eddy ashore!
Fight the weight of eleven states and half of Canada, something to think about swinging on your sodden shredded
branching root while fifty feet away—not an inch more—
a ship seven hundred and fifty feet long glides ghostly past,
soundless, what a thing to meet on a holiday beach! Not a
thing to swim too close to, glistening black walls rising
out of the water above you like an apartment building—
Scott Misener on the bows and the name of the line reading backward to the stern in letters twice your height,
swimmer, and not a sound from the ship, the current
moving the ship as easily as it moves you. A deckhand
leans incuriously at the rail, lifting a friendly hand, and is
gone, whirled away eastward while he lowers his arm.

*Scott Misener, Erika Hamburg, Tosui Maru, Bristol City,
Mooremacglen*—they hail from everywhere, upper lakers,
tankers, the few remaining canalers, ocean-going freight-
ers built by thrifty Danes for the lakes trade, drawing
twenty-seven feet precisely, up and down all day and all
night with their myriad of sirens sounding the whole range
of the tempered scale. The shipmaster confers anxiously
with his pilot through the forty perilous miles, threading
needle after needle. At Flowerlea the channel is so narrow the summer cottagers can lean over and assess the
deckhands' breakfast bacon. In the fall the last of the
cottagers sit around their barbecue pits with a liner in
the front yard, the shipmaster pacing about above them,
cursing them and their hot dogs, the handiest things to
curse. He is afraid of the Flowerlea channel, so narrow,
and of the weight of waters astern hurrying him along,
the navigation season waning and his insurance rate about
to jump sky-high if he doesn't clear the locks by the appointed day.

Late last autumn a shipmaster drove aground off Stoverville at the end of the season; he lost the closing date at
the locks and passed the winter iced into the river with a
ruined cargo. Each day the sailors walked to Stoverville
over the three feet of ice, but the captain, a ruined man,
brooded in solitary humiliation all winter in his cabin.
He was never seen in Stoverville, although hysterical cables
addressed to him arrived daily from Oslo.

He was unlucky, mistrusted his pilot, didn't know the

river, hated it, and the river ruined him. He missed all the signs, the waning of the islands, the widening of the channel, the three trees—tamaracks with fifty feet of bare trunk and perky coronas on top—that stand on the promontory west of Stoverville. Making his move to starboard toward the New York shore minutes too late, he felt the current drive his bows so deep into the river bottom he knew he'd never haul her off. He stared at the three tamaracks all winter, counting them and counting them and there were never more than three. This summer, in Oslo, he killed himself.

The tamaracks mark the end of the islands, the beginning of the river's free run from Stoverville to the Atlantic, nothing in the way but mammoth new locks, then Montreal, Quebec, wider and wider until you can't see across, at last the sleety Gulf. But at Stoverville the river's freedom is a newborn thing, the mass of water has just begun to run, eroding, finding the fastest way down. At Stoverville it's hardly two miles across.

Over there on the New York shore are the old resort towns, fading now, the gingerbread hotels coming down, their gilt furnishings sold off. Now and then a welterweight contender trains here and sometimes a powerboat regatta invites the curious. But the real tourist money goes to Europe or Montego Bay and the old millionaires, who found their way upstate in the seventies from Saratoga, are dead and gone. Between Watertown and Plattsburg, back a few miles from the river, there's nothing. An Army camp, a NIKE site, trees and woods and dunes and the snow belt. And that's it.

On the Canadian side there's Highway Number Two, the worst main highway in the world, with the small river towns dotted along it—Kingston, Gananoque, Stoverville, Prescott—dreaming their dreams dating from the eighteen-thirties of a prosperity which never came. Yet they sleep there along the shore waiting for things to pick up when the hundred and fifty years' slack season shall be over, an occasional coal boat putting in and water buses running thrice-daily tours of the islands up to the bridge and back.

Twenty miles north of the riverfront strip the towns begin to shrink in size—Tincap, Newboro, Athens; the farms are scrubbier and smaller and hillier. You still see

television aerials but now the rocks begin to stick up
through the thin topsoil and you are into the Laurentian
Shield with a rocky uninterrupted thousand miles clear to
James Bay of round old rock, polished by the last Ice
Age. Saint Lawrence again but this time choking off life,
not conferring it. And from this hinterland, from the little
towns like Athens, people have been moving back down to
the shore for sixty years, as soon as they broke their first
plowshares on the intractable rock humping up out of
the hillsides. They come back to Stoverville and cherish
their disappointments, the growth of their numbers limited
by their situation between the river and the rock, the same
smooth incredibly ancient rock which beds the river. Life
and power flowing beside them and old impregnable rock,
out of which nothing can be forced to grow, above them
northerly, so they come back one by one into Stoverville
from Athens and the other little towns, and here they
fashion their lamentations.

"They are painting the house," says Mrs. Boston venge-
fully, "green and white—so unoriginal. In the thirty years
we lived there they never offered to paint it for us. Your
father painted every four years, always green and white.
He spent thousands on paint, and always the best white
lead—money I might have had, or you, that has been
absorbed into the the walls of that place, with the Hungarians living in the other side."

"Hungarians must live somewhere," offers her daughter
mildly.

"But need they live in Stoverville?"

"They make their choices unknowingly, the poor things,"
says Maura even more mildly, "and I suppose once here
they must abide by the original choice. I must say, I think
it kind of Grover to let them have the other half of the
house."

"Most Stoverville people won't rent to them," says Mrs.
Boston, "but Grover does, in preference to me."

"You didn't wish to stay in the smaller half. You had
the opportunity."

"Taken a crumb from his table you mean? Accepted
the little half, and maintained it as we did the other side
for thirty years until they pushed us out? That I should
lie awake alone in my bedroom in the smaller half and
listen to Grover rattling around on the other side of the

wall! I don't know what he proposes to do with all that space, with just the two of them. Ellie, of course, doesn't go out any more, the poor unfortunate. Can you imagine it? Cooped up all day with that man, green and white? The very least he could have done would be to choose new colors. Green and white were your poor father's choice. Heavens, what it cost! It was that dirty gray, you know, but of course you couldn't know. You weren't five years old when we moved in. Your father had to pay for three coats of the finest white lead to cover the gray, the way they'd let it all run down, Ellie's crazy mother!"

"Was she crazy? I remember her."

"Undeniably, and her husband was worse. I tell you, Maura, there's a warped streak in that family somewhere, and it comes out, it comes out. I'm glad they're not my blood relations."

"But they were father's."

"He was a medical doctor, my dear," says Mrs. Boston stiffly, "and he understood these things."

"These things?" asks Maura delicately, lighting a cigarette. She does not wish to pass the entire weekend in these debates.

"Tubercular bone," says her mother, "congenital physical rot. And other things than physical for they've never been right, none of them. Your father at least went from Stoverville to the city, though in the end he came back. But these clumps of Phillipses—they move from the farm to Athens looking for the easy life, and from Athens to Stoverville believing they've found it because they don't have to rise at four in the morning. My dear girl, they infest the countryside, they're a positive plague."

"I'm one eighth Phillips," says Maura with a faint apprehension.

"But you live in Montreal where medicine and science have penetrated."

"The weak drive out the strong, Mother," says Maura, "like vines driving through rock. You're better off away from either side of that house."

"But to be driven out! And then those Hungarians." She smiles maliciously. "I understand that the ships' sirens terrify the Hungarians, wake them up at night. They think of Russians, I expect." The sirens give everyone dreams, thinks Maura to herself, everyone in Stoverville. *Paaaaa-rrrrrpppp*—I am going to starboard. *Mmeeeuuuhhhhhhhh*—I am going to port. They never collide in the channel, even at Flowerlea; they do not astonish us with freakish mishaps, sinkings, or groundings except for a single dead Norwegian, but they are all around us in the night. *Paaarrrrpppp. Mmeeuuuhhhhh.* They give us dreams in Stoverville, but in Montreal, though they circumnavigate the city, no one notices them. I forget the river in Montreal or in New York while here it rolls through me, head to thighs. I dreamed as a child in my bed at the dark top of the house, their house, probably Grover's room now; he can't sleep with Ellie, she'd never allow it, so virginal at sixty. Poor Grover Haskell, sleeping in my bed in my room listening first to the sirens and then to the cranky breathing of his good wife who has done everything for him, according to Mother, subjugated herself entirely to him, yielded him up her house, for of course it's her house, not his—she's legitimately Phillips. I'm only one eighth, thank God, so she has the house that was my father's by temporary arrangement because he was only a quarter Phillips and had the house at a nominal rent while Ellie, disguised as Mrs. Grover Haskell, tried to get away to other parts of the world. What is a nominal rent? Daddy never complained of the rent and we knew that one day the Haskells would drift back, allowing Daddy the smaller side while they all four enjoyed a polite Stoverville retirement, except that they didn't. Daddy is dead and Ellie is dying slowly and Grover is not. And my dear mother flourishes.

The year we moved in, the tamarack trees were lonely and beginning to lean over the river, earthfall exposing part of their roots on the promontory's side.

"We'll fix that," Daddy said, and he poured in cement and fill, so the trees are still there. "Those tamaracks look lonely," he said to me, "and they're important. Did you know, Maura," he said, talking as if I were an adult, "that sailors talk about our three trees from here to Duluth?" Then he told me where Duluth was and I remember it still. I think of the sailors at the Lakehead, talking about our three tamaracks, only of course they were never really ours at all but belonged first to her grandfather, who was the town saddler and unsuccessful, and then the town magistrate—and tubercular. Then they were her mad father's, whom I knew, who moved into the little half of the house to rent us the larger and to resent us—we paid a nominal rent for the privilege of becoming an object of resentment to that frustrated painter.

When I was five he would beckon to me from his side of the porch to show me his new picture, clutching at his brushes with arthritic paws and aiming unsteadily to pat me where he had no business to. "It's a schooner, Maura, do you see?" he said, pulling at the frill on my sleeve. "It's a schooner on the river."

"I like the steamers, Uncle Wallace," I said, and he changed color. "But I can't help it, I like them."

"This is a schooner, don't you see?"

"But I like the steamers' horns better."

Then Ellie came onto the porch, calming the morning with her still face. She picked up her father's pencils which were rolling hastily away along the porch toward the shrubbery, and handing them to him, kissed him while he stormed at me.

"The child's difficult, Ellie! She abuses my pictures. Everyone always does, everyone but you." She patted him and was silent, listening to his vacuities and smiling secretly at me from her still face around her lashes, drawing her father's sting as he went on rebuking me, not directly— he said nothing to me directly, but he let me hear. "My house, my house. I let them have my house, which I love, and their child must criticize. Let her stay on her side of the porch. Edward Boston is a young fool and his wife is malicious. When I asked him what was the matter with me, he declined to say, the coward—he knows all right but he daren't say. Only he sends his little girl around the corner of my house to make sure that my hands aren't right, that they shake, that my schooners look like steamers because I can't hold my pencil straight, a poor old man; they laugh at me. I'll raise his rent!"

Sitting on the arm of the deep chair in which her father crouches, mouthing his poison, she smiles sweetly along her lashes at me, frightened and trembling, five years old, misunderstanding it all because my father, young and poor as he is, worries about rent, cement, and fill and the three trees.

"Look at the new white paint," I wail, starting to cry.

"Daddy painted your old house for you." But old Mr. Phillips can't hear as he begins to slide into a soothed nearly senile sleep. Ellie tucks his blanket around him, watches him slide away, and takes me by the hand, walking me back around the corner of the porch to our front door.

"I only said I like the steamers. I didn't mean to make him mad."

"It's all right, darling, he's an old man. It's nothing you've said, he's an old man. He's been disappointed and he's sick."

"But he'll be all right, won't he?"

She stands with me at the door to our half of the house. We look through the screen into the hall, and at the back of the house my mother bustles, moving kitchen furniture with a cheerful scraping noise.

"He'll be all right soon," says Ellie full of comfort, placing her hand on her forehead and drawing me down after her onto the porch swing, which rocks gently with a creak of chains as we look into each other's eyes, hers the Phillips eyes, rapt, violet, staringly intense, and her face so sweet and still; mine the brown eyes my mother imported into the family, round and direct, eyes I hated as a child, so agatelike and unblinking, my mother's and mine, not glancing and vivid like Ellie's. All at once she hugs me and whispers secretly, "I wish you were mine."

I am appalled by the notion. "I belong to Daddy."

Ellie kisses me briskly and for a moment we stare together at the tamarack trees on the point. "We love our fathers," she says absently, and turning gives me again her ineffable saint's gaze, visionary, violet, preoccupied. "Find your mother, sweetheart," she tells me, and I trot into the house vaguely disappointed.

"If you were not such an intractable mule," says Mrs. Boston, fixing her agate eyes in a persuasive stare, "you might do well in Stoverville. There are four distinct pieces of house property you might inherit if only you'd be nice to people." She holds up her fingers, beginning to itemize them. "There's our house, to begin with."

Maura emerges from her reverie, balking at this projected deathwatch which jerks her suddenly over nearly thirty years to her pallid present prospects. What had been the frill on the arm of a child's frock becomes a table napkin across which she's thrown a suddenly adult arm, plumper and hairier than a five-year-old's.

"I've stayed away too much."

"Then come home more often!"

"This is home? Pardon me, Mother, but the only thing that brings me to Stoverville is you. And this isn't your home, any more than Montreal is mine. You weren't born here."

"It has grown into my home. The thought makes me weep sometimes now that your father is three years' dead."

"You don't go back to your birthplace." Maura hopes to make a point.

"I do not. Nobody there remembers me or my family. We're obliterated. If I have any home, which is dubious, it's here in this crazy town beside these damned ships."

"They're getting bigger and bigger. I don't know where it'll stop. It was never like this before."

"It's the new locks," says Maura. "The big ships used to stop at Montreal."

"You're past thirty, Maura," says Mrs. Boston. "Do you imagine that Montreal will provide you with a home?"

The faintest enlivening blush dabbles Maura's cheek as she folds and refolds a table napkin in her hands. "I meet men of my own age at the studios," she says reluctantly, "and you never can tell."

At this indecency her mother recoils, her life's scheme all at once readjusted. "You do not think of marriage?"

"I think of it all the time," says Maura, crossing her legs irritably, "all the blessed time and I wish somebody would ask me."

"A particular somebody?"

"Since you ask, yes." And then she grows defensive. "You were close to thirty when you married."

"But not past it."

"Thirty is no immutable barrier. Women past thirty have married before this, and will again."

"You mean that you will?"

"Given the chance!"

"Then think," says Mrs. Boston, adapting her tactics, "of the uses of our home as, perhaps, a summer place. Right on the river, a most desirable location."

"I thought that you disapproved of the location."

"I should disapprove less," says Mrs. Boston with regal dignity, "were the house legally mine."

"Ah!"

"There is no need to be ironic, Maura. I am your mother, after all, and I have your best interests at heart."

Maura thinks this over solemnly, seeming from her attitude to fancy a world in which fewer people have her interests more personally at heart. Identification with her interests, not cool appraisal of them, is the desideratum.

"I mean to protect you from Grover and his schemes," her mother pursues. "It is not a Haskell house but a Phillips house, and should come to you. He has no children."

"The poor man," exclaims Maura involuntarily.

"Poor man, bosh!" says her mother with energy. "He never wanted them and Ellie gave in to him everywhere. Poor woman, rather! You know that Grover Haskell is a monster of selfishness."

"Has he the necessary wit and tenacity?"

"All that he requires. You remember how, three years ago, he brutalized me, wouldn't even let me go on clinging to the littler half, but insisted on what he calls 'a proper rent, considering.' That man had the audacity to ask me to move your father's workbench from one side of the cellar to the other as soon as it was convenient—the tools still warm from your father's palms. I offered him a cord of firewood that your father had stored in the cellar to dry—out of the purest neighborly feelings—and he told me, as curtly as you please, that he meant to use the fireplaces ornamentally, to fit into their new decor."

"It is their house."

"It is her house, and will be yours, I tell you, if you behave properly. She must know by now what he is, even though she's sick. She has sacrificed everything to him, given in to him, followed him through all his failures like a saint, I tell you, like a saint, and now she's sick. She has never been well since her father died."

"When I was small," says Maura, remembering it with deep pleasure, "I really loved Ellie, she was so good."

"She is a saint. But queer, Maura, queer. She has these visions, you know." And Mrs. Boston begins a rambling account of the phenomenon called "second sight," by means of which events occurring at a distance in space or time may be observed directly by persons with certain particular spiritual equipment. "You father's great-aunt had it," she concludes, "and I believe Ellie has it, or something like it. When I go to see her I have the feeling that there are other people in the room."

"You go to see her?"

"I do."

"When Grover isn't there?"

"He is always there. He daren't leave her, you know, for fear she'll die while he's out of the house. But I'll grant him one good grace. He usually goes down to the cellar while I'm there. Can't face me, I suppose."

"How does she act?"

"Well, she wanders. She is sorry for what Grover has done to me; she is ashamed for him. She always asks for you, Maura, and you should go to see her, if only out of kindness."

"What's the matter with her?"

"She was always a visionary and religious, and of a self-sacrificing temperament, first her mother and father and now Grover. She seems to have gone completely religious, speaking in symbols and so on. She has been reading Revelation, I suspect."

"I'll go and see her," concedes Maura, not entirely reluctantly.

Peering through blue spruce and cedar, Grover studies the three tamaracks from the porch, trying to ignore the river below them which he has never loved, and assessing fondly the intervening plantings which have suddenly devolved upon Ellie and himself. When he courted his wife thirty years ago, coming fearfully to the old house because of the uncertainties of her father's temper, pausing on the front walk and studying the movement of dragonflies in the porch light, he had wished that it were warmer near the house, that someone might fill the space between the house and the tamaracks with sod, flowers, and other trees and vines, to take away something of the starkness of the house's situation, perched icily on the promontory unscreened from the winter reflection off the river's ice. He had been lucky. For most of the subsequent thirty years while he and Ellie tried their luck in Kingston, Belleville, and for a few desperate years in Toronto, they had had a caretaker who paid them for the privilege of keeping the property up and even improving it. A nominal rent but one that paid the taxes—and the house was regularly painted, heated, kept immaculate, ventilated, and the memory of Ellie's terrible father gradually expunged.

Grover had liked Dr. Boston, though he couldn't abide his widow, and had tried to deal fairly with him. He had accepted forty dollars a month from him for nearly thirty years and had never counted it up to see what it came to. Edward had had inexpensive living accommodation and had been free to improve the property for his own comfort if he wished. That the Bostons had come in time to think of his house as immutably their home was certainly natural enough but scarcely his concern. That Dr. Boston had planted and cultivated a perfectly splendid arbor, a lovely jungle of carefully selected trees and shrubs between the house and the tamaracks, that he had installed a darkroom and a new furnace, was his business, done with his eyes wide open. However much the Bostons might have resented their involuntary move into the smaller half of the house, they had been given fair—and more than fair, generous—notice of the event.

Grover knew that the enforced move was not what had killed Dr. Boston, although his death had certainly followed hard upon the move, coming three months after it had been accomplished. He didn't see why he shouldn't do over the house the way he and Ellie wanted it; but Dr. Boston had inconsiderately died and he was to be blamed for it, he supposed. The doctor's widow didn't seem at all interested to see what he was doing with so much unaffected delight to remodel the place according to his own ideas of comfort, his and Ellie's.

But they had gone ahead the way they'd planned during long years of living in inconvenient apartments, dreaming of the wealth of space they'd one day enjoy. They had saved, made sketches, eyed antique stores, and scrabbled around in back-concession attics looking for curly maple antiques, planning at length to reclaim the house and furnish their half with their painfully acquired and stored treasures. And when the time had come, despite Edward's inconvenient death, they had gone ahead with their plans. He had done it all for Ellie, had followed her in all things, had done everything for her because he'd cherished her and had hoped to exorcise the crazy memory of her parents.

"Softening of the brain" they'd called it when her mother died, the state of medical science being what it was in the Stoverville of thirty years ago. Like mother, like daughter, and like father, too. For Ellie was going the same way —he saw it though he tried not to—and here he was in a house, or half a house, that wasn't really his, had never been and would never be his, that now, watching her sicken prematurely, he hated and didn't want any more. He couldn't get out of the house, not even to go to the grocery store; there were razor blades lying loose in the medicine cabinets, mirrors that might be broken and wrists to slash. He didn't know what they might come to and couldn't leave the house for fear.

Light, not sunny light but cold white light, slides through the cedars and spruce, giving them a smoothy suave waxy sheen. Standing on the south corner of the porch, catching sharp gleams off the water through the glancing leaves, he wishes now that they'd kept their last mean apartment in Toronto. It is with a sense of felt physical release that he watches Maura push through a hole in the fence, enter the arbor, and make her way automatically, without pausing to place her feet safely on the springy overgrown turf, along winding paths aslant the promontory, coming to pay her call. Now he sees the oddness of their situation: Maura is a native of the place who's fled and felt no ties; he's an outsider who's gotten stuck fast inside. "Softening of the brain." They have a hospital of a kind these days in Stoverville and he knows what they'll call it.

Then the shrubbery shakes and parts and Maura stands revealed, mounting the sagging porch steps. Behind her the small green and copper leaves whisper together, and all at once, miles away to the east, a steamer hoots once.

"Hello," they say together, almost strangers, and again, with embarrassment, "well, hello!"

"I'm here for the weekend," she says with constraint, "and I wanted to see you both."

"You can see her," he says, forever an inside outsider. How the girl resembles her father! More and more he feels sixty-five and out of place.

"How is she? You know, Grover, she's the one person in Stoverville . . . well . . . she was a second mother to me."

"I wish we'd had children."

"You do?"

"Certainly I do. But her health was never up to it."

"Oh! How is she now?"

"Lying down," he says abruptly, with a shiver. "Come along, I'll show you what we've done with the house." He pauses. "You don't mind our doing it over, do you?"

"Of course not. It's yours, after all. But how is she?"

She won't be diverted, it seems. "When her mother died, you remember, it was the same thing. But they've a new name for it now, which sounds a little better."

"Most people said that old Mrs. Phillips was out of her mind."

"She wasn't, exactly. They called it 'softening of the brain.' That's the trouble. It runs in the family, don't you see?"

"But there isn't any such thing."

"They don't call it that any more. Now they call it"— and he rattles off the foolish phrase—"'premature senility induced by an insufficient supply of oxygen to the brain.' Her circulation is poor and the artery which feeds the brain is narrowing—like hardening of the arteries—I don't recollect the medical term."

"Sclerosis?"

"That's it. Arteriosclerosis affecting the brain, and hypertension, too, of course. She's all right sometimes but she wanders. And then she was always religious, you know."

"Is she still?"

"Worse, if anything. Good heavens, Maura, she sees ghosts. According to her the house is full of people. And I—I can't see anything. I tell you, it's frightening. Come inside, I'll show you around. You see on the floor here in the hall I've installed a parquet, black and white squares. Very cheerful, don't you think?"

He conducts her around the familiar rooms, exhibiting them in their novel guise. Soon they hear a voice calling from upstairs. Ellie's.

"I'm coming down. I've a housecoat here," she warbles with enthusiasm, "and I've had a good sleep, Grover."

She has no footfall. She had been soundless in Maura's memory, never letting the floorboards announce her coming. She had floated around her unfortunate father and mother like a creature from another world, a wraith. Now she floats down the quiet staircase more impalpable than ever, her face bloodless, her hair gone silver, white white white, like someone who lives in the river, Maura thinks, like somebody made of water. She stretches out her arms and floats along, singing that thin melody. What happens in her head, does she hear anything? She doesn't look at you but over your shoulder, seeing things beyond and to one side of you. Poor Grover. No wonder he's afraid that the house is full of people who can't be seen or heard. Her gaze closes around and behind you like water, and you aren't solid.

"My dear child," says Ellie moving soundlessly over the black and white squares while Maura, entranced, feels but doesn't see Grover melt away out of vision bound for his workbench, to feel the cutting edges of his chisels and wonder about them.

The two women embrace and Ellie is so weightless that Maura can hardly feel her hug. She, poor chunky brown-eyed girl, solidly there, whoever else vanishes, feels as if she's tearing an invisible tissue of air as she follows Ellie into the drawing room. So she takes good care to sit facing her across the room, not relishing the idea of that disturbing weightlessness at her side.

"You're always the same girl," says Ellie, plucking at the sleeves of her flowered housecoat with birdlike hands, blue in the veins, crooked fingers locked in an immutable grasp, "and I thank God you've got your mother's eyes and not ours."

Her own eyes can't be still but rove desperately around the room.

"I'm embarrassed for myself and Grover," she says. "I feel as though we've wronged you, although I'm thankful he feels nothing of it, the dear man, I don't believe he knows what's going on." All at once a nervous tic starts up in her left cheek and she straightens her spine, sitting up abruptly on the sofa.

"He showed me the river of the water of life, clear as crystal," she says, blinking.

There is just nothing to be said to this, for apparently she has left lucidity behind her, putting Maura in the position of an unwilling witness to a personal collapse. How can she get out, what can she do? There is nothing to do but sit there and make conversation during the rare lucid intervals.

"Seven stars and seven gold crowns, seven tapers, three trees, three thrones," says Ellie, shivering slightly. Then she shakes herself and tries to fix her eyes on Maura. "Grover wouldn't understand, would he?" she begs, and launches into the unforgettable.

"The house is full of gods," she begins, "all around us, gods and the dead. I saw my father yesterday, staring hatefully at the parquetry, and he told me that he didn't understand or like it, finding it bad taste and confusing to the eye. He told me not to marry and I wouldn't listen. I refused to listen though he told me from my cradle onward. I couldn't bear children though I wanted them so. I mustn't transmit my milky brains to them and yet I tried and tried because Grover wanted them so. They warned me against Grover, both of them. He'll never understand, they said, he'll never guess and you mustn't tell him. And yet our children might have been saved from it, if the doctors knew all they claimed, instead of letting my father go to his grave in the belief that he'd lost his mind."

"Naturally I meant to marry Edward. We were born in the same month to the same family, and outside the forbidden degrees of kindred by a hairbreadth. He might have helped me and there'd be no question about the house. Because he was a physician, don't you see, and could have stopped me before I came this far. You'd have been my child and you are my child though you won't admit it." She glares almost directly at Maura, just missing her eyes.

"There he is," she says flatly, "sitting beside you, your father." And Maura vainly resists the motion of her head which assures her that the three-years'-dead man is not there at all.

"I see him. The house is full of him, twenty-eight years of him, poor Edward. He lived his soul into this house and there he is."

"He's dead," says Maura, speaking for the first time in minutes.

"Don't stare at me with those hard brown eyes. They don't belong to you. God knows I wanted children and where am I now? A sick old woman being kept a prisoner by a stranger who won't let me alone. I know. He's afraid,

afraid." She spreads her palms over her cheeks and smoothes the twitches out. "Do you like the way we've changed the house?"

"I think it's all lovely, Ellie," says Maura, crossing the room and taking her by the arm, helping her to her feet. "I've been through it all with Grover. It's all lovely." She leads the other woman into the hallway.

"Are you leaving?"

"I think so. I told Mother I'd be home for lunch. Perhaps I can come over Sunday night."

"And then you go back to the city? You'll have children, Maura, I know it. You're going to be married, aren't you?"

At this prescience, Maura shudders. "I hope so," she admits, kissing a dry cheek, "and please take good care of yourself."

As she pushes the yielding shrubbery aside, as it whistles softly around her, she hears Ellie call, "It comes to Grover or to you, and soon, soon." And she resolves to herself that it can't possibly come to her.

"Oho!" says Mrs. Boston with delight of a kind. "Oho, oho! I told you, didn't I?"

"You told me something, but not all that," says Maura, utterly exhausted.

"She must have been having one of her bad days."

"All her days must be like that," reasons Maura tiredly. "She can't have any good days if she's as bad as that."

"It's partly assumed, you know."

"Oh, Mother, for goodness' sake! She's dying. She can't reason."

"The poor woman," says Mrs. Boston with real compassion, "and so she said that it would come to you or Grover."

"Yes."

"She must have meant the house."

"Oh, that and everything else."

"There's nothing else to inherit."

"You don't know. You don't know."

"There could be no two people more hardhearted, Maura, than you and Grover Haskell!"

"Why do you dislike him so much? You should be grateful to him."

"For heaven's sake, why?"

"Oh, I don't know," exclaims Maura, petulantly. "Per-

haps because he got her out of the way. He's not a malicious person at all. I like him. I pity him."

"And well you may," says Mrs. Boston, "because he's
caught; there's nothing he can do. He hoped for years to
get his hands on our house and now he hasn't got it—it's
got him. He caught a shark."

"I'll make a prediction," says Maura grimly, "and I
want you to remember it. If Ellie dies and leaves the house
to him, as I hope to God she does, you, Mother, will be
over there three nights a week playing cards with him
within six months."

Mrs. Boston springs to her feet and begins to pace up
and down the narrow bed-sitting room which comprises
the bulk of her small apartment. She doesn't resemble her
daughter, at this strained point in their relationship, nearly
as much as usual. She shows in her walk and in the de-
fiant toss of her head how completely she knows that there
can be no estrangement between them; she can trust
Maura.

"My God, how right you are," she confesses with a full
agitation, crushing a hand over her neat straw-colored
hair. "Of course I will be. Out of idle curiosity, you believe, and loneliness." She turns briskly to Maura. "I
know mine is not a dignified position. I'm quite aware of
what people say."

"People don't say anything, as far as I know."

"You live in Montreal."

"But I hear what goes on."

"Nonsense! You haven't been here in a year." As Maura
protests, her mother puts up a grim hand for silence. "I'm
not reproaching you. In your place I should do exactly the
same. Stay away! Hunt some man down! You can do it!"
She smiles at her daughter because they love one another.
"I sound like a cheerleader."

"I've nearly done it," grins Maura sourly, "and Ellie
knew all about it before I said a word."

"She has radar," says Mrs. Boston, "or second sight."

"You would adore your grandchildren if you had any."

Mrs. Boston winces. "My God, how right you are,"
she exclaims for the second time in three minutes. "Have
some!" she begs. "Start the whole thing off again. I don't
want you to be the last. We never meant you to be the
only child."

"I've borne it," says Maura.

"So you see me over at Grover's house, playing double solitaire with him, the two of us mourning our barrenness, all alone and exactly like each other. Very well, I've admitted that I don't hate the man. He's not a wicked man, I suppose."

"It's simply that you're both caught."

"He's caught worse than I am, Maura. He's planned and worked to possess himself of that place. He used to come to us on vacations, and when we had him in to dinner he'd look around as if it were already his. You could see his mind at work, estimating the cost of new velour drapes for the dining room. I used to laugh."

"Not tactful, anyway."

"No, he's like an infant. He has no notion of tact. And then he asked us to move while your father was sickening with what killed him, though I will admit in justice that he couldn't have suspected it, and then he moved in and Ellie began to collapse, and now she's gone the way her parents did and at the end they were both suicidal."

"Her mother killed herself."

"So she did, so she did. He knows it and he can't get out; the house owns him." It is complete triumph for her. "When your father and I lived there, we owned the house, we had tenants in the smaller side and we mailed their rent to Ellie. But we had the house, it didn't have us. Now the only people he can find to live in the smaller side are the Hungarians, because everybody in town who can speak English is afraid to go near the place. So the house has him. Oh, I'll go and see him," she concludes.

But Maura is ahead of her, already at the door. "You and he can do the gardening together," she observes. "You can preserve Daddy's arbor. Grover loves the trees."

"You don't have to go down there tonight. You're under no obligation and you've got a train to catch."

"It's been a long weekend," says Maura, "but I told him I'd drop in."

"Well, don't *you* get caught!"

It was a promise fairly made, though one which she repents of as she walks along the shore toward the three tamaracks which guide her into the leafy paths. The river is flat calm, an end-of-autumn calm, with here and there faint smudges on the surface moved by the slight breeze. Maura pauses for a moment before she pushes through the hole in the fence to study the river and wish it altered. What we need here, she decides, are docks and cranes, smoke, drydocks, slipways, a hundred factories; the river has strangled Stoverville. Straining her eyes she looks across to the desolate New York banks behind which, she remembers from the motor trips of childhood, there is nothing. Daddy promised me bears on the New York side but there weren't any, not a bear. Oh God, she allows herself for one second to reflect, oh God, I want children. I want two children.

She pushes through the hole in the fence, remembering the afternoon she caught her party frock on a nail in this same board, sneaking home late from a birthday party by her secret route. She looks for the hole in her frock and the red splash of the rust but there isn't anything there at all, and up she goes along the path to where Grover stands in the twilight on the sagging steps, anxiously looking out for her, with his hands outstretched to help her through the leaves.

"The husband," he begins shakily as soon as he can see all of her, "is not really a blood relation of the wife, is he? That is, he isn't related to her. After all I come from another part of the province and I'm not a Phillips. Am I?" He insists on it. "I'm not a blood relation to my wife, am I? Because this place should be transmitted according to the blood strain and should naturally come to you, all to you. I tell you, Maura, and I'd tell your father, too, if I could, that I never wanted this place for myself. We have no children and you're part Phillips. You should get it, and I'm going to see that you do. Because I don't want it. I never did, not for myself. Never. For two whole days Ellie has been going over and over the matter, threatening to leave the place to me, but I told her that I'm not a blood relation. I'm related to her by marriage only."

"That's a closer relation."

"No it isn't," he shouts, leaping like a trout in a still pool. "This place belongs to you through your father and I've insisted to Ellie for thirty-six hours that she leave it to you. I've torn up her will. I'll make her write another before she gets worse." He shudders. "I'm afraid she's going to die soon." It has gone from twilight to dark through his speech.

"Where is she now?"

"She made me move her bed. She's lying down in your room at the top of the house. She's exhausted. I tell you, Maura, when she isn't herself she says things you wouldn't believe. I don't mean to complain or bear tales but I've never seen her like this and I can't bear it." His throat dries up and closes convulsively and then miraculously opens for his final words as they pace up and down hand in hand on the creaking porch.

"You'll take it, won't you? Look at me, Maura, please! It's so dark I can't see you." He turns to face her and throws his arms stiffly wide apart. "It's yours. It's yours! I don't want it. You will take it, won't you? Take it, take it, please!"

Her little bedroom is dark like a virginal cell in a cloister and Ellie lies on her bed with arms folded on her chest like an effigy on a tomb, her mind whirling with the effort to concentrate and control her thoughts. At regular intervals of maybe thirty seconds her body arches rigidly, projecting her torso and thighs forward and upward into the air, drawing her lower back up off the sheets, the cramped writhings of a woman in childbirth forcing her thighs apart and racking her abdomen, and all to no purpose. But her consciousness doesn't record these convulsions as the stream of her ideas grows fuller and stronger, swollen by many tributaries, sliding faster and faster. *Ppaaaarrrrpp*— I am going to starboard. *Mmeeeeuuuuhhhh*—I am going to port. S.S. *Renvoyle* upbound with package freight for Toronto. M.V. *Prins Willem Oranje* downbound for the locks and the Atlantic, half laden, looking for a full hull at Quebec City. The horns grow louder and merge with the full downward current of her thoughts. They were never like this before, never so loud, never right in my room like this. The ships are swimming over me and the river through me and the horns are inside my head muddling my ideas all together with the family downstairs in the living room with the captain from Oslo, seven stars and seven coronets and the three trees on the point for Christ and the two thieves hanging so straight and dark

in the twilight on the darkening water. I am going to starboard under the stars on the current down the river down
east past the Plains of Abraham, farther, to where, the
river yawns its mouth eleven miles wide, invisibly wide,
bearing me away at last to the darkness, the sleety im-
passible impassable Gulf.

THE OFFICE

Alice Munro

The solution to my life occurred to me one evening while I was ironing a shirt. It was simple but audacious. I went into the living room where my husband was watching television and I said, "I think I ought to have an office."

It sounded fantastic, even to me. What do I want an office for? I have a house; it is pleasant and roomy and has a view of the sea; it provides appropriate places for eating and sleeping, and having baths and conversations with one's friends. Also I have a garden; there is no lack of space.

No. But here comes the disclosure which is not easy for me: I am a writer. That does not sound right. Too presumptuous, phony, or at least unconvincing. Try again. I write. Is that better? I *try* to write. That makes it worse. Hypocritical humility. Well then?

It doesn't matter. However I put it, the words create their space of silence, the delicate moment of exposure. But people are kind, the silence is quickly absorbed by the solicitude of friendly voices, crying variously, how wonderful, and good for you, and well, that is intriguing. And what do you write? they inquire with spirit. Fiction, I reply, bearing my humiliation by this time with ease, even a suggestion of flippancy, which was not always mine, and again, again, the perceptible circles of dismay are smoothed out by such ready and tactful voices—which have however exhausted their stock of consolatory phrases, and can say only, *"Ah!"*

So this is what I want an office for (I said to my husband): to write in. I was at once aware that it sounded like a finicky requirement, a piece of rare self-indulgence. To write, as everyone knows, you need a typewriter, or at least a pencil, some paper, a table and chair; I have all these things in a corner of my bedroom. But now I want an office as well.

And I was not even sure that I was going to write in it, if we come down to that. Maybe I would sit and stare at the wall; even that prospect was not unpleasant to me. It was really the sound of the word *office* that I liked, its sound of dignity and peace. And purposefulness and importance. But I did not care to mention this to my husband, so I launched instead into a high-flown explanation which went, as I remember, like this:

A house is all right for a man to work in. He brings his work into the house, a place is cleared for it; the house rearranges itself as best it can around him. Everybody recognizes that his work exists. He is not expected to answer the telephone, to find things that are lost, to see why the children are crying, or feed the cat. He can shut his door. Imagine (I said) a mother shutting her door, and the children knowing she is behind it; why, the very thought of it is outrageous to them. A woman who sits staring into space, into a country that is not her husband's or her children's is likewise known to be an offense against nature. So a house is not the same for a woman. She is not someone who walks into the house to make use of it, and will walk out again. She is the house; there is no separation possible.

(And this is true, though as usual when arguing for something I am afraid I do not deserve, I put it in too emphatic and emotional terms. At certain times, perhaps on long spring evenings, still rainy and sad, with the cold bulbs in bloom and a light too mild for promise drifting over the sea, I have opened the windows and felt the house shrink back into wood and plaster and those humble elements of which it is made, and the life in it subside, leaving me exposed, empty-handed, but feeling a fierce and lawless quiver of freedom, of loneliness too harsh and perfect for me now to bear. Then I know how the rest of the time I am sheltered and encumbered, how insistently I am warmed and bound.)

"Go ahead, if you can find one cheap enough," is all my husband had to say to this. He is not like me; he does not really want explanations. That the heart of another person is a closed book is something you will hear him say frequently, and without regret.

Even then I did not think it was something that could be accomplished. Perhaps at bottom it seemed to me too improper a wish to be granted. I could almost more easily have wished for a mink coat, for a diamond necklace— these are things women do obtain. The children, learning of my plans, greeted them with the most dashing skepticism and unconcern. Nevertheless I went down to the shopping center which is two blocks from where I live; there I had noticed for several months, and without thinking how they could pertain to me, a couple of *For Rent* signs in the upstairs windows of a building that housed a drugstore and a beauty parlor. As I went up the stairs I had a feeling of complete unreality; surely renting was a complicated business in the case of offices; you did not simply knock on the door of the vacant premises and wait to be admitted; it would have to be done through channels. Also, they would want too much money.

As it turned out, I did not even have to knock. A woman came out of one of the empty offices, dragging a vacuum cleaner and pushing it with her foot toward the open door across the hall, which evidently led to an apartment in the rear of the building. She and her husband lived in this apartment; their name was Malley; and it was indeed they who owned the building and rented out the offices. The rooms she had just been vacuuming were, she told me, fitted out for a dentist's office, and so would not interest me, but she would show me the other place. She invited me into her apartment while she put away the vacuum and got her key. Her husband, she said with a sigh I could not interpret, was not at home.

Mrs. Malley was a black-haired, delicate-looking woman, perhaps in her early forties, slatternly but still faintly appealing, with such arbitrary touches of femininity as the thin line of bright lipstick, the pink feather slippers on obviously tender and swollen feet. She had the swaying passivity, the air of exhaustion and muted apprehension, that speaks of a life spent in close attention on a man who is by turns vigorous, crotchety, and dependent. How much of this I saw at first, how much decided on later is of course impossible to tell. But I did think that she would have no children; the stress of her life, whatever it was, did not allow it, and in this I was not mistaken.

The room where I waited was evidently a combination living room and office. The first things I noticed were models of ships—galleons, clippers, Queen Marys—sitting on the tables, the windowsills, the television. Where there were no ships there were potted plants and a clutter of what are sometimes called "masculine" ornaments—china deer heads, bronze horses, huge ashtrays of heavy, veined, shiny material. On the walls were framed photographs and what might have been diplomas. One photo showed a poodle and a bulldog, dressed in masculine and feminine clothing, and assuming with dismal embarrassment a pose of affection. Written across it was "Old Friends." But the room was really dominated by a portrait, with its own light and a gilded frame; it was of a good-looking, fair-haired man in middle age, sitting behind a desk, wearing a business suit and looking preeminently prosperous, rosy and agreeable. Here again, it is probably hindsight on my part that points out that in the portrait there is evident also some uneasiness, some lack of faith the man has in this role, a tendency he had to spread himself too bountifully and insistently, which for all anyone knows may lead to disaster.

Never mind the Malleys. As soon as I saw that office, I wanted it. It was larger than I needed, being divided in such a way that it would be suitable for a doctor's office. (We had a chiropractor in here but he left, says Mrs. Malley in her regretful but uninformative way.) The walls were cold and bare, white with a little gray to cut the glare for the eyes. Since there were no doctors in evidence, nor had been, as Mrs. Malley freely told me, for some time, I offered twenty-five dollars a month. She said she would have to speak to her husband.

The next time I came my offer was agreed upon, and I met Mr. Malley in the flesh. I explained, as I had already done to his wife, that I did not want to make use of my office during regular business hours, but during the weekends and sometimes in the evening. He asked me what I would use it for, and I told him, not without wondering first whether I ought to say I did stenography.

He absorbed the information with good humor. "Ah, you're a writer."

"Well yes. I write."

"Then we'll do our best to see you're comfortable here," he said expansively. "I'm a great man for hobbies myself. All these ship models—I do them in my spare time; they're a blessing for the nerves. People need an occupation for their nerves. I daresay you're the same."

"Something the same," I said, resolutely agreeable, even relieved that he saw my behavior in this hazy and tolerant light. At least he did not ask me, as I half expected, who was looking after the children, and did my husband approve? Ten years, maybe fifteen, had greatly softened, spread, and defeated the man in the picture. His hips and thighs had now a startling accumulation of fat, causing him to move with a sigh, a cushiony settling of flesh, a ponderous matriarchal discomfort. His hair and eyes had faded, his features blurred, and the affable, predatory expression had collapsed into one of troubling humility and chronic mistrust. I did not look at him. I had not planned, in taking an office, to take on the responsibility of knowing any more human beings.

On the weekend I moved in without the help of my family, who would have been kind. I brought my typewriter and a card table and chair, also a little wooden table on which I set a hot plate, a kettle, a jar of instant coffee, spoon, and a yellow mug. That was all. I brooded with satisfaction on the bareness of my walls, the cheap dignity of my essential furnishings, the remarkable lack of things to dust, wash, or polish.

The sight was not so pleasing to Mr. Malley. He knocked on my door soon after I was settled and said that he wanted to explain a few things to me—about unscrewing the light in the outer room, which I would not need, about the radiator and how to work the awning outside the window. He looked around at everything with gloom and mystification and said it was an awfully uncomfortable place for a lady.

"It's perfectly all right for me," I said, not as discouragingly as I would have liked to, because I always have a tendency to placate people whom I dislike for no good reason, or simply do not want to know. I make elaborate offerings of courtesy sometimes, in the foolish hope that they will go away and leave me alone.

"What you want is a nice easy chair to sit in while you're waiting for inspiration to hit. I've got a chair down in the basement, all kinds of stuff down there since my mother passed on last year. There's a bit of carpet rolled up in a corner down there; it isn't doing anybody any good. We could get this place fixed up so's it'd be a lot more home-like for you."

"But really," I said, "but really I like it as it is."

"If you wanted to run up some curtains, I'd pay you for the material. Place needs a touch of color; I'm afraid you'll get morbid sitting in here."

"Oh, no," I said, and laughed, "I'm sure I won't."

"It'd be a different story if you was a man. A woman wants things a bit cosier."

So I got up and went to the window and looked down into the empty Sunday street through the slats of the Venetian blind, to avoid the accusing vulnerability of his fat face and I tried out a cold voice that is to be heard frequently in my thoughts but has great difficulty getting out of my cowardly mouth. "Mr. Malley, please don't bother me about this any more. I said it suits me. I have everything I want. Thanks for showing me about the light."

The effect was devastating enough to shame me. "I certainly wouldn't dream of bothering you," he said, with precision of speech and aloof sadness. "I merely made these suggestions for your comfort. Had I realized I was in your way, I would of left some time ago." When he had gone I felt better, even a little exhilarated at my victory, though still ashamed of how easy it had been. I told myself that he would have had to be discouraged sooner or later; it was better to have it over with at the beginning.

The following weekend he knocked on my door. His expression of humility was exaggerated, almost enough so to seem mocking, yet in another sense it was real and I felt unsure of myself.

"I won't take up a minute of your time," he said. "I never meant to be a nuisance. I just wanted to tell you I'm sorry I offended you last time and I apologize. Here's a little present if you will accept."

He was carrying a plant whose name I did not know; it had thick, glossy leaves and grew out of a pot wrapped lavishly in pink and silver foil.

"There," he said, arranging this plant in a corner of my room. "I don't want any bad feelings with you and me. I'll take the blame. And I thought, maybe she won't accept furnishings, but what's the matter with a nice little plant, that'll brighten things up for you?"

It was not possible for me, at this moment, to tell him that I did not want a plant. I hate house plants. He told me how to take care of it, how often to water it and so on; I thanked him. There was nothing else I could do, and I had the unpleasant feeling that beneath his offering of apologies and gifts he was well aware of this and in some way gratified by it. He kept on talking, using the words *bad feelings, offended, apologize.* I tried once to interrupt, with the idea of explaining that I had made provision for an area in my life where good feelings, or bad, did not enter in, that between him and me, in fact, it was not necessary that there be any feelings at all; but this struck me as a hopeless task. How could I confront, in the open, this craving for intimacy? Besides, the plant in its shiny paper had confused me.

"How's the writing progressing?" he said, with an air of putting all our unfortunate differences behind him.

"Oh, about as usual."

"Well, if you ever run out of things to write about, I got a barrelful." Pause. "But I guess I'm just eatin' into your time here," he said with a kind of painful buoyancy. This was a test, and I did not pass it. I smiled, my eyes held by that magnificent plant; I said it was all right.

"I was just thinking about the fellow was in here before you. Chiropractor. You could of wrote a book about him."

I assumed a listening position, my hands no longer hovering over the keys. If cowardice and insincerity are big vices of mine, curiosity is certainly another.

"He had a good practice built up here. The only trouble was, he gave more adjustments than was listed in the book of chiropractic. Oh, he was adjusting right and left. I came in here after he moved out, and what do you think I found? Soundproofing! This whole room was soundproofed, to enable him to make his adjustments without disturbing anybody. This very room you're sitting writing your stories in.

"First we knew of it was a lady knocked on my door one day, wanted me to provide her with a passkey to his office. He'd locked his door against her.

"I guess he just got tired of treating her particular case. I guess he figured he'd been knocking away at it long enough. Lady well on in years, you know, and him just a young man. He had a nice young wife, too, and a couple of the prettiest children you ever would want to see. Filthy some of the things that go on in this world."

It took me some time to realize that he told this story not simply as a piece of gossip, but as something a writer would be particularly interested to hear. Writing and lewdness had a vague delicious connection in his mind. Even this notion, however, seemed so wistful, so infantile, that it struck me as a waste of energy to attack it. I knew now I must avoid hurting him for my own sake, not for his. It had been a great mistake to think that a little roughness would settle things.

The next present was a teapot. I insisted that I drank only coffee and told him to give it to his wife. He said that tea was better for the nerves and that he had known right away I was a nervous person, like himself. The teapot was covered with gilt and roses and I knew that it was not cheap, in spite of its extreme hideousness. I kept it on my table. I also continued to care for the plant, which thrived obscenely in the corner of my room. I could not decide what else to do. He bought me a wastebasket, a fancy one with Chinese mandarins on all eight sides; he got a foam cushion for my chair. I despised myself for submitting to this blackmail. I did not even really pity him; it was just that I could not turn away, I could not turn away from that obsequious hunger. And he knew himself my tolerance was bought; in a way he must have hated me for it.

When he lingered in my office now he told me stories of himself. It occurred to me that he was revealing his life to me in the hope that I would write it down. Of course he had probably revealed it to plenty of people for no particular reason, but in my case there seemed to be a special, even desperate necessity. His life was a series of calamities, as people's lives often are; he had been let down by people he had trusted, refused help by those he had depended on, betrayed by the very friends to whom he had given kindness and material help. Other people, mere strangers and passersby, had taken time to torment him gratuitously, in novel and inventive ways. On occasion, his very life had been threatened. Moreover his wife was a difficulty, her health being poor and her temperament unstable; what was he to do? You see how it is, he said, lifting his hands, but I live. He looked to me to say yes.

I took to coming up the stairs on tiptoe, trying to turn my key without making a noise; this was foolish of course because I could not muffle my typewriter. I actually considered writing in longhand, and wished repeatedly for the evil chiropractor's soundproofing. I told my husband my problem and he said it was not a problem at all. "Tell him you're busy," he said. As a matter of fact I did tell him; every time he came to my door, always armed with a little gift or an errand, he asked me how I was and I said that today I was busy. Ah, then, he said, as he eased himself through the door, he would not keep me a minute. And all the time, as I have said, he knew what was going on in my mind, how I weakly longed to be rid of him. He knew but could not afford to care.

One evening after I had gone home I discovered that I left at the office a letter I had intended to post, and so I went back to get it. I saw from the street that the light was on in the room where I worked. Then I saw him bending over the card table. Of course, he came in at night and read what I had written! He heard me at the door, and when I came in he was picking up my wastebasket, saying he thought he would just tidy things up for me. He went out at once. I did not say anything, but found myself trembling with anger and gratification. To have found a just cause was a wonder, an unbearable relief.

Next time he came to my door I had locked it on the inside. I knew his step, his chummy cajoling knock. I continued typing loudly, but not uninterruptedly, so he would know I heard. He called my name, as if I was playing a trick; I bit my lips together not to answer. Unreasonably as ever, guilt assailed me but I typed on. That day I saw the earth was dry around the roots of the plant; I let it alone.

I was not prepared for what happened next. I found a note taped to my door, which said that Mr. Malley would be obliged if I would step into his office. I went at once to get it over with. He sat at his desk surrounded by obscure evidences of his authority; he looked at me from a distance, as one who was now compelled to see me in a new and sadly unfavorable light; the embarrassment which he showed seemed not for himself, but me. He started off by saying, with a rather stagey reluctance, that he had known of course when he took me in that I was a writer.

"I didn't let that worry me, though I have heard things about writers and artists and that type of person that didn't strike me as very encouraging. You know the sort of thing I mean."

This was something new; I could not think what it might lead to.

"Now you came to me and said, Mr. Malley, I want a place to write in. I believed you. I gave it to you. I didn't ask any questions. That's the kind of person I am. But you know the more I think about, well, the more inclined to wonder. . . ."

"Wonder what?" I asked.

"And your own attitude—that hasn't helped to put my mind at ease. Locking yourself in and refusing to answer your door. That's not a normal way for a person to behave. Not if they got nothing to hide. No more than it's normal for a young woman, says she has a husband and kids, to spend her time rattling away on a typewriter."

"But I don't think that—"

He lifted his hand, a forgiving gesture. "Now all I ask is that you be open and aboveboard with me—I think I deserve that much—and if you are using that office for any other purpose, or at any other times than you let on, and having your friends or whoever they are up to see you—"

"I don't know what you mean."

"And another thing—you claim to be a writer. Well I read quite a bit of material, and I never have seen your name in print. Now maybe you write under some other name?"

"No," I said.

"Well, I don't doubt there are writers whose names I haven't heard," he said genially. "We'll let that pass. Just you give me your word of honor there won't be any more deceptions, or any carryings-on, et cetera, in that office you occupy—"

My anger was delayed somehow, blocked off by a stupid incredulity. I only knew enough to get up and walk down the hall, his voice trailing after me, and lock the door. I thought—I must go. But after I had sat down in my own room, my work in front of me, I thought again how much

I liked this room, how well I worked in it, and I decided not to be forced out. After all, I felt, the struggle between us had reached a deadlock. I could refuse to open the door, refuse to look at his notes, refuse to speak to him when we met. My rent was paid in advance and if I left now it was unlikely that I would get any refund. I resolved not to care. I had been taking my manuscript home every night to prevent his reading it, and now it seemed that even this precaution was beneath me. What did it matter if he read it, any more than if the mice scampered over it in the dark? Several times after this I found notes on my door. I intended not to read them, but I always did. His accusations grew more specific. He had heard voices in my room. My behavior was disturbing his wife when she tried to take her afternoon nap. (I never came in the afternoons, except on weekends.) He had found a whisky bottle in the garbage.

I wondered a good deal about that chiropractor. It was not comfortable to see how the legends of Mr. Malley's life were built up.

As the notes grew more virulent our personal encounters ceased. Once or twice I saw his stooped, sweatered back disappearing as I came into the hall. Gradually our relationship passed into something that was entirely fantasy. He accused me now, by note, of being intimate with people from Numero Cinq. This was a coffeehouse in the neighborhood which I imagine he invoked for symbolic purposes. I felt that nothing much more would happen now; the notes would go on, their contents becoming possibly more grotesque and so less likely to affect me.

He knocked on my door on a Sunday morning, about eleven o'clock. I had just come in and taken my coat off and put my kettle on the hot plate.

This time it was another face, remote and transfigured, that shone with the cold light of intense joy at discovering the proofs of sin.

"I wonder," he said with emotion, "if you would mind following me down the hall?"

I followed him. The light was on in the washroom. This washroom was mine and no one else used it, but he had not given me a key for it and it was always open. He stopped in front of it, pushed back the door and stood with his eyes cast down, expelling his breath discreetly.

"Now who done that?" he said, in a voice of pure sorrow.

The walls above the toilet and above the washbasin were covered with drawings and comments of the sort you see sometimes in public washrooms on the beach, and in town hall lavatories in the little decaying towns where I grew up. They were done with a lipstick, as they usually are. Someone must have got up here the night before, I thought, possibly some of the gang who always loafed and cruised around the shopping center on Saturday nights.

"It should have been locked," I said, coolly and firmly as if thus to remove myself from the scene. "It's quite a mess."

"It sure is. It's pretty filthy language, in my book. Maybe it's just a joke to your friends, but it isn't to me. Not to mention the art work. That's a nice thing to see when you open a door on your own premises in the morning."

I said, "I believe lipstick will wash off."

"I'm just glad I didn't have my wife see a thing like this. Upsets a woman that's had a nice bringing up. Now why don't you ask your friends up here to have a party with their pails and brushes? I'd like to have a look at the people with that kind of a sense of humor."

I turned to walk away and he moved heavily in front of me.

"I don't think there's any question how these decorations found their way onto my walls."

"If you're trying to say I had anything to do with it," I said, quite flatly and wearily, "you must be crazy."

"How did they get there then? Whose lavatory is this? Eh, whose?"

"There isn't any key to it. Anybody can come up here and walk in. Maybe some kids off the street came up here and did it last night after I went home; how do I know?"

"It's a shame the way the kids gets blamed for everything, when it's the elders that corrupts them. That's a thing you might do some thinking about, you know. There's laws. Obscenity laws. Applies to this sort of thing and literature, too, as I believe."

This is the first time I ever remember taking deep breaths, consciously, for purposes of self-control. I really wanted to murder him. I remember how soft and loathsome his face looked, with the eyes almost closed, nostrils extended to the soothing odor of righteousness, the odor of triumph. If this stupid thing had not happened, he would never have won. But he had. Perhaps he saw something in my face that unnerved him, even in this victorious moment, for he drew back to the wall, and began to say that actually, as a matter of fact, he had not really felt it was the sort of thing I personally would do, more the sort of thing that perhaps certain friends of mine— I got into my own room, shut the door.

The kettle was making a fearful noise, having almost boiled dry. I snatched it off the hot plate, pulled out the plug and stood for a moment choking on rage. This spasm passed and I did what I had to do. I put my typewriter and paper on the chair and folded the card table. I screwed the top tightly on the instant coffee and put it and the yellow mug and the teaspoon into the bag in which I had brought them; it was still lying folded on the shelf. I wished childishly to take some vengeance on the potted plant, which sat in the corner with the flowery teapot, the wastebasket, the cushion, and—I forgot—a little plastic pencil sharpener behind it.

When I was taking things down to the car Mrs. Malley came. I had seen little of her since that first day. She did not seem upset, but practical and resigned.

"He is lying down," she said. "He is not himself."

She carried the bag with the coffee and the mug in it. She was so still I felt my anger leave me, to be replaced by an absorbing depression.

I have not yet found another office. I think that I will try again some day, but not yet. I have to wait at least until that picture fades that I see so clearly in my mind, though I never saw it in reality—Mr. Malley with his rags and brushes and a pail of soapy water, scrubbing in his clumsy way, his deliberately clumsy way, at the toilet walls, stooping with difficulty, breathing sorrowfully, arranging in his mind the bizarre but somehow never quite satisfactory narrative of yet another betrayal of trust. While I arrange words, and think it is my right to be rid of him.

PLAYING BALL
ON HAMPSTEAD HEATH

Mordecai Richler

Drifting through Soho one hot sticky evening in June, too early for the theater, Jake stopped at the Nosh Bar for a sustaining salt beef sandwich. He had only managed one squirting mouthful and a glance at the unit trust quotations in the *Standard* (S & P Capital was steady, Pan-Australian was down again) when he was distracted by an American couple. The bulging-bellied man wore a seersucker suit and his wife clutched a *London A to Z* to her bosom. The man opened a credit-card-filled wallet, briefly exposing an international medical passport which listed his blood type, extracted a pound note, and slapped it into the waiter's hand.

"I suppose," he said, winking, "I get twenty-four shillings change for this?"

The waiter shot him a sour look.

"Tell your boss," the man continued, unperturbed, "that I'm a Galicianer, just like him."

"Oh, Morty," his wife said, bubbling.

And the juicy salt beef on rye turned to leather in Jake's mouth. It's here again, he realized, heart sinking—the season.

At the best of times, American and Canadian show business plenipotentiaries domiciled in London had many hardships to endure. The income-tax tangle, scheming and incompetent workmen, uppity nannies, smog, choosing the right prep school for the kids, doing without real pastrami, and of course keeping warm. But come the season, life was impossible. Come summer, ocean liners and airplanes began to dump clamorous hordes of relatives, friends of friends, long and better forgotten schoolmates and army buddies, on London, thereby transmogrifying the telephone, charmingly inefficient all winter, into an instrument of terror. Everyone who phoned, no matter how remotely connected at home, exuded warmth and demanded a night on the town. "Waddiya say to a pub crawl, old chap?" Or an invitation to dinner at home. "Well, Jakey, did you tell the Queen your Uncle Moish was coming? Did she bake a cake?" You agreed, oh how many times you agreed, the taxis were cute, the bobbies polite, and the pace slower than New York or, in Jake's case, Montreal. "People still know how to enjoy life here. I can see that." On the other hand, you've got to admit the bowler hats are a scream, hotel service is from the stone ages, and the British have snobby British accents. "Look at it this way, it isn't home."

Summer also meant, even if you had lived in London for years, though possibly paying your tax in Liechtenstein or Bermuda, being mistaken for a tourist everywhere. Suddenly truculent taxi drivers insisted on larger tips. Zoom went the price of antiques and pornography. The waiters in the Guinea were ruder and more condescending about wines, if possible. It required the sharpest of elbows to get close enough to put down a bet on the roulette table at the White Elephant. Summer was charged with menace, with *shnorrers* and greenhorns from the New Country. So how sweet and soothing it was for the hard-core show biz expatriates to come together on a Sunday morning for a fun game of softball on Hampstead Heath, just as the Rajas of another dynasty had used to meet on the cricket pitch in Malabar.

Manny Gordon drove in all the way from Richmond, clapping a sporty tweed cap over his bald head and strapping himself and his starlet of the night before into his Aston-Martin at nine A.M. Bernard Levine started out from Ham Common, stowing a fielder's mitt and a thermos of martinis in the boot of his Jag, picking up Al Herman and Stan Cohen in Putney and Jimmy Grief and Myer Gross outside Mary Quant's on the King's Road. Moey Hanover had once startled the staff at the Connaught by tripping down the stairs on a Sunday morning, wearing a peak cap and a T shirt and carrying his personal Babe Ruth bat. A Bentley with driver, laid on by Columbia films, waited outside. Another Sunday Ziggy Alter had flown in from Rome, just for the tonic of a restorative nine innings. Frankie Demaine drove in from Marlow-on-Thames. Lou

Caplan, Morty Calman, and Cy Levi usually brought their wives and children, while Monty Talman, ever mindful of his new twenty-one-year-old wife, always cycled to the Heath from St. John's Wood. Wearing a maroon track suit, he lapped the field eight or nine times before anyone else turned up.

Jake Hersh, a comparative novice, generally walked to the Heath from his flat in Swiss Cottage with Nancy and the kids, his tattered fielder's mitt, nappies, a baby's bottle, and three enervating bagels filled with chopped liver concealed under *The Observer* in his shopping bag.

Other players, irregulars, were drawn from the directors, actors, writers, producers, and agents who just happened to be in London working on a picture. The starting lineup on Sunday, July 25, 1965, was:

AL HERMAN'S TEAM	LOU CAPLAN'S BUNCH
Manny Gordon, ss.	Stan Cohen, 3b.
Bernard Levine, 2b.	Myer Gross, ss.
Jimmy Grief, 3b.	Frankie Demaine, lf.
Al Herman, cf.	Morty Calman, rf.
Ziggy Alter, lf.	Cy Levi, 2b.
Jack Monroe, rf.	Moey Hanover, c.
Monty Talman, 1b.	Johnny Roper, cf.
Sean Fielding, c.	Jason Storm, 1b.
Alfie Roberts, p.	Lou Caplan, p.

Jake, an unusually inept player, was one of the subs. A utility fielder, he sat on the bench with Lou Caplan's Bunch. It was a fine, all but cloudless day, but looking around Jake anticipated friction, because some of the players' first wives, or, as Ziggy Alter put it, the Alimony Gallery, was already fulminating on the grass behind home plate.

First Al Herman's Team and then Lou Caplan's Bunch, both sides made up of men mostly in their forties, trotted out, sunken bellies quaking, to take a turn at fielding and batting practice. Last Sunday Frankie Demaine's analyst, walking the dog, had passed accidentally and lingered to watch the game, his smile small but constant, and Frankie had gone 0 for 5; but today Frankie looked his old lethal self. Morty Calman, on the other hand, was in trouble.

His first wife, Ethel, had come to watch and whenever Morty called for a fly ball her sour piercing laughter cut across the field, undoing him.

Nate Sugarman, once a classy shortstop, but since his second coronary the regular umpire, strode onto the field and called, "Play ball!"

First man up for Al Herman's Team was small, tricksy Manny Gordon, ss.

"Let's go, boychick!"

Manny, hunched catlike over the plate, was knotted with more than his usual fill of anxiety. If he struck out, his starlet might glow for somebody else; Lou Caplan, however, who was pitching for the first time since he had signed his three-picture deal with 20th, would be grateful, and flattering Lou was a good idea, especially since Manny had not been asked to direct since *Chase. Strike one, called.*

"Atta boy, Lou. You've got a no-hitter going for you."

If, Manny thought, I hit a single I will be obliged to pass the time of day with that stomach-turning queen, Jason Storm, 1b. *Ball one, inside.* He had never hit a homer, so that was out, but if just this once (*Adonoi, Adonoi*) he could manage a triple, he could have a word with— KNACK! *God damn it, it's a hit! A double!* As the players on Al Herman's bench rose to a man, shouting encouragement—

"Go, man! Go!"

—Manny, suffering under Lou Caplan's glare, scampered past first base and took myopic, round-shouldered aim on second, wondering should he say something rotten to Cy Levi, 2b., who was responsible for getting his name on the blacklist years ago, or should he greet him warmly because after all Cy had married Manny's first wife, the *putz*, and so taken him off the alimony hook. Decisions, decisions. Manny charged into second base, flat feet flying, trying to catch Cy with a belt in the balls. He missed, but beat the throw, grinned, and said, "Hi."

"You should come to visit the kid sometimes," Cy said. "He asks for you."

"I'd love to, but I'm too sensitive. If I see him I'll cry."

Bernard Levine struck out, which brought up Jimmy Grief, who was in a state. Jimmy had to hit but quickly, urgently, before bigmouth Cy Levi let it slip to Manny, who had not been invited, that the Griefs were giving a cocktail party on Friday. Jimmy swung at the first pitch, hitting it high and foul, and Moey Hanover, c., called for it and made the catch.

Which brought up big Al Herman, who homered, bringing in Manny Gordon ahead of him. Manny immediately sat down on the bench next to Grief. "Oh, Jimmy baby," he said, his smile ingenuous, "I was wondering, I mean if you and Estelle aren't busy on Friday, could you come to dinner at my place?"

"Have to check with Estelle. I'm not sure what we're doing on Friday yet."

Monty Talman scooped out the last of the Wholefood yogurt, stepped up to the plate, and immediately ground out to Gross, ss., retiring the side. Al Herman's Team, first inning: two hits, no errors, two runs.

Leading off for Lou Caplan's Bunch, Stan Cohen singled to center and Myer Gross struck out, bringing up Frankie Demaine and sending all the outfielders back, back, back. Frankie whacked the third pitch long and high, an easy fly had Al Herman been playing him deep instead of outside right, where Manny Gordon's starlet was sprawled on the grass. Herman was the only man on either team who always played wearing shorts—shorts revealing an elastic bandage which began at his left kneecap and ran almost as low as the ankle.

"Oh, you poor darling," the starlet said, making a face at Al Herman's knee.

Herman, sucking in his stomach, replied, "Spain," as if he was tossing the girl a rare coin.

"Don't tell me. The beach at Torremolinos. Ugh!"

"No, no. The Civil War, for Christ's sake! Shrapnel. Defense of Madrid."

Demaine's fly fell for a homer, bringing in a panting Stan Cohen. Morty Calman popped to short and Cy Levi struck out, retiring the side.

Lou Caplan's Bunch, first inning: one hit, one error, two runs.

Neither side scored in the next two innings, which were noteworthy only because Moey Hanover's game began to deteriorate. In the second Moey muffed an easy pop fly and actually let Bernard Levine, still weak on his legs after his colonic irrigation and all but foodless week at Forest Mere Hydro, steal a base on him. The problem was Sean Fielding, the young Liverpoolnik whom Columbia had put under contract because Hy Silkin's son-in-law Jerry thought he looked like Peter O'Toole. The game had only just started when Lillian Hanover had sat down on the grass beside Fielding, which was making Moey nervy. Moey, however, had not burned his young manhood up at a yeshiva to no avail. Not only had he plundered the Old Testament for his *Bonanza* plots, but now his intensive Jewish education served him splendidly yet again. Moey remembered, *And it came to pass in the morning, that David wrote a letter to Joab, and sent it by the hand of Uriah. And he wrote in the letter, saying, Set Uriah in the forefront of the hottest battle, and retire ye from him, that he may be smitten, and die.* Amen.

Lou Caplan yielded three successive hits in the third and Moey Hanover took off his catcher's mask, called for time, and strode to the mound.

"I'm all right," Caplan said. "Don't worry."

"It's not that. Tell me, love, when do you start shooting in Rome?"

"Three weeks tomorrow. You heard something bad?"

"No."

"You're a friend now. Remember. No secrets."

"I've had second thoughts about Sean Fielding. I think he's very exciting. He's got lots of appeal. Real magnetism. He'd be a natural to play Domingo."

Multicolored kites bounced in the skies over the Heath. Lovers strolled on the tow paths and locked together on the grass. Old people sat on benches sucking in the sun. Nannies passed, wheeling toddlers. The odd baffled Englishman stopped to watch the Americans at play.

"Are they air force chaps?"

"Film makers, actually. It's their version of rounders."

"Whatever is that enormous thing that woman is slicing?"

"Salami. Kosher."

"*On the Heath?*"

"Afraid so. One Sunday they actually set up a bloody folding table, right over there, with cold cuts and herrings and mounds of black bread and a whole bloody side of smoked salmon. *Scotch. Eight and six a quarter, don't you know?*"

"On the Heath?"

"Champagne. Mumm's. Out of paper cups. One of them had won a bloody award of some sort. *Look!*"

Alfie Roberts, the next man up, had connected on the first pitch. Only it wasn't a softball he hit, but a cherante melon, which splattered over the infield. A double, Nate Sugarman ruled.

Going into the bottom of the fifth, Al Herman's Team led 6–3.

Cy Levi, first man up for Lou Caplan's Bunch, hit a triple, but heading for third he saw Jimmy Grief, 3b., waiting there with a mean expression on his face, and guessed that Jimmy knew Lou Caplan had hired him to rewrite Jimmy's script and so, instead of pulling up at third, Cy scooted for home and was caught in a rundown. Jimmy charged Cy, grinning, actually grinning, as he whacked the ball into his stomach, knocking him down. The two men rolled over in the dirt, where Cy managed to land Jimmy a good one in the nose with his shoe. "Sorry," he said.

Sorry? Nate Sugarman, the umpire, who had had nothing but heartache with the Jag he had bought from Cy Levi, waved him out of the game.

Which brought in Tom Hunt, a surly colored actor, to play second.

Next man up, Moey Hanover, lifted a lazy fly to left field, which Ziggy Alter trapped rolling over and over on the grass, until—just before getting up—he was in a position to peek under Natalia Calman's skirt. Something he saw there so unnerved him that he dropped the ball, turning pale and allowing Hanover to pull up safely at second.

Which brought up Johnny Roper, who crossed his eyes, dropped his bat, knocked his knees together, and did the twist, finally working a convulsed tearful Lou Caplan for a walk.

Which brought up Jason Storm to the delight of a pride of British queers who stood with their dogs on the first baseline, squealing and jumping. Jason hit a line drive to center and floated down the baseline to second, obliging the queers to move up a base.

With two out and the score tied 7–7 in the bottom of the sixth, Alfie Roberts was unwillingly retired for a new pitcher. It was Gordie Kaufman, a blacklisted writer for years, who now divided his labors between Rome and Madrid, asking $100,000 a spectacular. Gordie came in with the go-ahead run on third and Tom Hunt stepping up to the plate for the first time. Big black Tom Hunt figured that if he homered he would be put down for another buck nigger, good at games, but if he struck out, which would require rather more acting ability than was required of him on the set of *Othello X,* what then? He would enable a bunch of fat foxy Jews to feel big. Goysy. Screw them, Hunt thought.

Gordie Kaufman was perplexed, too. His stunning villa on Mallorca had ten bedrooms, his two boys were boarding at a reputable British public school, and Gordie himself was president, sole stockholder, and the only employee of a company that was merely a plaque in Liechtenstein. And yet—and yet—Gordie still subscribed to *The Nation;* and his spectaculars had content, that is to say, he filled his Roman slaves with antiapartheid dialogue and sagacious Talmudic sayings. If Hunt touches me for even a scratch single, he thought, I'll come off as a patronizing ofay. If he homers, I'm a shitty liberal. And so with the count 2 and 3 and a walk, the typical social democrat's compromise, seemingly the easiest way out for both men, Gordie, his proud Trotskyite past emerging, threw a burning fast ball right at Hunt, bouncing it off his head. Hunt threw away his bat and started for the mound, fists clenched, but not so hurried that players from both sides couldn't rush in to separate the two men, both of whom felt glowingly emancipated because they had triumphed over impersonal racial prejudice to recognize and hit each other as individuals on a fun Sunday on Hampstead Heath.

Something else of note happened in the sixth.

Going into the bottom of the inning the prime diversion had been Manny Gordon's toreador-trousered starlet. Again and again the men had meandered over, asking if she wanted to catch, a salami on an onion roll, or a drink. Then, in the bottom of the sixth, burly Alfie Roberts had been retired from the mound. He had been humiliated before his wife and children. He had been made to look a

zero before hostile agents and producers and, he added
to himself, dirtygoyhomosexual actors. Alfie, his last picture still riding in *Variety's* top money-making ten, walked
to his Jag and returned to sit on the grass alongside the
third baseline reading a book. A hardcover book. A hardcover book in a plain brown wrapper.

The word leaped from one bench to another, it electri-
fied the field, making it spark with speculation. A hardcover book in a plain brown wrapper meant either Alfie
only had an option on the property, and so it could possibly be wrested from him, or even more intriguing, the
property was in the public domain. *My God, my God.*
Woody Farber, the agent, strolled down the third baseline to where Alfie sat, his smile open, touchingly honest,
only to have the suspicious bastard slam the book shut
and sit on it. Next Phil Berger drifted over toward Alfie,
forcing him to sit on the book again. Alfie slammed the
book shut in Lou Caplan's face. Even Manny Gordon's
starlet couldn't get anywhere.

Then, going into the crucial seventh inning, Alfie shook
up the infield and was directly responsible for a failed
double play, when he was seen to take out a pencil, lick
it, and begin to make notes in the margin of his book.
Enough is enough. Monty Talman called for time and
walked over to confront Alfie. "Can't you work somewhere
else?" he asked.

"Darling," Alfie said, "I didn't know you cared."

Come the crucial seventh, the Alimony Gallery grew
restive and began to move in on the baselines and benches,
demoralizing former husbands with their heckling. When
Myer Gross, for instance, stepped up to the plate with
a man on base and his teammates shouted, "Go, man. Go,"
one familiar grating voice floated out over the others, "Hit,
Myer. Make your son proud of you just this once."

What a reproach the first wives were! How steadfast!
How unchanging! Still Waiting for Lefty after all these
years. Today maybe necks had gone pruney and stomachs
had lowered and breasts had flattened, like yesterday's
latkas, but let no man say that these ladies had aged in
spirit. Where once they had petitioned for the Scottsboro
Boy, spit on their families over mixed marriages, packed
their skinny scared boyfriends off to defend Madrid, split

with old comrades over the Stalin-Hitler Pact, raised funds for Henry Wallace, demonstrated for the Rosenbergs, and never, never yielded to McCarthy, today they clapped hands at China Friendship Clubs, petitioned for others to Keep Hands Off Cuba and Vietnam, and made their sons chopped-egg sandwiches and sent them marching off to Aldermaston.

The sons. How well and honestly they had raised the sons. When Georgie Gross, for instance, had returned from the hospital after his appendicitis operation and had tried, first morning home, to climb into bed with his mother, she had not rebuffed him with sweet old-fashioned lies. Instead she had said, "You must understand *why* you want to get into bed with me. It's because you desire to make physical love to me. You wish to supplant your father."

Davey Hanover did not have to sit through windy religious instruction at his private school. On the contrary, he had a note which entitled him to leave the classroom for the period and stand alone in the corridor, sometimes, it's true, wetting the floor. When nine-year-old Dickie Herman had put on lipstick and got into his older sister's dress for a hallowe'en party, he was told, no punches pulled, all about homosexuality. None of the children played with guns. Or watched violent shows on television. And when ten-year-old Judd Grief rebelled, he was taken to see a special screening of a concentration camp documentary so that he could understand clearly where gunplay led to.

Davey Hanover stammered. Dickie Herman suffered nightmares. Judd Grief wanted to grow up to be an SS Colonel. But all the children had been honestly brought up and knew there was no God and that all men were brothers and all wars bad.

The wives, nicely alimonied but bitterly alone, had known the early struggling years with their husbands, the rejections and the cold-water flats, but they had always remained loyal. They hadn't altered, their husbands had. Each marriage had shattered in the eye of its own self-made hurricane, but essentially the men felt, as Ziggy Alter had once put it so succinctly at the poker table, "Right, wrong, don't be *narish*, it's really a question of who wants to grow old with Ana Pauker when there are so many juicy little bits we can now afford."

So there they were, out on the grass chasing fly balls on a Sunday morning, short men, Jake thought fondly, over-paid men, tubby men, all well within the coronary and lung cancer belt, allowing themselves to look ridiculous in the hope of pleasing their new young girls. What appe-tites, Jake thought, what self-redeeming appetites they had. There was Ziggy Alter, who had once directed a play for the Group Theater. Here was Al Herman, who had used to throw marbles under horses' legs at demonstrations and now raced two horses of his own at Epsom. On the pitcher's mound stood Gordie Kaufman, who had once carried a banner that read *Non Passaran* through the streets of Manhattan and now employed men specially to keep Spaniards off the beach at his villa on Mallorca. And sweating under a catcher's mask there was Moey Hanover, who had studied at a yeshiva, stood up to the committee, and was now on a sabbatical from Desilu.

Usually the husbands were able to avoid their used-up wives. They didn't see them in the gaming rooms at the White Elephant or in the Mirabelle or Les Ambassadeurs. But come Brecht to Shaftesbury Avenue and without look-ing up from the second row center they could feel them squatting in their cotton bloomers in the second balcony, burning holes in their necks.

And count on them to turn up on a Sunday morning in summer on Hampstead Heath just to ruin a game of fun baseball. Even homering, as Al Herman did, was no answer.

"It's nice for him, I suppose," a voice on the bench observed, "that on the playing field, with an audience, if you know what I mean, he actually appears virile."

In the eighth inning Jack Monroe had to retire to his Mercedes-Benz for his insulin injection and Jake, until now an embarrassed sub, finally entered the game. Jake Hersh, thirty-four years old, one-time relief pitcher for Room 41, Fletcher's Field High, Montreal (1–4), trotted out to right field, mindful of his disc condition and hoping he would not be called on to make a tricksy catch. He assumed a loose-limbed stance on the grass, waving at his wife, grin-ning at his children, when without warning a sizzling drive came right at him. Jake, startled, did the only sensible thing; he ducked. And then outraged shouts from the bench reminded him where he was, in a softball game, that is, and he started after the ball.

"Fishfingers!"

"Putz!"

Runners on first and third broke for home as Jake, breathless, finally caught up with the ball. It had rolled to a stop under a bench where a nanny sat watching over an elegant perambulator. "Excuse me," Jake said.

"Americans," the nurse said.

"I'm a Canadian," Jake protested automatically, fishing the ball out from under the bench.

Three runs scored. Jake caught a glimpse of Nancy, unable to contain her laughter. The children weren't looking at him.

In the ninth with the score tied 11–11, Sol Peters, another sub, stepped cautiously to the plate for Lou Caplan's Bunch. The go-ahead run was on second and there was only one out. Gordie Kaufman, trying to prevent a bunt, threw right at him and Sol, forgetting he was wearing contact lenses, held the bat in front of him to protect his glasses. The ball hit the bat and rebounded for a perfectly laid-down bunt.

"Run, you *shmuck*."

"Go, man."

Sol, astonished, ran, carrying the bat with him.

Going into the bottom of the fourteenth, Al Herman's Team was leading 13–12. There were two out and a runner on third when Morty Calman stepped wearily up to the plate. If I hit, he thought, sending in the tying run, the game will go into yet another inning, and it will be too late for the pub. So Calman struck out, ending the game, and hollering, "I say, chaps, who's for a pinta?"

Monty Talman phoned home.

"Who won?" his wife asked.

"We did, 13–12. But that's hardly the point. We had lots of fun."

"How many are you bringing back for lunch?"

"Eight."

"Eight?"

"I couldn't get out of inviting Johnny Roper. He knows Jack Monroe is coming."

"I see."

"A little warning. Don't, for Christ's sake, ask Cy how Marsha is. They're separating. And I'm afraid Manny Gordon is coming with a girl. I want you to be nice to her."

"Anything else?"

"If Gershon phones from Rome while the guys are there please remember I'm taking the call upstairs. And please don't start collecting glasses and emptying ashtrays at four o'clock, it's embarrassing—Bloody Jake Hersh is coming and it's just the sort of incident he'd pick on and joke about for months."

"I never—"

"All right, all right. Oh, Christ, something else. Tom Hunt is coming."

"The actor?"

"Yeah. Now listen, he's very touchy, so will you please put away Sheila's doll."

"Sheila's doll?"

"If she comes in carrying that bloody gollywog I'll die. Hide it. Burn it. Lock it up somewhere. Hunt gets script approval these days, you know."

"All right, dear."

"See you soon."

THE HARD-HEADED
COLLECTOR

Dave Godfrey

They came through the mountains themselves unscathed, although Piet Catogas nearly tumbled into the gorges beneath Yellowhead Pass when his horse skittered out from under him. The last horse. When they entered North Battleford they were all seven afoot, but they were well entertained in front of the tent of the bread baker, who kept them amused with juggling tricks and poured them many cups of hot tea in blue galvanized cups filled to the brim then with swirling milk.

The bread baker's final trick was to keep seven round oranges up in the air at once, and when the rotund man had heard enough of their clapping he gave one orange to each man. His own children clustered around and his wife walked back into the tent, so the men were careful to divide, but Pier dela Ombre, throwing his filthy black hair out of his eyes so that the firelight could blaze back out of his pupils, asked for a second orange from Piet Catogas, the leader, and began to explain to the children why the earth did not fall into the sun. He sang to them.

Katrina, the wife of the bread maker, came out of the tent and said to her husband, "Why not offer Mr. dela Ombre two loaves of wheat bread every morning so that he will be encouraged to stay here."

The bread maker started the offer to Piet, but Piet refused. "We are on our way to a strange land and there is not one man that I can afford to lose. We have the return journey on our minds, too."

Pier dela Ombre's orange sun rotated around and around the orange earth held stationary by little Katrina, the bread baker's only daughter. The mother smiled.

At midnight, when all the men except Ole Siuk and

Scrop Calla were seated around the fire drinking the white lightning which the Scottish whisky maker distilled in North Battleford, Katrina came out of the tent with the bread baker.

"We will give you your own tent," she said directly to Pier dela Ombre. "And a complete set of the *European Encyclopedia,* and after twenty years' service a golden shovel. Which will no doubt help to make you feel glorious as you clear away the blizzards from your door or clean out the many ashes from your stove. Around here we have very little anthracite."

Pier dela Ombre smiled and said that he needed no time to consider their kindness. "We do not even know how far we now need to travel," he said to the woman, "but we must be there by May and then there is the long journey back before we can really set down to work, and for each stage I will have to learn the new strophe that the good Calla writes. In fact, if he were not out now stealing the settlement's horses, he would probably be putting one together, telling of our dangerous passage through the mountains. I cannot stay."

They both laughed at his humor of the horses and determined even more to persuade him to stay.

"Little Katrina will be disappointed you were unable to explain to her the proportions of the sun and the earth," the woman said. "At times in the summer I have heard her say that they almost seem equal. It does get very hot here in the summer, but we arrange many boat picnics on the Saskatchewan, and of course there is nothing like sawdust to keep the winter's ice safely stored."

They kept after him, gently, until the bread maker fell asleep.

Ole and Scrop came back very early in the morning, before the sun, but little Katrina had risen and was adding yeast to the sugar water for the day's baking.

"If you let him stay long enough to explain the proportions of the earth and the sun," she said to Piet, "I will not awaken my father and tell him that the man with the sunken eyes has taken possession of Elder Clough's gray horse and silver bridle. And six other poorer horses."

Piet nodded to Pier dela Ombre. He laid the golden orange of the sun on the ashes of last night's fire and took Katrina by the hand.

"If the sun were made that small," Pier said, "let us say about a thousand to one, then the earth would still be so large that in a whole day we could not walk around its edge."

He held her hand more tightly and began walking with her away from the tent and the fire, in the gentle circle of one who is uncaringly lost.

The six men were glad to have the extra horse and the mountains behind them, with the summer not completely gone.

"He'll be in real trouble when they discover the loss," Scrop Calla said to Piet when they next stopped.

"The mother will get him out of it," Piet replied, "if the little girl can't. God, they start them young here. I can't believe there's anywhere they start them so young. Even among the Sasarians."

Why had he decided to present the works to the United States!

"Well, a lot of people wanted it . . . but I couldn't do what I did in any other country. What I did I accomplished here in the United States. It belongs here."

Did he have any comment about President Johnson!

"I told him I've adopted him. I love him."

They went eastward safely for five days across the lush prairie grass until they heard gunfire in the distance ahead and what they thought might be a tornado, a dust storm. Coming over the rise they saw a Nanarian Indian from one of the reserves who shouted at them as he drove his almost collapsing wagon at a dangerous pace toward the west. His wife and children sat on mounds of hay in the back, firing whence they had come. The men rode on, although they knew there was a fire ahead which would block their way.

"We can return later," Piet said, "and cross over the ashes. Or look for the river again."

"I'm sure I can find it if you let me lead," said Torah Black.

He rode back whence they had come—the mountains were invisible—and the others followed, although Piet had said nothing.

The wagon was overturned less than a mile to the west.

Besides the wife and the four children there was a milk-white goat among the hay.

"This will save us all," Black said and slit its throat. He held it by the hind legs as it kicked its way to death and circumscribed a large circle around the wagon, the men, the four children, and the woman.

"We had better ride on," Piet said.

After a time the firing started again, and once or twice the five men could distinguish the sound of Torah Black's shotgun. Scrop Calla could see the gold engraving on its stock glittering in the sun.

"What does a gunsmith know about old superstitions," Piet said as they rode back eastward over the powdery black ashes. Looky McLaww nodded sagely.

Mr Hirshhorn lives with his fourth wife, Olga, in Greenwich. He is the father of six children, two of them adopted, and is a grandfather several times over. He is board chairman of the Callahan Mining Company, and the principal stockholder in Prairie Oil Royalties, a Canadian concern.

He has been trying to follow doctor's orders to take it easy, but finds it a trial. When he appears at Parke-Bernet, the auctioneer knows that he has to keep a sharp eye for the little man with the expressive face who signals vigorously with his program. If there is any doubt, Mr. Hirshhorn lets the auctioneer know what he is up to. He calls out his bids in a loud clear voice.

"He's a tiger," an old, close friend said.

Beyond the death of Torah Black they had no more difficulties until they reached Winnipeg. It was difficult to find a place that would take all of them, for the Leagues were busy, but eventually they found a large old house on the river in Ste. Vital. All the girls spoke French, so that André was kept busy as a translator; but after all, what is there to say?

"We have made it over the hard part," Piet said. "We have still eight months to go. Let us hope that the winter will be easy. Tonight you may enjoy yourselves; there is no more need of the horses in any case."

The first girl did not satisfy Looky because the pleasure of her body simply filled his head with memories of the wife he had left on Queen Charlotte Island.

"That damn Hunky won't want more than a snack," he said and walked into Ole Siuk's room and threw him out of bed. *"J'ai une qualité inestimable,"* he said to the girl, and she shone with delight.

"He is afraid for his wife," Piet said to Ole Siuk. "There are many other carvers and poets on the island. She is a loving model; puts her heart into it."

"Mineur, how's about a free and equal exchange of riches," Looky later said to André. But when André tried his new girl he found her cold and exhausted. She swung a condom full of black beetles over his head and threatened him with death.

Looky took Scrop Calla's girl also, a plumper one than the first three, but when he came to Piet's room he found him gone.

The old woman, the girl provider, still lay in the bed and offered herself to Looky, but she was dark haired and hidden-eyed like Looky's wife and he could not take her.

"There's the matter of the bill," she said, "but that's not important. I have the horses. If you had slept with me those bay-tárds would have beaten you to death with horseshoes on the end of pikes and we would have put you out in the stable to freeze until spring, but as it is you will save us the cost of putting an ad in *The Free Press* for some able body to haul our ashes all winter."

"At least McLaww won't have to go about with a gold shovel in his hands," Piet Catogas said to Scrop Calla as the four men trudged on bear-paw snowshoes through the wine-dark snows north of Fort Frances, as the sun fell.

But, with the end of World War I, he guessed wrong on the market and found his fortune had shrunk to $4,000. Mr. Hirshhorn says he has always learned by his mistakes. At any rate, he was back on top in a few years and intuitively got out of the market with $4 million just before it broke in 1929.

When he was a child, Mr. Hirshhorn was attracted to the pictures on the Prudential Life Insurance Company's calendars.

Mr. Hirshhorn was attracted to the possibilities of Canada, bought 470 square miles of land, and by 1950 was mining uranium. His biggest coup occurred in 1952. On the advice of Franc Joubin, a geologist who had little audi-

ence elsewhere, Mr. Hirshhorn secretly put together 56,000
square miles of claims in Ontario's Algoma Basin and
struck a uranium bonanza in Blind River.

When the four men were only twelve miles from Chapleau, they came across a group of Hémonites at prayers. They had built a great square wall of snow blocks out onto the lake, no more than a foot high, and at intervals, dressed in brown worsted cowls, stood women, men, and the older children, praying into the sky.

"This is a chance for Calla to use his four iamb line," said Ole Siuk, who had taken over the post of religious cynic since they had lost McLaww.

Piet could see no altar, but in the center of the square was a tall ancient man standing above a slender circular hole cut deep into the ice down to the dark water below.

"In the summer you can see clear down thirty-two feet," the old man said.

Near him were three boys tending nine blanketed cattle. On a high easel, facing in the direction in which all prayed, was an old lithograph of an Essex County dairy farm, coated in plastic to protect it against the weather but torn in one corner so that the gold of cut hay was stuck to a piece of flapping plastic and glittered in the frosted sunlight.

"No one will do it," the old man said.

"I'm out of grass, acid, and mushrooms," said Scrop Calla, "but I know what you want and I will attempt it."

He stripped himself naked and lowered himself into the water three times so that not only his heavy beard and hair were covered with a sliver of ice, but his whole body. It shone.

He held his arms outward in the direction of them all and said loudly and with no sound of rhythm, "I know, I know, I know."

Upon the horizon appeared as though on the edge of a highly polished silver punch bowl, a simple inverted image of all: the penitents, the wall of snow blocks, the old priest, Scrop Calla, the strangers, and the forests and the snow-covered meadows behind them. With the exception that, in the inverted image, the cows were unblanketed and moved about freely, their udders thick with milk, their coats sleek as threshed grain.

"You're a genius and a half," the old priest said. "You'll have to settle here. In the summer you can see down thirty-two feet and the fishing license's only two bucks—to natives that is."

"During the war," said Piet to Ole Siuk as they came near French River, "Calla once deserted and tried to find the enemy, but a handful of men went unknowingly after him and became so enthused with their fear that they broke through the lines of the Sasarians and covered themselves with loot and glory."

At night when they stopped now, Ole Siuk read in Calla's leather-bound notebooks and occasionally was seen stamping his left foot heavily and repeatedly on the hard earth of the world.

"Poverty has a bitter taste," Mr. Hirshhorn said years later, recalling how his mother was sent to the hospital when a fire gutted their tenement on Humbolt Street and the family was dispersed to various homes in the neighborhood. "I ate garbage."

In French River the three men were fed and lodged in a building as tall as the smallest of the foothills they had long left behind them.

"Perhaps we have gone far enough," said André. "That is a building tall enough to house Egsdrull. The tools must be rusty and I long to hear the chips shatter, even a practice stroke."

All the people there had a small exact circle of soot on each cheek, but they were kind to the voyagers, gave them fat for their stiff-thonged snowshoes, and did not laugh loudly at Ole Siuk's awkward attempts at song.

"You can see God's fish," they said at the end of the recital. "Perhaps then you will stay and teach us to sing."

Inside the tall building sat rows and rows of old men and women, all dressed in heavy blue robes, but seemingly divided into three groups.

Some had two circles of dark soot on their cheeks, so that only the blue robes distinguished them from the guide. These sat reading from a book that was passed slowly down the rows, meditating while they awaited their turn. Others had only one circle of soot, that on their right cheek, and were busy at workbenches, hammering tiny marbles of gold into large, almost circular flakes. Their blue robes seemed cumbersome, and many seemed too old for such a task.

The third group had no marks on their cheeks, but on their foreheads was a slightly larger, more oval, circle of soot. These seemed to be neither reading nor hammering, but once, while the strangers were there, one of the old men among them went up to the forty-foot fish which dominated the entire building, a *mashkinoje*. Only its skeletal frame was finished; the outer covering was not yet half done. The old man laid in place on the others his own interlocking golden scale. Then fire consumed him.

"Each year," said the guide, "we get just about done before the Sasarians come raiding. We've calmed the Nanarians. One year the Sasarians will be awed by God's fish and will allow us to finish. Below God's fish, you will see the coffins of the fifty original scale craftsmen. Each holds an ivory tooth on his breast, and on the day that the Sasarians are awed, they will all arise and the teeth will complete the fish of unity."

When Piet and Ole left, André Mineur was talking in Arabic to the God's fish's tail. He was not speaking of their own voyages and their many losses.

"He's a sucker, that Mineur," said Piet Catogas to Ole Siuk as they crossed the St. Lawrence at Three Rivers. "It won't sell. I've seen men making them in Boston, twice the size, every scale machine-polished, and for half the price."

"I think you have the right reason," said Ole Siuk. "Hah, hah, hah." His teeth had all fallen out because of the bad diet they had endured during the winter and he looked very old and ugly.

"It's almost the end of April," he said.

The President added:
"Washington is a city of powerful institutions—the seat of government for the strongest government on earth, the place where democratic ideals are translated into reality. It must also be a place of beauty and learning, and museums should reflect a people whose commitment is to the best

that is within them to dream. We have the elements of a great capital of beauty and learning, no less impressive than its power."

The two men avoided all contact with the Sasarians, although Piet was certain he could communicate with them if necessary, but when they arrived in Edmundston and stated that they were determined to reach the Bay of Chaleur even though only two of them remained, they ran into the united opposition of all the Town Fathers.

"The *day* of judgment is only possible as a concept because of our notions of the duration of time," the mayor said. "In reality there is a summary court in perpetual session and we're going to beat your knackers down to your knees."

They turned upon Siuk, stripped off all his clothing, tore away his fingernails with their teeth, gnawed his fingers with the fury of famished dogs and thrust a sword through one of his hands. They drove the two men between them in a hastily formed aisle, and beat them with clubs and thorny sticks. Then they hung them by the wrists to two of the poles that supported the Town Hall. A woman was commanded to cut off Piet's thumb, which she did; and a thumb of Siuk was also severed, a clam shell being used as an instrument, in order to increase the pain.

In the morning the children came to castrate them, and then they were set free. Hair was pulled from their beards and their wounds were lacerated before they left.

In the night Ole Siuk wrote out a message for Piet, the leader, although he did not awaken him.

I guess I've followed Areskoui and that crew long enough. I feel the need of those Edmundston men more than anything. My great-aunt was a nun in the Ukraine, but she was of unsound motives in her religious pursuits. When she was not made Mother Superior at a time she had appointed, she stripped herself naked during a Sunday mass and declared herself to the world as an atheist. The family has had bad luck ever since. Maybe this act of mine will atone in some way. I wouldn't visit us, however, on your way back. I'll probably be married to the woman who collects thumbs.

Piet had no one to talk to, but he chuckled to himself as he came upon the birch bright sea.

"It's lucky old McLaww didn't make it to that part of the contest. He would have hated me for the rest of his life."

"This is a magnificent day for the nation's capital and for millions of Americans who will visit Washington in the years to come," the President said, smiling at Mr. Hirshhorn at his side.

"Throughout the world," the President said, "Mr. Hirshhorn has sought the great art of our time—those expressions of man's will to make sense of his experience on earth, to find order and meaning in the physical world about him, to render what is familiar in a new way."

It was late June when he arrived at the bay.

"I've come for Egsdrull," said Piet to the manager of the lumber yard. "I'm the carver from Queen Charlotte." He handed him the receipt.

"You're a little late," replied the manager. "And as well there's the little matter of the seven terms: shape an axe, sing its joints, engrave its shaft, bless its point, name it in ten tongues, knit soul and intent, determine where lies its enemy."

"I had men who could do all that. Ole Siuk could have shaped it out of brittle rock; Pier dela Ombre was once with the Scala; the best man with a graver you ever saw was Torah Black; Looky McLaww would have had a libation for the blade; André Mineur knew a baker's-dozen tongues; Scrop Calla would have taught you a thing or two about serpents biting their own tails and how to hoop a barrel hoop. And I, why do you think I came all this way? Put that axe in my hands and show me the tree, show me Egsdrull, and God himself will not be able to catch the bloody chips."

"Terms is terms," the manager said. "The sea probably has fish who could do all that, but you don't see him standing there begging."

Piet could find nothing to say.

"I've got something out behind the slab pile that might do for you," the manager said. "We flooded those ten or twelve years back when we gave up hope on you."

Beyond the slab pile, where a small red forklift truck scurried with its swaying load of sixteen- and eighteen-foot slabs, was a scene of desolation. The creek which once had there flowed into the Bay of Chaleur was dammed. Forty feet or more on either side was flooded. All the trees that once had grown there were black stubs. Not ankle high, as a good piece of future meadowland might look waiting for the years to rot the stumps, but man high, totem high—trunks like amputated limbs.

"You're free to make something of one of those if you like," said the manager. "But I don't expect any of them is fit for a trip back to the coast. Hollow rotten."

"I did not come all that way," said Piet. He was screaming. "Lose all those men, suffer all that laceration. Father, father, I am a grown man. You promised me Egsdrull. I discovered the Pacific; I fed China for three months; I played poker with Lord Astor; I kissed the dirty Hun's lady. I courted death. You have forsworn me. Thiefman."

"Forsworn you, my ass. Terms is terms. There it is in black and white. Ninth of May or all terms void. Seven terms to be fulfilled before delivery. It's time you earned your daily bread for a change, young fellow. Don't 'father' me. Perhaps we can fit you in on the butt saw, if you can keep up. You're not so spry as you once were. What do you say, young fellow? Want to try Newfoundland?"

President Johnson formally accepted the Hirshhorn art collection today "on behalf of the American people" in a ceremony at noon in the Rose Garden of the White House.

Piet Catogas lasted a week at work before his death. Not on the butt saw, which is a skilled task and requires a young and agile man, but out in the yard in the sunlight, sorting the lumber by lengths, widths, and grades.

This was a job for the young or the very old, but he found no sympathy among his comrades and was unable to speak to them of the carvings that he had made before he was half their age, back on the island.

More than one of his wounds was infected, and though he bathed in the warm sea he knew it was futile and awaited his death with great equanimity. At night he wondered if dela Ombre would have blond sons later with Katrina or what Torah had thought about as he fired into the flame and smoke; he chuckled at the thought of Looky beaten by the horseshoes on pikes and wondered how many winters Calla would survive; he was afraid Mineur had sold out to those madmen and prayed for Ole Siuk.

In the mornings he slept later and later. He would have been fired on the morning he died if ever he had reached the yard where men sorted the sixteen-foot one-by-sixes into four grades without a passing glance at the ship which came for his body.

KEYS AND WATERCRESS

John Metcalf

David, with great concentration, worked the tip of his thumbnail under the fat scab on his knee. He carefully lifted the edges of the scab enjoying the tingling sensation as it tore free. His rod was propped against his other leg and he could just see the red blur of his float from the corner of his eye. He started to probe the center of the crust.

"Had any luck?" a voice behind him said suddenly.

Startled, his thumbnail jumped, ripping the scab away. A bright bead of blood welled into the pit. The sun, breaking from behind the clouds, swept the meadow into a brighter green and made the bead of blood glisten like the bezel of a ring.

"Had any luck?" the old man said again. David twisted around to look at him. He wasn't in uniform and he wasn't wearing a badge and anyway he was far too old to be a bailiff. Unless he was a Club Member—and they could report you, too. And break your fishing rod.

David glanced down the river toward the bridge and the forbidding white sign. "I'm only fishing for eels," he said. "With a sea hook."

"Slippery fellows, eels," said the old man. "Difficult to catch."

"I haven't caught any yet," said David, hoping the old man wouldn't notice the gray eel slime on the bank and the smeared fishing bag.

The old man started to sit down. Wheezing harshly with the effort, he lowered himself until he was kneeling, and then, supporting himself on his hands, laboriously stretched out each leg like a dying insect in a jam jar. His anguished breathing eased slowly away into a throaty mutter. David felt more confident because he knew he could run nearly to the bridge by the time the old man had struggled to his feet.

Taking a blue silk handkerchief from the top pocket of his linen jacket, the old man dabbed at his forehead. "My word, yes!" he said. "Extremely slippery fellows." He took off his straw hat and rubbed his bald head with the blue handkerchief.

"They're a nuisance," said David. "The Club Members don't like catching them."

"And why is that?"

"Because they swallow the hook right down and you can't get it out," said David.

"You've hurt your knee," said the old man. The bead of blood had grown too large and toppled over, trickling down his knee to run into the top of his stocking.

"Oh, that's nothing," said David. "Only a scab."

"Yes," said the old man reflectively, "it's a pleasant day. A beautiful sky—beautiful afternoon clouds."

They sat silently staring across the flow of the river. Near the far bank in the shallows under the elderberry bushes the huge roach and chub basked in the sunshine, rising every now and then to nose soft circles in the water.

"Do you know the name of clouds like those?" asked the old man suddenly. "The *proper* name, I mean."

"No," said David.

"Well, the correct name is *cumulus*. Cumulus. You say it yourself."

"Cumulus," said David.

"Good! You won't forget, will you? Promise me you won't forget." There was a silence while the old man put on his spectacles from a tin case. Then, taking a fountain pen and a small black book from his inside pocket, he said, "But boys forget things. It's no use denying it—boys forget. So I'm going to write it down." He tore a page from the notebook and printed on it "CUMULUS (CLOUDS)."

As David tucked the paper into his shirt pocket, he looked across at the old man, who was staring into the water, a vague and absent look in his eyes. David watched him for a moment and then turned back to his float, watching the current break and flow past it in a constant flurry. He tried to follow the invisible nylon line down into the depths where it ended in a ledger weight and a turning, twisting worm.

"Every evening," said the old man, speaking slowly and more to himself than David, "when the light begins to fail, the cattle come down here to drink. Just as the night closes in."

"They've trampled the bank down further upstream," said David.

"And I watch them coming across the fields," said the old man as though he hadn't heard. "I see them from my window."

The old man's voice died away into silence, but suddenly, without warning, he belched loudly—long, rumbling, unforced belches of which he seemed quite unaware. David looked away. To cover his embarrassment, he started reeling in his line to check the bait and the clack of the ratchet seemed to arouse the old man. He groped inside his jacket and pulled out a large flat watch. With a click the lid sprang open. "Have you ever seen such a watch before?" he asked. "Such a beautiful watch?" He held it out on the palm of his hand.

"Do you know what watches like these are called?"

"No," said David. "I've never seen one before."

"They're called Hunters. And numbers like these are called roman numerals."

As the old man counted off the numbers on the watch face, David stared at the old man's hand. The mottled flesh was puffy and gorged with fat blue veins which stood beneath the skin. He tried to take the watch without touching the hand which held it.

"What time does the watch say?" asked the old man.

"Half-past four," said David.

"Well then, it's time we had our tea," said the old man. "And you shall come and have tea with me."

"Thank you," said David, "but I've got to go home."

"But tea's prepared," said the old man, and as he spoke he started to struggle to his feet. "Tea's prepared. In the house across the bridge—in the house with the big garden."

"But I really have to go," said David. "My mother'll be angry if I'm late."

"Nonsense!" said the old man loudly. "Quite untrue."

"Really. I do have to—"

"We won't be long," said the old man. "You like my watch, don't you? You do like my watch."

"Oh, yes."

"Well, there you are then. What more proof do you need? And," said the old man, "I have many treasures in my house." He stared at David angrily. "You would be a rude boy to refuse."

"Well . . ." said David. "I really mustn't be long."

"Do you go to school?" the old man asked suddenly.

"Parkview Junior," said David.

"Yes," said the old man. "I went to school when I was a boy."

As David was sliding the rod sections into the cloth case, the old man gripped his arm and said, "You may keep the watch in your pocket until we reach the bridge. Or you could hold it in your hand. Whichever you like." Then stopping David again he said, "And such a watch is called a . . . ?"

"A Hunter," said David.

The old man relaxed his hold on David's arm and said, "Excellent! Quite excellent! Always be attentive. Always accumulate *facts*." He seemed very pleased, and as they walked slowly along the river path toward the bridge made little chuckling sounds inside his throat.

His breath laboring again after the incline from the bridge, the old man rested for a few moments with his hand on the garden gate. Then, pushing the gate open, he said, "Come along, boy. Come along. Raspberry canes everywhere, just as I told you."

David followed the old man along the path and into the cool hall. His eyes were bewildered at first after the strong sunlight, and he stumbled against the dark shape of the hall stand.

"Just leave your things here," said the old man, "and we'll go straight in to tea."

David dropped his fishing bag behind the door and stood his rod in the umbrella stand. The old man went ahead down the passage and ushered him into the sitting room.

The room was long and, in spite of the French windows at the far end, rather dark. It was stuffy and smelled like his grandma.

In the center of the room stood a table covered with green baize, but tea was layed out on a small card table at the far end of the room in front of the French windows.

Bookshelves lined the walls and books ran from ceiling to floor. The floor, too, was covered with piles of books and papers—old books with leather covers, musty and smelling of damp and dust, and perilous stacks of yellow *National Geographic* magazines.

A vast mirror, the biggest he'd ever seen, bigger even than the one in the barber's, stood above the fireplace, carved and golden with golden statues on each side.

David stared and stared about him, but his eyes kept returning to the lion which stood in front of the fireplace.

"Do you like it?" asked the old man. "It's stuffed."

"Oh, yes!" exclaimed David. "Can I touch it?"

"I've often wondered," said the old man, "if it's in good taste."

"Where did it come from?"

"Oh, Africa. Undoubtedly Africa. They all do, you know."

"I think it's terrific," said David.

"You may stay here, then, and I will go and put the kettle on," said the old man. As soon as the door had closed, David went and stuck his hand into the lion's snarling mouth and stroked the dusty orbs of its eyes with his fingertips. When he heard the old man's footsteps shuffling back down the passage, he moved away from the lion and pretended to be looking at a book.

"Do you take sugar?" asked the old man as they sat down at the card table in front of the French windows.

"No thank you," said David. "Just milk."

"No? Most interesting! Most interesting! In my experience, boys like sweet things. A deplorable taste, of course. Youth and inexperience."

He passed the teacup across the table and said sternly, "The palate must be educated." David didn't know what to say, and because the old man was staring at him looked away and moved the teaspoon in his saucer. Putting down the silver teapot, the old man wrote in his notebook, "The love of sweetness is an uneducated love." Handing the note across the table he said, "Facts, *eh? Facts.*" He chuckled again inside his throat.

"And now," he continued—but then broke off again as he saw David staring out of the window into the orchard. "If you're quite ready? We have brown bread. Wholemeal.

Thin-cut. And with Cornish butter." He ticked off each point on his fingers. "To be eaten with fresh watercress. Do you think that will please you?"

"Very nice, thank you," said David politely.

"But it's not simply a matter of *taste*, you see," said the old man fixing David with his eye. He shook his head slowly. "Not simple at all."

"What isn't?" asked David.

"Not at all simple. Taste, yes, I grant you," said the old man, "but what about texture? Umm? Umm? What about vision?"

"What isn't simple?" David asked again.

The old man clicked his tongue in annoyance and said, "Come along, boy!" He glared across the table. "Your attention is lax. Always be attentive." He leaned across the card table and held up his finger. "Observe!" he said. "Observe the tablecloth. Cotton? Dear me, no! Irish linen. And *this*." His fingertips rubbed slowly over the facets of the bowl. "Waterford glass—brilliant. Can you see the colors? The green of the cress and the drops of water like diamonds? Brilliant. A question of the lead content, you see. You do see, don't you? You do understand what I'm telling you."

"Well . . . please," said David, "what's a texture?"

And once again the old man took out his notebook and his fountain pen.

When tea was finished, the old man wiped his lips with a linen napkin and said eagerly, "Well? Do you think you're ready? Shall you see them?"

"Please," said David, "I'd like to very much."

The old man pulled on the thick, tasseled rope which hung by the side of the window and slowly closed the red velvet curtains. "We don't want to be overlooked," he whispered.

"But there's no one there," said David. The old man was excitedly brushing the green baize and didn't seem to hear. With the red curtains closed, the room smelled even more stuffy, hot, and stifling, as if the air itself were thick and red. And in the warm gloom the lion lost its color and turned into a dark shape, a pinpoint of light glinting off its dusty eye. As David crossed over to the table he saw himself moving in the mysterious depths of the mirror.

"Come along, boy!" said the old man impatiently. "We'll

start with the yellow box. There. Under the table."

The old man lifted the lid of the box and took out three small leather sacks. They were like the pictures in pirate books, and as he laid them on the baize they chinked and jangled. Slowly, while David watched, very slowly, the old fingers trembled at the knots, and then suddenly the old man tipped the first sack, spreading keys across the table-top.

There were hundreds of keys—long rusted keys, flat keys, keys with little round numbers tied to them, keys bunched together on rings, here and there sparkling new Yale keys, keys to fit clocks and keys for clockwork toys. The old man's fingers played greedily among them, spreading them, separating large and small.

"Well?" he said, looking up suddenly.

"I've never seen so many," said David.

"Few people have," said the old man. "Few people have." His eyes turned back to the table, and he moved one or two of the keys as though they were not in their proper place. And then, as if remembering his manners, he said, "You may touch them. I don't mind if you do."

David picked up a few keys and looked at them. His hands became red with rust, and he dropped them back on the table, stirring them about idly with his fingertip.

"Not like that!" snapped the old man suddenly. "Do it properly! You have to heap them up and scatter them. If you're going to do it do it properly."

He pulled at the strings on the other bags and cascaded a stream of keys onto the table. The air swam with red dust. David sneezed loudly and the old man said, "Pay attention!"

He raked the keys together into a large heap and burrowed his hands deep into them. When they were quite buried, he stopped, his eyes gleaming with a tense excitement. His breathing was loud and shallow. He looked up at David, and his eyes widened. "Now!" he shouted, and heaved his hands into the air.

Keys rained and rattled about the room, clicking against the mirror, breaking a cup on the card table, slapping against the leather-covered books, and falling loudly on the floorboards. A small key hit David on the forehead. The old man remained bent across the table as if the excitement had exhausted him. The silence deepened.

Suddenly, a key which had landed on the edge of the mantelpiece overbalanced and fell, rattling loudly on the tiles of the hearth. Still the old man did not move. David shifted his weight restlessly and said into the silence, "I think I'll have to be getting home now. My mother's expecting me."

The old man gave no sign that he had heard. David said again, "I'll have to be going now." His voice sounded flat and awkward in the silent room.

The old man pushed himself up from the table. Deep lines of irritation scored the sides of his mouth. David began to blush under the fierceness of the old man's eyes. "I can't quite make up my mind about you," the old man said slowly. He did not take his eyes from David's face.

"Sometimes I think you're a polite boy and sometimes I think you're a rude boy." He paused. "It's unsettling." David looked down and fiddled with one of the buttons on his shirt.

"Lift up another box of keys," said the old man suddenly.

"But I have to go home," said David.

"Quite untrue," said the old man.

"Really I do."

"A lie!" shouted the old man. "You are lying. You are telling lies!" He pounded on the table with his fist so that the keys jumped. "I will not tolerate the telling of lies!"

"Please," said David, "can I open the curtains?"

"I'm beginning to suspect," said the old man slowly, "that you don't really like my keys. I'm beginning to think that I was mistaken in you."

"Please. Honest. I have to," said David desperately, his voice high and tight with fear of the old man's anger.

"Very well," said the old man curtly. "But you are a rude boy with very little appreciation. I want you to know that." Reaching inside his jacket, leaving brown rustmarks on the lapel, he took out his notebook and wrote in it. He passed the piece of paper across the table. David read, *"You have very little appreciation."*

The old man turned away, presenting his silent and offended back. David didn't know what to do. Hesitantly he said, "I do like the keys. Really I do. And the lion. And thank you for the tea."

"So you're going now, are you?" asked the old man without turning around.

"Well, I have to," said David.

"It's a great pity because I don't show it to many people," said the old man.

"Show what?"

"It would only take a moment," said the old man turning around, "but you're in too much of a hurry."

"What is it?"

"Can you really spare me two minutes? Could you bear to stay with me that long?" Suddenly he chuckled. "Of *course* you want to," he said. "Go and sit on the settee over there and I'll bring it to you."

"Can I open the curtains now?" asked David. "I don't . . . I mean, it's hot with them closed."

"Don't touch them! No. You mustn't!" said the old man urgently. He was struggling to take something from one of the bookshelves. He came and stood over David and then stooped so that David could see the black leather case in his hands. It was so stuffy in the room that it was difficult to breathe properly, and when the old man was so close to him David became aware of a strong smell of urine. He tried to move away.

Almost reverently, the old man opened the leather case, and lying on the red silk lining was a small gray ball. They looked at it in silence.

"There!" breathed the old man. "Do you know what it is?"

"No," said David.

"Go on! Go on!" urged the old man.

"I don't know," said David.

"Try."

"A marble?"

"A marble!" shouted the old man. "Why would I keep a marble in a leather case! Of course it isn't a marble! That's one of the most stupid remarks I've ever heard."

"I'm sorry," said David, frightened again by the anger in the old man's glaring face.

"You're an extremely silly boy. A brainless boy. A stupid boy." He slammed shut the leather case. "Stupid! Silly!" shouted the old man.

"I want to go home now," said David, beginning to get up from the settee. The old man pushed him back. "A marble!" he muttered.

"Please . . ." said David.

"It's a bullet!" shouted the old man. "A rifle bullet."

"I didn't know," said David. He tried to get up again, but he was hemmed in by an occasional table and the crowding presence of the old man. The dim light in the room seemed to be failing into darkness. David's throat was dry and aching.

"This bullet," said the old man, "was cut out of my leg in 1899. December 1899. Next I suppose you'll tell me that you've never heard of the Boer War!"

David said nothing, and the old man's black shape loomed over him.

"Have you heard of the Boer War?"

David began to cry.

"Have you?"

"I want to go home," said David in a small and uncertain voice.

"Quite untrue," said the old man. "I will not tolerate liars. You told me you went to school, and yet you claim not to have heard of the Boer War." He gripped David by the shoulder. "Why? Why are you lying to me?"

"Please," said David. "I'm not telling lies. Please let me go."

"Oh, very well," said the old man. "Maybe you aren't. But stop crying. It irritates me. Here. You may touch the bullet." He opened and held out the leather case. "There's no need to cry."

"I want to go home," snuffled David.

"I know!" said the old man. "I know what you'd like. I'll show you my leg. The bullet smashed the bone, you know. You *would* like that, wouldn't you?"

"No," said David.

"Of course you would."

The old man moved even nearer to the settee, and leaning forward over David, lifting with his hands, slowly raised his leg until his foot was resting on the cushion. The harsh wheezing of his breath seemed to fill the silent room. The smell of stale urine was strong on the still air. Slowly he began to tug at his trouser leg, inching it upward. The calf of his leg was white and hairless. The flesh sank deep, seamed, and puckered, shiny, livid white and purple toward a central pit.

"If you press hard," said the old man, "it sinks right in."

David shrank further away from the white leg. The old man reached down and grasped David's hand. "Give me your finger," he said.

David tore his hand free, and kicking over the coffee table, rolled off the settee. At first, in his panic, he wrenched the doorknob the wrong way. As he ran out of the darkened room, he heard the old man saying, "I've tried to teach you. I've tried to teach you. But you have *no appreciation.*"

NOTES BEYOND A HISTORY

Clark Blaise

She lived on the same curve of the lake as we did, but in a stone cottage that was a good eighty years old and set far back, because Oshacola had not been tame in those days. She had not wanted to see the lake—what was it but an ocean of alligators, the breeder of chilling fevers? She didn't need the water. Her wealth, back then, had been a Valencia grove two miles square, planted in her youth. Yet all that remained, by the time we arrived, were the two hundred yards of twisted trees between her door and the matted beach. Cypress and live oak had replaced her untended citrus. From where she used to sit on her porch, I doubt that she had even seen the lake in thirty or forty years. Her name was Theodora Rourke and she was ninety-two. The year was 1932.

We were the second year-round residents on the lake, having built a fine Spanish-style home of tawny stucco in 1938, set about fifty yards from the beach with a rich Bermuda lawn reaching to the water in front and to the hedge at the side that separated us from Theodora Rourke. By '32 there were other residents, not yet neighbors, but none so well established. It was still a risky five-mile drive into Hartley over sand trails given to flooding or sifting, and no one but my father trusted his car enough to drive in daily. When I say we were the second family most Hartleyans of today would be surprised; we've always been known as the leading family and one of the oldest. Theodora Rourke, however, was the first by such a gulf that a comparison with anyone else is absurd. I should divide the history of Oshacola County into "Modern Era" and "All Time" so that both the Rourkes and the Sutherlands could enjoy their prominence, like Cy Young and Early

Wynn, with no one confusing the equivalence of the records they set. We were the first family of Lake Oshacola, then; the Rourkes had come with the place.

She was Catholic. That was important, for we had no admitted Catholics in Hartley, and since she was the lone example of an absent conspiracy, we were taught that everything strange about her must be typical of the faith. My mother—poor tormented woman—was a South Georgia disciple of Tom Watson, and what she told my brother Tom and me about Catholics (especially the Black Sisters, which Theodora must have been) was enough to keep us awake, sweating together under our sheets. Black Sisters walked in loose black robes, two at a time in the day, and then at night they shed their robes and took to flight on the black leather wings their robes had hidden, invisible on moonless nights but for their white human faces and their cruel white teeth for sucking blood. My mother's full-time job, aside from raising Tom and me to love each other, Florida, FDR, and the Christ of her choice, was collecting the goods on Theodora Rourke. Who delivered food to her and her daughter? What shape of clothes were drying from the trees, what black people visited and were taken inside, and what language did they speak in?

My father was a Hartley man with education; being that, he had been mayor three times, schoolteacher, principal, state senator, and judge. Thirty years ago in Florida that was omnipotence. He was an old father to Tom and me (his first wife had died and he remarried at fifty), and his bent walk, white suits, stoutness, and eclectic learning have forever merged wisdom with self-righteousness, justice with legality, and history with just a little priggishness. He left us a great gift, however: an assurance that we need never answer for anything he did. It freed me for my manhood, this history, as it did for Tom, and his rockets.

I have never stopped wondering what it was that made my brother a builder of rockets—Apollo moon probes—and left me here in Hartley, a teacher.

My office is air-conditioned, wrapped in tinted glass, eight floors up on the main quadrangle overlooking the lake. Eight floors more than commands the lake. Oshacola is beautifully landscaped now, a pond on some · giant's greens. The city of Hartley and its suburbs are gleaming white among the smoky citrus groves. More smoke rises from the processing plants—the stench of orange pulp— and the Interstate slices west from here in an unbroken line to the Gulf. That haze that never lifts, way way to the west, it could be Tampa; fifty miles isn't far, and if eight floors of perspective can do *this* to Oshacola, why shouldn't Tampa be creeping slowly to my front lawn?

Oshacola was always this small, I'm forced to admit, but never this humanized. I was smaller then, of course, and places are always remembered as larger and more un-ruly—but *why*, precisely? I've only grown six inches in the past thirty-five years: why then does my memory insist on an Oshacola too broad to be seen across, on whitecaps that would swamp a weekend cruiser, on soft-shelled tur-tles Tom and I could only drag with ropes, on clusters of snakes threshing mightily on Theodora Rourke's warm sand beach? Not only has the lake been civilized, but so has my memory, leaving only a memory of my memory as it was then. I'm not a shrewd man (and more than a little bit my father's son), but I have a probing memory and what I see with my eyes closed, books shut, was also true, also happened, and Oshacola was once that inland sea and the things in it would startle an expert today, men like my colleagues on the first seven floors.

Hartley had a population of forty-three hundred in 1932, approximately three thousand of whom were white. My father knew them all. Hartley had one main street and cars were still so rare that even a lost Yankee could make a U turn in broad daylight with the sheriff looking on and chances were he wouldn't be stopped. We had a movie house, open on Wednesday for Negroes and the week-ends for us. The buildings were mostly dark brick—those were the days before we learned we were in the tropics and should show off everything in pink and white.

A few weeks ago I went roaming through the old Main Street section and couldn't find much I remembered. It's now on the fringes of a Cuban and Negro ghetto, and there were a few used-car lots, *casas del alimiento,* laun-dromats, and *tavernas.* The real center now is east, creep-ing toward the complex at the Cape. A year or two from now the first Hartley outpost, a pizza stand most likely, may find itself on national television at blast-off time.

Hartley now is—I can't describe the difficulty of adding

to that phrase—*bigger*. One hundred thousand white souls, ten thousand black, and seven thousand Cuban exiles. The power is still in local hands, the boys from my class at Hartley High, despite the eighty thousand Yankees now among us, and though they no longer wear white suits or practice oratory they've not improved on my father's generation. They're a measly, brainless lot, owned ear-high by the construction, citrus, and power companies. And not one of these local boys has an accent or curries a drop of character. As the wisest of all wise men said, the more things change, the worse they remain. The reason of course is that *change* merely reflects the unacknowledged essence of things. That's what history is all about.

In 1932 I delivered a Jacksonville paper to the row of cabins that were strung along the beach road that ran past our back door. A bundle was delivered to the courthouse and my father would have a janitor take the pile to the drugstore, where I would pick it up after school. Then I'd ride home with my father, eat, and Tom and I would later carry them down the road by kerosene lamp. Sometimes, when it rained, we didn't deliver till the next morning.

Big Mamma—Theodora Rourke—was ninety-two; her daughter Lillian was in her middle seventies. It was the daughter who sent me a note one day (it took four days to reach us by customary post though she lived but sixty yards away): *Please to have boy commence the paper for Big Mamma and Me. L. Rourke (Miss)*.

My father handed it to me discreetly; it would never do for my mother to know I was trafficking with witches, visiting at night and taking part of their hoarded treasures. The fear of personal contact actually did delay my collecting until after Christmas. Their two months' bill had hit a dollar and there was always the chance of a tip.

One day I showed up at the foot of the steps to Big Mamma's back porch. I wasn't going to climb up or go inside.

"Paper boy, ma'm," I managed when the younger old woman answered the door. From the bottom of the stairs, she looked dark and immense.

"How much are it?" she asked.

"Ma'm?"

"Mind to me what I say."

"A dollar and a dime," I said, guessing what she wanted. She turned away, black behind the ancient screen, leaving me to wonder if I had asked for too much. Should she complain, I was willing to take a fifty-cent cut.

Then Big Mamma appeared and shuffled to the door. Her daughter opened it and Big Mamma started down toward me, her spotted brown hand trembling on the wooden railing. I took a step backward, wanting somehow to accommodate her presence. She straightened up when she reached the bottom step and I noticed she didn't even challenge my chin. I was looking down on the oily, brownish-pink swath of her scalp, the clumps of cottony hair stuck amateurishly, it seemed, to its flesh. My mother had said the Black Sisters were bald as buzzards under their bonnets—she was right.

Then she looked at me. Her skin was tarnished and wrinkled on a thousand planes; her eyes simply colorless—not even the rheumy blue I had expected. Her nose seemed to have receded into her face and her jaw had almost melted away. It was a long time—it seems now an eternity that I looked into her face!—before I noticed she was holding her cold fist on my arm. I looked, and she opened it.

Her palm was pink, darkly lined. I'd never seen such coins as she held. Two round, golden ducats lay flat and heavy in her hand, like the hammered heads of copper spikes. She brought them closer and I took another step back: they were medals, I thought, charms to mesmerize me.

"You never seen these here things before, have you, boy?" she asked, looking behind me with those pale, opaque eyes.

"No, ma'm."

"Take aholt of them."

"No, ma'm."

She dropped them on the sand at my feet and I jumped back, half expecting them to leap at me, like snakes from Aaron's rod. The daughter, watching from the porch, laughed. "You skeered, boy?" she called down.

"You just owe me for the paper," I said.

"Boy, I done paid you for the rest of your life. Now pick up what I throwed. Them is genuine ten-dollar gold pieces—" She finished in midsentence, as though she had decided I was not worth the rest, and when she ceased talking, she seemed to shrink.

The pieces were half buried in the sand. I picked them up; they were cool, half coated with sand where her moist palm had held them. But wasn't it magic, I wondered, that both the coins had dug edge-first into the sand instead of landing flat? I was still cautious.

"Would you be wanting a bite of cake?" the daughter suggested suddenly. She held the screen door open. "You can have it on the porch."

"No, ma'm."

"Johnnycake?"

I climbed to the porch, then followed Big Mamma inside, but not into the house. I could see into the parlor and it was filled unlike any room I have ever seen since, except perhaps an auction house. Paintings and photos lined the walls with a single desire to be displayed; the tables were piled with metal and porcelain objects that reflected the pale sunlight like the spires of a far-off, exotic city. How I wanted to step inside! And I might have, but for a gold cross centered above the sofa and its remarkable crucified Christ, whose face was lifted in agony to the door where I was standing.

Around the Christ several paintings were hung and they now caught my eye, for even in the dullness they were vivid. Wildlife scenes, watercolors or India ink on white stock. The artist had wisely allowed the white itself to animate the studies of birds, fish, and smaller game of Florida . . . not like the murky, quasi-fabulous things my father collected, the overworked paintings by those New England gentlemen in floppy straw hats who merely observed the shoreline from the deck chairs on St. Johns River steamers. . . . These fish and bird and otter's eyes seemed to stare into mine and follow as I glanced away. Their scales and pelts and feathers were eternally moist, eternally in the sun.

"I see you are coveting my daddy's paintings," Miss Lillian noticed as she handed me the plate of cake.

"They're right nice," I said. "They are the nicest things I've ever seen."

"He executed them in the winter of eighteen hundred and fifty-seven."

I ate the cake silently. Christ's head, it seemed, had nodded.

"You live just over yonder, don't you, boy? I seen you."

I picked up the last piece of cake and underneath it was a fine gold crucifix, the type a schoolgirl might wear on a light gold chain. I pressed the last crumbs into a wafer and let it drop back on the plate.

"Now you kiss the Lord, boy," the daughter commanded. "Put your lips on Him and tell Him you are sorry for all you done."

"No," I cried. "I ain't going to!"

"You have got to. Else He will follow you. You have accepted the gift of His immortal body and so now you must be forgiven." She lifted the crucifix as though she might a dime, and thrust it in my face. I could see the faint outline of a Christ, head bowed, dripping blood, vague as an Indian head on an old penny. Had it been worn from so much kissing? The daughter held it now to her thick, puckered lips. Her eyes were closed and her lips were quivering with prayer, forming sounds I couldn't understand. Magic! And that was my only chance to get away before she could drain my blood into a cup. I don't think she opened her eyes until I slammed the door, but as I threw myself into the briar hedge between our properties, I heard her crying out, "Remember, He's a-goin' to foller you. . . ."

Facts: Theodora (?) parents unknown; birthplace (presumed), Oshacola County, Florida, 1840 (c.). Died, 1937.

Bernard Rourke, birthplace, C. Galway, Ireland, 1822. Arrived New York, 1838. Buffalo, 1839–44. Mexico and California, 1845–52. New York, 1852–55. Sent to Florida on canal crew, 1856. Married Theodora (?), 1858. Captain CSA. State Senator, 1882–84. Judge, 1886–88. Died, Oshacola County, Florida, 1888.

Children (records incomplete, but births recorded):
Lucretia (d. infancy, 1859)

Lillian (1859–1946). Barren.

Bernard, Jr. (1866–1902). Issue suspected; unknown.

John Ryan (1870–1894). Issue suspected; unknown.

Theodora Rourke, parents and birthplace unknown, according to the records I'm at the moment responsible for. But I know where she came from, though my *History of Hartley* will never record it, and therein lies the rest of my story.

Her birthplace is in Oshacola County, probably now within the city limits of Hartley. I've often looked for the exact spot, but the traces of the old canal have been filled in and chewed over for at least twenty years. Perhaps from a helicopter I could spot it—something subtle in the pattern of streets, a patch of parkland primordially rich, a shack or two that no one thought of removing. But from a car all Hartley is the same.

A word, historically, on the old canal scheme. Some states are driven by dreams—gold, oil, timber, ore—but Florida (long before the sun and oranges counted for much) was weaned on a dream of the Mighty Ditch. The maps show why: the St. Johns is wide and navigable from Jacksonville down; central Florida is blessed with a chain of deep, virtually continuous lakes, and there are a dozen accommodating estuaries on the Gulf side, the best perhaps at Tampa. To the early speculators it looked as though nature herself had merely lacked the will or Irish muscles to finish what she had so obviously begun. Cuba was Spanish, and the Keys were often treacherous—and a canal through Florida offered no natural or diplomatic barriers. A guaranteed safe passage between New York and New Orleans. Nature had never smiled so sweetly on the schemes of capital. Not only that, certain local politicians reasoned, the canal would be a natural divider between the productive and enlightened north of Florida and the swampy pestiferous south. We could sell the rest to Spain, give it to the freedmen, or make it a federal prison— "What Siberia is to the Czars of Imperial Russia," a local editor once wrote. A dozen companies had been involved in a thirty-year period to effect the cut from Atlantic to Gulf, and at least a couple had sent crews down to dynamite the forest and butcher the indigenous tribes—all before Bernard Rourke's arrival in 1856. Theodora, we can assume, had been born some sixteen years earlier to an unmarried mother of unknown origins and an Irish father similarly anonymous. By 1856 the heroic age of the canal was actually over; not many of the crew sent to Florida from New York ever saw the North again.

The summer of the year I had run from the Rourkes' stone cottage, I made a discovery that determined my life. My brother Tom, the builder of rockets, must have been affected, too.

One morning in August we were fishing from the frog boat we had tied to our dock. A political fish fry was coming up, so we were keeping everything edible: shellcrackers, warmouth, some channel cats, and dozens of bream. The boat was filling. We quit awhile and stuffed a burlap sack with fish, then tied it to the dock.

"Look!" Tom cried.

We saw a black, blunt tub rounding the arm of the cove, with a tall man in black robes poling furiously toward us. He was close to the shore, at poling depth, and we huddled behind the dock, afraid that he would see us. A man who would pole a frog boat like it was a canoe, in black robes, in August, from Lord knows where—terrifying! The visitor swung beyond us, not looking, and then put it on Rourke's scummy beach and made his way through the jungly orange grove to their cottage.

"The devil hisself," Tom whispered.

And he looked it—a dark leathery face, sideburns, black cape and white collar, and a white sleeve with ruffles showing under his robes. He even carried a little black bag. It was a priest, I told Tom, a Catholic priest.

He was inside about an hour. We heard no noises from the stone cottage, no shrieks, no moans. When the priest emerged, we noticed that he had taken off his hat and robes, and he proceeded to pole out into the lake in his ruffled white shirt, without a look backward or to us. We had a better look at him this time. Tom shook my arm, but I was already nodding. The priest had Negro blood; which meant, in a flash, that Big Mamma did, too.

We had to follow—I wonder *why* we did; Tom would say, as he does of the moon, because it's there—but how did we ever find the nerve? He was already rounding the cove, poling rhythmically. We only wanted to keep him in sight.

About a mile from our place, Buck's Cove got sealed in with lily pads. Beyond the pads a stagnant creek emptied in. We'd never explored it—the pads repulsed a boat like rubber, and the mosquitoes hummed above creek like a far-away powersaw—but the priest was prying his way through the pads into the mouth of the creek. We followed.

Cypress overhung the mossy water. In the shade, the water was brown, the color and tepidness of tea. Mosquitoes hummed. The water was the calmest I had ever seen, rich with moss and minnows. The ripples died so quickly we barely left a wake. I could feel the bass and turtles knocking against my pole, but I couldn't see six inches underneath the surface. There was no real shoreline, just a thicker and thicker tangle of cypress and floating mangroves, and the heat was increasing as all the breeze died down. Our breath came hard, but when we tried to catch it, we sucked in gnats. The sweat rolled off my nose and chin, and my arms were spotted with flies, drinking in the salt. I looked up and the priest was out of sight.

I poled half an hour, never catching him. The creek curved and branched, trees thinned and thickened, birds hooted and then were gone. There were pockets of breeze, then deadness; places where the water dimpled around my pole and pushed with a sudden current, and places where I felt I was sliding on a thicker surface. Then a consistent current came up, and the mosquitoes died down. The water was deeper. I thought we were coming to another lake.

Up ahead I spotted a bright yellow cloth draped from a cypress whose roots overhung the water. To the right of the marked tree there was a broad, open ditch that emptied into the creek at right angles to where we were. The ditch, about thirty feet wide, was lined with a high dike of mud and crushed limestone and stretched before us straight as an avenue. We took it.

It was deep, very deep; we couldn't pole, so I paddled. I told Tom I could *feel* the fish knocking against my paddle and knocking on the bottom of the boat just like someone was hammering. Bass were jumping all around us, and a few gar were floating in the middle.

"Somebody made this," said Tom.

But where did they come from? I was wondering. *We shouldn't be here,* I thought; my father told terrifying stories of Seminole bands, still wild on the hummocks, that had never signed a treaty. They stole white boys and fed them to their hunting 'gators.

"Reckon it's Indians made it?" he asked.

I kept paddling. Seminoles or something—I couldn't picture white men so deep in nature. *Maybe niggers,* I'd wanted to say to Tom, but my voice was gone.

"Look, smoke!" Tom cried. We smelled it as soon as we saw it, and it wasn't just a campfire; it was lumber mill smoke. *Jackpiners,* I thought with relief. The ditch was narrower, and beginning to curve.

There were voices, children's and women's, not far away. We couldn't make out anything, but we smiled.

"I'm getting me a coke as soon as we get down," said Tom.

"I'm getting me *two,*" I said.

The settlement was just ahead. *Work crew,* I thought as soon as I saw the gray shanty shapes behind the dike. Two boys, our age, were squatting in the water on either side of the dike, dragging a seine and netting our way. They were thin blondish boys and Tom laughed suddenly, for they weren't wearing a stitch of clothing. I waited for them to spot us but they didn't look up from the water. "Hey, y'all," I finally shouted, "what you call this pl⌒ce?"

They stood up slowly, still holding the corners of the seine. They didn't move toward us. I looked down at Tom and I saw his smile begin to sag, and his eyes grow wide and frightened. He held that look for several seconds, and then he began to retch. Then he screamed.

"There's something wrong with them—" he cried, his voice high and quivering, "there's something wrong with them—they ain't . . . they ain't—" The boys dropped the tips of their net and pinned it in the mud with sticks. They were as light as we were but not the way we were, and their hair was light but it wasn't blond, it was just colorless. And then I seemed to be looking into the opaque, colorless eyes of Big Mamma, and into the bleeding side of Jesus, and I could hear Miss Lillian commanding me to kiss Him, *kiss Him.* . . . The boys' hair was fair and kinky and we could see they weren't any whiter than the priest we'd been following. They were only lighter.

"Let's get out of here," Tom wailed, his voice already breaking. I started paddling backward as the boys climbed their respective sides of the dike and approached us slowly from above.

I looked up one last time and saw far behind them a gold cross on top of a pink stucco building, then it dropped from view.

"Say something to him," Tom cried. He held the useless pole, ready to defend himself somehow. Then one of the boys let out a hoop. People came running.

We were reeling backward now, as fast as I could paddle and Tom could slash. I tried to stay near the middle, but what good was it—ten feet on either side—when the rocks started flying?

"No!" Tom was screaming. "I didn't do nothing—quit it!" He was ten years old; he didn't know it wasn't, finally, a game. I knew, but I couldn't believe it was happening. He curled himself under the poling ledge where I was sitting.

Each rock, as it struck me, took my breath away before it started burning. Tom was praying, *dear God, get me home*, and I paddled with one arm and then with both, dodging what I could, trying to protect my head. They didn't have rocks, nothing big, just limestone gravel, but I remembered the story of David and the picture I loved of Goliath with blood between his eyes. Once more I looked up, hoping they'd see how young I was, how frightened, but all I could see were swarms of children, all the color of dirty sand, and darker adults screaming down at me, *"Morte, morte!"* and others, "Kill, kill!" They followed us to the end of the ditch, to the cypress hung with yellow, and then there was no place for them to stand as the dike and dry land petered out. We were suddenly back on the creek and I fell to the bottom of the boat, crying. We drifted awhile, until the current died, and then I poled and Tom paddled the rest of the way home.

The records show no settlement of mixed-blood Catholics in Oshacola County in 1932, or at any other time. The parish records, begun in 1941 by Father Enrique Fernandez, of Tampa, show no significant Spanish or Creole population this far east of Tampa. Theodora Rourke and Lillian are both listed as "White" on their death certificates, as was Bernard, Jr. (John Ryan Rourke, who died in 1894, was apparently buried privately without any record being kept); and since Big Mamma's estate later endowed a public park and Bernard Rourke's paintings hang in the State Galleries, there is no great enthusiasm in Hartley to investigate. Nor am I concerned about her genes in any quasi-legal sense—only historically. Theodora Rourke and her line are dead, unless the suspected issue of her sons Bernard and John could ever be traced; but she is one of many who have left scars on my body and opened a path that time has all but swallowed up. If my instincts are correct, her race degenerated into whiteness a generation ago and melted back to Hartley, or Tampa, or anywhere a lost people congregate. And the two children who discovered them a few years too early, before the transformation was complete, they, too, are only wanderers.

A passage I once marked from a story of Henry James reads, "The radiance of this broad fact had quenched the possible sidelights of reflection." I, too, am a partisan of the broad sweep, of mystery that sweetens as its sources grow deep and dim. I live in the dark, Tom in the light; I wonder, to return to the original question, if my experience that afternoon thirty-five years ago did not compel me to become a historian—and prevent me from becoming a good one. And made Tom, eyes skyward in St. Louis, indifferent to it all—the broad facts and the sidelights— and everything else around us crumbling into foolishness.

THE DWARF IN HIS VALLEY ATE CODFISH

Ray Smith

I. THE GREAT MAN

Long noses and petulance; the Great Man himself used to sit here, but that was in the old days when things were not as they are now. Is it a sense of loss we feel? Yes, I believe so, for we are weak. I do not like a south wind blowing.

There are many things to forget. See, here, carved into the doorstep: "M.E." Neat lettering, deep, straight, and with every serif in fine proportion, to commemorate the night the buffalo passed by, surly and awesome, a shadow and a rumble. *You* remember!

Make a vista for yourself; I will not disturb it; I am going round to the back of the house to the trees. Come if you wish, or not as also you wish. I will not trouble you.

I'm glad; one worries about proportion.

I have always wanted power; I begin to fear I have not got it in me. Oh yes, at times, under some circumstances, but always artificial. We ponder the fate of the codwife and her dark lover. . . .

Remember this shed from back over the (so many!) years. It was in there that we played the rumple game. How did it go? Yes. After all, what else can you do with a daffodil? You have a sleek sense of humor, sliding otter jokes that end with a splash. Ah! The tyranny of delight!

I see horses, one flesh-colored, one lime green, two red and two orange, and the second orange one is leaping over a lime-green sawhorse. It has not moved in six years. Beyond that (beyond the six years) I cannot (would not) vouch for it. Perhaps the Great Man . . . but that is no matter. Not *now*.

Was Alexander the Great's horse called Bucephalus? I have a feeling he was. History lacks sincerity; so I have always thought. The Great Man once accused history of three crimes, none of which was committed in the name of passion. The magistrate tossed the case out of court for lack of evidence. This tree will mean something to you. . . .

Curious, doubtless, I never knew. But then, there is so much one never knows. Don't you find that so? I once saw a falcon and thought myself lucky. If you enquire into the history of playing cards you will find, I surmise, that the Queen of Spades has always been evil . . .

Utopian characters always play a local variation of chess, inferior because of the writer's blind spots. But think! Think of the wildman or the fascinating mystery of Basilisk-Thorpe at Arras in '93. But then, even I sing at times for no reason at all. Yes.

Save string.

Fatuity is excusable for the same reason that sincerity is insufferable; it all depends upon the bending of the reeds when, under the scudding clouds, the wind comes in over the marshes, nervous, chill, agèd. . . .

The long grass. . . . I once thought happiness was balanced tension but the nostrum is no longer of much use to me. That does not make it less true—you'll recall the crow and the rune.

Have a lemon . . . go ahead. No lemon groves o'erhang the hoary Don. Did you know (you who have loved a redhaired girl) that the shell (of the oyster) is still around; I think it is in one of those cupboards you browse through on a rainy day. Old books, chocolate boxes full of trinkets, etc.

Red and blue stripes: that is the key.

Say something.

Plantagenet.

Codfish.

Nettles.

There's a political pun to be made out of Caesar's crossing the Rubicon; I can't be bothered explaining it for it is complicated and, I expect, of little interest to any but me.

Fol-de-ree
Fol-de-ray
Turn a key
End the day.

One sometimes wonders about dimensions. He did, frequently . . . mused upon the difference between weight
and specific gravity . . . made several cunning observa-
tions. Or: consider a planet. Yes, exactly, the Great Man
said as much himself numerous times.

He looked into the alcove (the buffalo again) and
thought to himself: any God worth a damn would surely
have the sense of humor to put up real red, white, and
blue striped north and south poles. Well, he said, really,
I don't think it's too much to ask, after all, he said, the
agèd pederast once. . . .

Thus (or so) the Agèd Pederast:

An old room, very old, with small sooty windows, old
objets d'art from years past (why the past itself!) cluttered
about. The fireplace doesn't draw well. In his worn chair
sits the agèd pederast reading a pornographic book. The
pederast is snickering; he wipes the saliva from his chin
with a dirty, hardened handkerchief. . . . We steal
closer. . . .

Possibly. I'm not sure.

What is it about marzipan? There's something about
marzipan. You can't trust people with pens.

"France, Spain, Italy, Germany, Poland, Russia, Sweden,
Turkey,/ Arabia, Palestine, Persia, Hindustan, China,
Tatary, Siberia,/"—the feet upon the endless stair—
"Egypt, Libya, Ethiopia, Guinea, Kaffraria, Negroland,
Morocco,/ Congo, Zara, Canada, Greenland, Carolina,
Mexico,/ Peru, Patagonia, Amazonia, Brazil. . . ." You
quote from the bard.

Have a handkerchief, his nose is running.

Wouldn't it be great, she thought, to be a walrus! (I
have a friend who is happy much of the time.)

No, not you, of course. . . . We wonder what to do
about the Beautiful and so we draw maps showing holes
in the ground; but when we try to use the maps the holes
have unaccountably moved. Holes do that.

See . . . there. . . a man on crutches.

Now the Great Man used to be brought out here in the

evenings to . . . listen I suppose. He was blind as a bat by then, but the ears of a bat, too. The women used to say it was so touching, but women always say that sort of thing. See, here is the trailing arbutus; it was his favorite flower for some reason unknown to the rest of them. Here, have a colander. No, really, I have a whole carton in my room.

Yes, all right. Perhaps we could wear sweaters, as I know your dislike for clouds which assume the shape of earthly objects.

I beg your pardon?

Possibly; in any case, I'm off to the beach now. Think upon the broken pillar and the goatherd's jolly song.

Harrooo. . . .

II. GLADYS

Gladys: but then she nevèr knew the difference. You wonder sometimes, you really wonder how long, how long O! Israel. You can try erasing but the whole web is ersatz. It's like trying to extract minutes from yesterdays. She had style; she also had long hair. The hair probably explained more. I don't know.

"So," he said and walked down the mountain. What the hell can you do, he asked himself, what can anyone do about panoramas? He just walked down the mountain until he came to a tavern and he went into the tavern and got drunk. No one cared. They didn't even ask him for money. "You don't care," he yelled, "you don't give a damn. What the hell do I have to do, expose myself?" (It was one of those countries.)

So he exposed himself and no one gave a damn.

Gladys! Gladys! he cried and they turned away. Out in the street his feet tended naturally on down the mountain. God knows what happened to him after that. Perhaps we'll find out later. I wasn't there at the time, but I heard it from someone or other. It is substantially true.

You were sitting at the far end of the long table (so elegant) and I could hardly see you because the candles were the only light in the room and you said to me, "Marjorie, this is the damndest best bouillabaisse I've ever tasted," and I thought about it not having *racasse,* which you can't get here. When *was* that? I remember the glitter; there was at least as much inside me. But I don't know; what are you supposed to say about crimes of this sort? Are they really crimes? Perhaps that's more to the point. We talk about Macedonian blood feuds that were ageless when Alexander the Great was counting his fingers for Aristotle, we talk about wergild and we can go to an art gallery and see paintings worth a king's ransom. So.

Take for example a fellow I knew in the army. Mashie-Niblick was his name. An officer and a gentleman, a really despicable piece of humanity. He got himself cashiered for gambling debts, and having learned his role well from a chintzy potboiler, never got back up again. Finally hung himself from a sconce by his regimental tie. It was pretty silly, really, he was eighty-seven at the time. I believe he was afraid of lightning.

In any case, this is the lino print block. I suppose it should have been destroyed but my wife restrains me. He listened to the radio a lot while Gladys was still alive and she thought he was in love with me. "Marjorie," she would say, "he has to be in love with you, you're so much more beautiful." Although I wasn't really, just more photogenic. Gladys could never see the difference. I mean, she never wore a girdle and I think men adored her for that. I tried not wearing one but it just didn't work, I have these solid childbearing hips. It was the same even when I was young enough that it mattered. In any case here is, as I said, the lino print block.

Gladys, Gladys: I always loved her, I always feel that when she dies the world will end. It was cool and bright the morning he set out. The only sounds were birdsong and the rustling of the dew. Clear, so clear! and bright. He sang a song as he walked along and the song he sang was "The Bottom Rung." (And ring it did . . . later.) There's nothing like beginning a journey; we've all done it. It was a shame his ended so quickly and so tragically. Ten girls in the county swore they never would marry and at least one, the ugliest and stupidest, was able to keep her threat. Revelation is the bread of fools, the bane of merchants, and the salve of kings. So much for bloody journeys.

Take this street, for instance. Fifty years ago it was nothing but a quaggy swamp. Progress, they say, marches on. But when you're my age you find your mind back in that swamp. The swamp harbored wildfowl, doubtless, and there were sedges of one sort and another. The world should make a place for bogs. Yes, I mean that, in spite of what happened to Gladys. You see, in spite of it all, she wasn't too bright. Midnight wanderings: well really, now, what can you expect?

Once I was sitting in a bleak tavern. It was the wrong time of day and the only other person there (besides the arthritic barmaid who appeared every now and then) was a rather dispirited prostitute doing a crossword puzzle. She had propositioned me earlier in a sadly apologetic way and I had thanked her, apologetically no. We chatted a bit about the weather while she chipped away at her memory. Then she asked me for a six-letter word for "yoke" beginning with "z." I said, "Zeugma," and she said, no, it wasn't a Polish crossword. We got it worked out after a while. The funny thing—macabre if you wish —was that it was in this very tavern that Gladys had first met Stanislaus Zeugma, her—shall we say?—fate. . . .

O, see that fellow just going into that house across the street . . . yes . . . well, he wears a chastity belt . . . yes, voluntarily . . . and his wife is a prostitute, too. It's all over the place but it's keeping me alive because it's milled from washed wheat.

She liked gambling a lot and was rather good at it. So it was with some misgivings that I heard them ask her, "Hey Margie, how about a game of strip poker?" There were six men and just her and when the game was over she was fully clothed. After she had teased us a bit she took off, too. She was always a good sport, which is why, I think, everyone disliked her so much. She disliked artichokes.

I remember Gladys at school; she was the cause of much violence. Old Nosey's life was ruined by the scandal. It was then we saw she was utterly amoral. Doorways meant nothing to her. It's infuriating, you see; you work and work building something and at the very last minute you find out you've used water instead of glue. (You wonder what happened to the glue and then you brush your teeth. . . .) Oh yes, she had a way about her. If only she hadn't giggled so much.

"Why?" he yelled when he had emerged from the sewer, "Why?"

"Who wants to know?" they called back.

"A wayfaring stranger."

"Screw strangers."

And so. Usually they were a hospitable bunch but you'd be unwise to depend on it. Oh, he stumbled about, muttering, trying as we all do to find a dignified out, but all he came up with was Gladys's name. So he took another swig from his bottle and cried, "Gladys . . . Gladys!" As he should have expected, they tore him apart and fed him to the dogs. That was the sort of effect she had on people. The morning the duel was to be fought she said to me, "Margie, I deserve this, don't I?" And I replied, "Gladys, you sure do." It seemed to make her happy; God knows, she needed happiness.

III. THE SHADOW PEOPLE

I remember the one with the artificial breasts saying how deep do you have to go anyway? Isn't there a limit? I mean. . . . She crossed her legs so that her skirt rode up, the exposure giving her as much pleasure as it gave us. The secret, she once told Madeleine, is an aura of prurience. Along with the perfume she wore some secret scent with aphrodisiacal qualities. We found out later it was a drop of fish oil.

It just goes on. The frightening part of is that nothing gets added, but things die and get taken away until there's nothing left but the going on. Process is horrible. But there are still hedgehogs. Remember the hedgehog; consider the hedgehog; venerate the hedgehog. So also:

Codfish

Cauliflowers

And Mira the Wonderful.

Here, you can't do that. . . . Really, though, in a place like this we'll have no stories about altarboys and streetlights. I've heard them all anyway. Try one about the raven.

Take the Marianas Trench, for e.g.; you can't go a hell of a lot deeper than that. Or in people, is the sole or the soul the deeper? Or the gut? Or how many fish live deeper than the sole, as if that solved anything. What a lot of nonsense; there's nothing more meaningless than connections.

That far under the water there was no light and he

found himself feeling his way along the stainless-steel wall, his fingers probing for a break, a turning. It was not much after that his brother found a moose head in the piano, and an unnamed girl, dressed in white, looked up and down the street before stepping into a dark doorway. It went on like that day after day until the old man died. His last request was for a kipper and when they said he shouldn't eat kippers in his condition he bawled at them, "Not to eat, you fools, to look at. Bah!" And so expired.

The question he was putting to them was this: Why can't it all happen on a seashore? You have your eel grass, your driftwood, waves, sea urchins, rocks, wind, sky, weather, sea. . . . Hell, what else is there? Run it up over a dune and add some sex and there you are. To hell with formalizations; to hell with inlaid ceilings and pillars; what the· hell do they matter? He was a brash young fellow, they said, and you know what they're like. J.D. (going under the name of A.C.) once told the feeble crow to go castigate the rood. People listened to him, though, because whatever he said had the heft of an anvil.

Once she got mixed up with a shoe salesman who read Blake. He had a great mind, that shoe salesman, really, just great. Some people would have said great in the sense of fat-headed but that was all they knew. Things can be learned from driving rods into the ground, but nowadays they use explosives and that's taken all the fun out of it, all the mystery. She thought the seismograph was a device used by charlatan mind readers. The last we had heard of her she had eloped with the gimpy alchemist and his retarded assistant. Presumably he changed her.

Once they tried to do fireflies; sat around a meadow one night, friendly at first then silent, then snarling at each other. Oh, the fireflies came all right, but never enough at once and they could never anticipate a blink. After that they pretty well stuck to artificial flowers. Once they went to Stonehenge and came back with the flu. But they could work together and every man Jack of 'em had a taste for endive. They hung together . . . just like pirates. *You* know.

Chessmen and the far-off lights; things like that drove her crazy after a while. He knew it was coming, he had seen it from very early on. When she had been gone three months, he went too. The memory of them is sharp but it is only a few pictures and the color is too bright for truth. It's like a one-eyed man catching a ball: lunge at truth and you get a broken nose. (At least that was what he said, but neither he nor his father much believed in the epigrams they both rolled out so easily. "Epigrams are like doughnuts," the father wrote from Burma. "They got holes in the middle.") Everyone pretended to believe it. They were very understanding; and very loathesome.

So the time passed and passes. One wonders how long it can go on. It's the happiness that goes first, and it matters damn little what goes after that. We pick up daisies and dream of train rides. Hate sneaks in like juice into a grapefruit. One day it leaps out at your eye. Something will snap somewhere. Somehow it will get at them sooner or later, the Great Man, Gladys, and The Shadow People. Until then: long noses and petulance.

NOTES ON THE AUTHORS

THOMAS CHANDLER HALIBURTON (1796–1865)

Haliburton had distinguished professional and literary careers. He was born and educated in Windsor, Nova Scotia, where in 1815 he received a B.A. degree (from King's College) and where, in 1820, he began practicing law. By 1826 he had won a seat in the Legislative Assembly. Three years later he had become a judge of the Inferior Court of Pleas, and by 1841, a judge of the Supreme Court of Nova Scotia, a position he held until 1856. He then retired to England, where he lived until his death. There he was almost as renowned as in his native land, receiving an Honorary degree from Oxford and sitting as a member of the British House of Commons from 1859 to 1865.

Haliburton began his full-fledged career as a writer with *A Historical and Statistical Account of Nova Scotia* (1829), but he made and has retained his reputation with a series of books (amounting finally to eleven volumes) describing the adventures of a shrewd and boastful Yankee peddler, Sam Slick, and with a collection of tales, in two volumes, *The Old Judge, or Life in a Colony* (1849). In these books, Haliburton proved himself a forerunner of much American humorous writing and a master of the genre. He knew the value of dialect, anecdote, tall tale, "character" sketch, and local color in themselves. In addition he knew their worth as sugarcoating for his social satire, for Haliburton as a Tory aimed almost constantly at what he considered colonial sloth in the face of the merits of self-help and the great opportunities presented in the new world (and especially in Nova Scotia) for the triumph of individual initiative through honest and hard work. Yet he is a moralist with the saving grace of a generally pervasive geniality.

V. L. D. Chittick's biography (1924), Fred Cogswell's article in *Literary History of Canada* (1965), and R. L. McDougal's, in *Our Living Tradition* (1959), are excellent studies of Haliburton.

EDWARD WILLIAM THOMSON (1849–1924)

A veteran of the American Civil War and a Boston news-paperman for twenty years, Thomson was a Canadian for all that. He was born in Peel County, Upper Canada, and educated at Trinity College School, Weston, and in his stories turns consistently to Canada (and especially the Ottawa Valley, where he was once a land surveyor) for his material.

Thomson was highly regarded as a man of letters in his day and in 1909 was elected a Fellow of the Royal Society of Literature, and in the following year, a Fellow of the Royal Society of Canada. By that time he had proved himself a lively and well-read newspaper editor, and a man quite at home in literary circles, where he had soon become a close friend of the poet Archibald Lampman. He had, besides, published three books of stories for young readers and three of poetry. One of these, *The Many Mansioned House, and Other Stories* (1909; also entitled *When Lincoln Died, and Other Stories*) has been praised for its "good vernacular verse," but Thomson's literary reputation rested mainly on *Old Man Savarin, and Other Stories* (1895). (The book was later expanded under the title *Old Man Savarin Stories, Tales of Canada and Canadians,* 1917.) Today, however, his reputation rests largely on one story, "The Privilege of the Limits." Thomson's stories are often sentimental-heroic and sometimes unduly farcical, but, at their best, contain excellent portraits and are good as narratives, gaining strength from their author's genuine feeling for the people he writes of and from his convincing presentation of local color.

There is no full study of Thomson's work, but A. S. Bourinot has examined it in part, and there are comments on it in the *Literary History of Canada* and similar books.

SIR CHARLES G. D. ROBERTS (1860–1943)

A maritimer born in Douglas, N.B., Roberts spent his boyhood in Westcock near the great Tantramar marshlands and his youth in Fredericton, where his father, an Anglican clergyman, became rector in 1874 and where Charles was to receive his B.A. degree from the University of New Brunswick five years later. A classical scholar of considerable merit and a close student of English poetry, Roberts soon rose to prominence in Canadian literature as a spokesman for the spirit of the new Canada, which by the 1880s had begun to sense its potential. As a teacher, magazine editor, and a professor of English, Roberts was well prepared for a career that eventually produced ten volumes of poetry, several historical romances, and some twenty books of short stories, most of which he wrote after he left Canada (in 1897) when, living for some twenty-seven years in the United States and England, he established himself as a successful professional man of letters.

As a novelist Roberts was derivative and melodramatic. As a poet he wrote excellent descriptive and mood pieces, and his influence on Canadian poetry, beginning with the publication of *Orion and Other Poems* (1880), can scarcely be overestimated. As a story writer, especially of the animal story, Roberts achieved much, his *Red Fox* (1905), a full-length animal biography, ranking among the very best of the kind. In the shorter fiction, nearly all of which centered on nature, Roberts wrote biographies, sketches, and adventure stories tailored in general to the requirements of the genre. He developed a tendency to write to formula in his later work, but at his best he combines authentic natural history with both an imaginative sympathy (generally free of sentimentality) for his animal heroes and an impressive talent as writer.

James Cappon's *Charles G. D. Roberts* (1925), E. M. Pomeroy's *Sir Charles G. D. Roberts* (1943) and W. J. Keith's *Charles G. D. Roberts* (1969) are full and excellent studies of Roberts's life and work.

DUNCAN CAMPBELL SCOTT (1862–1947)

Scott was born in Ottawa and was educated there and at Stanstead College in the Eastern townships of Quebec. He was employed from 1879 to 1932 as a civil servant in Indian affairs in his native city. There, also, he became a friend of the poet Archibald Lampman, who encouraged him to try writing, a pursuit he continued until his death, producing nine volumes of poetry; two of short stories (*In the Village of Viger*, 1896; and *The Witching of Elspie*, 1923); a collection of essays, poems, and short stories, *The Circle of Affection* (1947); and a play, *Pierre* (1923). In 1899, Scott was elected to the Royal Society of Canada in appreciation of his writing and interest in literary affairs.

Scott's education in the different Ontario and Quebec schools and his work in Ottawa were as influential as the encouragement he received from Lampman, for in large part they determined his subject matter—nature *vis-à-vis* man, habitant and Indian life, and the early and frontier history of the country. His stories often contain both delicately romantic and precisely realistic elements and vary from the nostalgic and the whimsically humorous to the violent and the strange, if not the macabre. He is a careful artist, and his touch is generally sure, so that the sentiments implied, the elements of adventure, and the moral are kept in bounds. If his stories seem to lack power, they are suffused with a sensibility (often with a fine sense of irony) and a mood that suggest a depth of understanding of the central issues of life, even if they are generally only intimated.

Scott's poetry has received far more attention from critics than his fiction, but there are usually some comments on the latter in most histories and handbooks of Canadian literature.

STEPHEN LEACOCK (1869–1944)

Leacock was born in England, but at the age of seven came to Canada with his mother when his father, a ne'er-do-well remittance man, took up a farm near Sutton in the Lake Simcoe area. Leacock attended Upper Canada College in Toronto (where he became a Master in 1889) and also attended the University of Toronto. He received his B.A. degree there in 1891 and remained as a master at Upper Canada College until 1899. He then left to study economics and political science at the University of Chicago, and received his Ph.D. degree in 1903, two years after he had taken the position at McGill University in the Department of Economics and Political Science that he continued to hold until he retired in 1936.

Among Canadian writers, Leacock is certainly one of the most prolific and probably the best known both at home and abroad. He published some fifty-five books, not to mention a play, two collections of verse, and many pamphlets and addresses. He wrote for and was written of in periodicals in the United States, England, and Canada, and publishers in all three countries eagerly sought his books. He was elected Fellow of the Royal Society of Canada in 1910. A building at McGill has been named after him, a postage stamp issued in his honor, and his summer home at Orillia (the model of the "Little Town") on his beloved Lake Simcoe has been preserved as a memorial to him.

As an economist and political scientist, Leacock wrote on trade, tariffs, Imperialism, the Depression; as an amateur historian, on the early days of Montreal and of the country at large; and as a man of letters he produced books on humor, writing, and education, and on his favorites Dickens and Twain. Yet his fame rests but lightly on these serious works, for he made his name as a humorist with *Literary Lapses* (1910), *Nonsense Novels* (1911), and *Sunshine Sketches of a Little Town* (1912), and so on through some twenty-five similar books until the nostalgic-humorous (and, unfortunately, fragmentary) autobiography, *The Boy I Left Behind Me* (1946).

Like Roberts, Leacock fell prey to writing by formula in his later years, but many of the first vital and witty pieces which helped establish his reputation have lost nothing with the passing of time. His satire has kept its edge; his genial appreciation of the incongruous remains attractive and valid; and beneath all the mockery and buffoonery, all the laughter and high spirits, there is often a suggestion of Leacock's sympathetic understanding of their close relationship to the darker, if not quite tragic, side of life. As a result Leacock's humor at its best has a depth and tension that lift it above the farcical and the merely clever.

Three recent full-length studies of Leacock have appeared: Ralph Curry's *Stephen Leacock, Humorist and Humanist* (1959), Donald Cameron's *Faces of Leacock* (1967), and David Legate's *Stephen Leacock*.

FREDERICK PHILIP GROVE (1871–1948)

The facts that Grove records about his early life in his autobiographical books, *A Search for America* (1927) and *In Search of Myself* (1946), are open to serious question, as Douglas Spettique's *Frederick Philip Grove* (1969) makes clear. Yet it does seem certain that Grove was born in Europe and that as a young man he spent considerable time working as an itinerant laborer on the prairie farms of the western United States. Whatever doubts there may be about Grove's early years, there is little question, however, that his later life in Canada was hard and sometimes even desperate, despite his wife's loyalty and unstinting dedication to his cause, as he struggled to become a writer against great odds—a long illness, a serious accident, and the terrible grief that followed his daughter's death in 1927. Besides, there was the almost constant need to earn a living as someone other than writer, first as a teacher in Manitoba and later as a farmer near Simcoe, Ontario, where he settled in 1931 after a dismal year as director of the Graphic Press in Ottawa.

If Grove received considerable acclaim from critics for his books, he earned little from their sales, although he did make some money from *Our Daily Bread* (1928)—but from it alone among all his works—and he did make three lecture tours in the 1920s on the strength of his reputation as a writer. Later, in 1934, a year after he published *Fruits of the Earth*, his fourth and last novel of life on the prairies, he won the Lorne Pierce Medal for his contribution to the nation's literature. Toward the end of his life even greater honors were bestowed on him. He became a Fellow of the Royal Society of Canada in 1941. Four years later, he received an honorary degree from the University of Toronto, and in the following year won a Governor General's Award. In 1937, however, the Lorne Pierce Medal went to pay for a radio, and by the 1940s the other tributes to his talent were too late to help much.

As a short-story writer, Grove reveals many of the qualities that he demonstrated in his novels, although he seems generally less at home in the story, since it denied him the vast time scheme and sprawling narrative he used so tellingly in his full-length books. Yet he could handle the short form effectively, as "Snow" indicates, to work out his familiar theme of the struggle between man and nature, and to suggest, if not illustrate, his tragic vision of the even more destructive and baffling struggles of man with man and of man within himself.

For all their failure to sell well, Grove's realistic novels, such as those already mentioned and *Settlers of the Marsh* (1925), *The Yoke of Life* (1930), and *The Master of the Mill* (1944), and his two books of essays belong with the best of Canadian literature. As yet Grove's stories have not been collected. "Snow" was first published in the *Queen's Quarterly* (1932), but has since appeared in at least four anthologies.

Desmond Pacey, who is preparing Grove's letters for publication, Douglas O. Spettique, and Ronald Sutherland have written full-length studies of Grove.

ETHEL WILSON (1890–   )

Ethel (Bryant) Wilson is South African by birth, but has been a resident of British Columbia since she was eight years old. She did most of her schooling in England, but then returned to Vancouver, where she became a teacher and where, in 1920, she married Doctor Wallace Wilson, onetime President of the Canadian Medical Association.

Mrs. Wilson did not begin publishing until 1937. Since then she has written five novels and published many short stories in journals and magazines in both Canada and England. Several of these stories have appeared again in recently published anthologies and many of them have been collected under the title *Mrs. Golightly and Other Stories* (1961).

Although Mrs. Wilson has made her name as a novelist, she has been equally good with the short story. In it she reveals the strengths that mark such longer works as *Hetty Dorval* (1947), *The Innocent Traveller* (1949), and *Swamp Angel* (1954)—the same lively sense of humor, often genially satirical, the same sympathetic understanding of the feminine point of view, and the same urbanity of style and subtle organization of the details in the narrative.

There is no comprehensive study of Mrs. Wilson's work, but several critics—Livesay, Pacey, and Walters—have published articles on it.

MORLEY CALLAGHAN (1903–   )

A lifetime resident of Toronto (except for a brief period in Paris and in the United States), a graduate of the University of Toronto (1925), a lawyer, and a friend of Hemingway (whom Callaghan met when he and Hemingway were reporters for the Toronto *Daily Star*), Callaghan has had a long and successful career as an author. Beginning with short stories, which Hemingway encouraged him to try, he soon branched out into the novel and with *Strange Fugitive* (1928) proved his talent beyond a doubt. Since then he has added nine more novels to a list that includes *The Loved and the Lost* (1951), for which he received a Governor General's Award, and such other excellent novels as *Such Is My Beloved* (1934), *They Shall Inherit the Earth* (1935), and *More Joy in Heaven* (1937).

Despite the acclaim Callaghan received for his novels, he continued writing short stories, publishing three volumes of them and a novella between 1929 and 1937 and a collected edition in 1959. Revealing Callaghan's sensitive social conscience and marked by a deftness of style and concision of organization, the stories attempt to present setting and characters as directly as possible. Callaghan tried to isolate the subtle nuances of personality of his through the trivial events that make up their lives. Never a sensationalist, he is content to try to demonstrate that what may seem insignificant to an ordinary observer may be most significant to the person involved. As a collection, his stories tend to a sameness in manner, attitude, and theme, but there is no question of his mastery of the kind he chose to develop. There is none either of the sincerity of his sympathy for the misfits who usually people the pages of his books and for their counterparts in real life. Compassion is the keynote of all that he has to say.

Brandon Conron and Victor Hoar have each recently written a book-length study of Callaghan, and he himself has published the autobiographical *That Summer in Paris* (1963).

SINCLAIR ROSS (1908–   )

Like Grove, Ross writes at his best realistically of man's harsh and often tragic struggle with nature on the Canadian prairies of some forty or fifty years ago. Again like Grove, Ross knew his subject first hand, for he was born and brought up in Saskatchewan, where he began working in a bank when he was sixteen. It is scarcely surprising, then, that prairie life forms the core of his first and very impressive novel *As for Me and My House* (1941) and of all his short stories, many of which have been collected in *The Lamp at Noon and Other Stories* (1968).

For all the harsh realism of the picture that Ross paints, his imaginative sympathy with his characters and his perspicacious insight into their motives and reactions preclude his stories from becoming gritty fictionalized documentaries of a period in his own life and in the nation's history. In *The Well* (1958) and again in a forthcoming novel, Ross turns to the West for much of his setting and material. Neither years in the army during the Second World War nor years in Montreal, where he continued working in a bank until 1967, when he retired and moved to Greece, have really diverted him from his attempt to describe and explain prairie life. Although depicted less somberly in his latest books, the West remains for Ross the emotional and imaginative center of all his fiction.

The short story seems admirably suited to Ross. Its very size lends force to his intensity of feeling and enables him to focus directly on the elemental in both man and nature.

There are articles on Ross by Donald Stephens and Warren Tallman in the magazine *Canadian Literature,* and a book by R. Chambers is in preparation.

MALCOLM LOWRY (1909–1957)

An immigrant from Great Britain, Lowry lived at Dollarton, near Vancouver, during his most productive period, which ran, generally speaking, from 1939, when he arrived in Canada, until 1954, when, evicted from his shack at Dollarton, he left for Sicily. He finally settled in England, but died there suddenly three years after leaving Canada. Before going to British Columbia, Lowry had lived a varied life and had accumulated a rich store of experience to call on for his fiction. He had studied at Cambridge, where he received a B.A. degree in 1932. He had sailed as a deckhand on a tramp steamer for a year, had traveled extensively in Europe and North America, worked as a script writer in Hollywood, and had lived in Paris, New York, and Cuernavaca, Mexico. It was at Cuernavaca in 1936, when living with his first wife, Jan, that he wrote the short story "Under the Volcano," which he later expanded under the same title into the very impressive novel about a drunkard that he published in 1947. He was then living with his second wife, Margerie Bonner, herself a novelist, whom he had married in 1940.

She helped him greatly and is doing much now to make available the pile of manuscript that Lowry left unpublished at his death.

Lowry's novels *Ultramarine* (1932, 1962), which stems from his life at sea, *Lunar Caustic* (1963), and *Dark as the Grave Wherein My Friend Is Laid* (1968) do not have Canadian settings. *Hear Us O Lord from Heaven Thy Dwelling Place* (1961), a collection of seven of his short stories, for which Lowry was posthumously granted a Governor General's Award, does, however, manifest a direct Canadian influence.

The story "Under the Volcano" reveals in miniature the qualities of Lowry's novels—his meticulously wrought, flexible, and subtly metaphoric prose, his ability to catch the shades of mood and thought of his characters as individuals and at the same time to disclose through them a sympathetic understanding of human social experience.

Some of Lowry's poems and letters have been published recently. Many articles have been written about Lowry, and a monograph on him is to appear shortly. There is, also, a valuable introduction by Mrs. Lowry to *Ultramarine,* and by Douglas Day to *Dark as the Grave Wherein My Friend Is Laid.* "Under the Volcano" was first published in a journal, the *Prairie Schooner* (1964), and has been reprinted in N. Levine's anthology, *Canadian Winter's Tales* (1968).

GABRIELLE ROY (1909–)

A French-Canadian novelist and one of Canada's foremost authors, Gabrielle Roy (Mrs. Marcel Carbotte) was born and grew up in St. Boniface, Manitoba. As a young woman she was active in the theater there, attended the Winnipeg Normal School, and later taught round about the province for several years, an experience that supplied the material of *La Petite poule d'eau* (1950; *Where Nests the Water Hen,* 1951). Miss Roy left Manitoba in the 1930s and, after a brief stay in France and England during 1937–38, went to Montreal to take up free-lance writing.

In 1945 she published her first novel, *Bonheur d'occasion* (*The Tin Flute,* 1947), a book that in its realism broke new ground in French-Canadian fiction and won her a Governor General's Award and Le Prix Fémina in France. Within two years, also, Miss Roy was elected Fellow of the Royal Society of Canada. She set her next novel, *Alexandre Chenevert* (1954; *The Cashier,* 1955), in Montreal, but for all her other books she has turned back to her life in Manitoba and generally away from the harsher aspects of her realism. One of these, *Rue Deschambault* (1955; *Street of*

Riches, 1957), a collection of reminiscent and nostalgic short stories, received a Governor General's Award. Linked by a common narrator, Christine, the youngest daughter of a large French-Canadian family, these stories present a lively, sensitive, and perceptive study of child-parent relationships and of the inner worlds of the child and the adolescent. A second collection (a kind of sequel to the earlier book) *La Route d'Altamont* (*The Road Past Altamont*) appeared in 1966. All six of Miss Roy's books have been translated into English. Guy Sylvestre, Alan Brown, and Hugo McPherson have written articles on Miss Roy's work, and Phyllis Grosskurth published a lengthy monograph on it in 1969.

IRVING LAYTON (1912–   )

In 1913 Irving Lazarovitch came with his family from Rumania, his birthplace, to Montreal, which was to be his home until he moved to Ontario to become Poet-in-Residence at Guelph University in 1968 and a Professor of English at York University, Toronto, in 1969. Layton attended Montreal public schools, then MacDonald College, where he received a B.Sc. in Agriculture in 1939, and, finally, after a stint in the armed forces, entered McGill University, where in 1946 he took his M.A. degree in Economics and Political Science. Following graduation, Layton taught at the Herzliah High School in Montreal until he left it in 1960 to take a position as lecturer at Sir George Williams University.

A writer with some twenty volumes of poetry to his credit, and a Governor General's Award for one of them, *A Red Carpet for the Sun* (1959), Layton turned to the short story only intermittently in his literary career, publishing *The Swinging Flesh* (1961), a collection of poems and stories, nineteen years after his poetry began appearing in the Montreal "little" magazine *First Statement*. An angry young man once, Layton reveals in his recent poetry that he has become more reflective with the passing of time. The same may be said of his short stories. Yet, no matter when Layton wrote them, they continue to examine the values of a society that, as he sees it, threatens constantly by the very nature of its organization to undermine the values of both the imaginative and the independent-spirited.

L. Dudek, W. Francis, and N. Frye, among several others, have written articles on Layton, but Eli Mandel's *Irving Layton* (1969) is the first lengthy study of his work.

HUGH GARNER (1913–)

Born in Yorkshire, England, but a Canadian by adoption, Hugh Garner has been a Torontonian ever since he was six. He was educated in Toronto at Danforth Technical High School. During the Depression he worked here and there about the city whenever he could find a job, and later, during the Second World War, he spent five years in the Royal Canadian Navy. But, it was his life in Toronto during the Depression that contributed most to his writing. It was then he developed the social conscience that impelled him to fight in Spain as a machine gunner with the International Brigade and to take up the cause of the downtrodden in an industrialized, capitalistic society as the subject of so much of his fiction.

Garner has written many successful TV plays, timely articles and essays, four novels, and three books of short stories, one of which, *Hugh Garner's Best Stories* (1963), gained him a Governor General's Award. "A Trip for Mrs. Taylor," which comes from that book, is a bit more fanciful than most of Garner's work, but conforms to its general pattern (of a central and ordinary incident involving an ordinary person) through which Garner, as a writer with a purpose, implies or demonstrates social criticism. In some of the stories Garner fails because he weights them unduly with message, but in many he does infuse his details and moral indignation with an imaginative sympathy that produces good realistic fiction.

Garner's fiction is discussed at some length in the *Literary History of Canada* (1965).

YVES THÉRIAULT (1916–)

Although born in Quebec City, Thériault received his education in Montreal at Notre-Dame-de-Grâce and le Mont-Saint-Louis, but gave up his studies so that he might devote his time to tennis, boxing, and radio broadcasting. His ambition to become a professional athlete came to nothing when he fell ill and had to enter a sanatorium at Lac Edouard. When he recovered, he became a jack-of-all-trades as he struggled to make a living as tractor salesman, truck driver, M.C. in a night club, newspaper manager before finally settling into radio work in Montreal after jobs at no fewer than five different stations in the province between 1936 and 1943. Always energetic, Thériault soon began writing radio scripts and then fiction, and within the next two decades produced many pseudonymous potboilers, a half-dozen romances for young readers, ten novels, three volumes of short stories, and a play, not to mention

1,500 radio and TV scripts he wrote for the CBC from 1944 to 1962 and three lengthy stays in Europe, the latest as the recipient of a Canada Council scholarship. Thériault is a Fellow of the Royal Society of Canada and a winner of a Governor General's Award for *Ashini* (1960), his novel of Indian life.

The story selected for this anthology is taken from *Contes pour un homme seul* (1944), Thériault's first book. It typifies most of Thériault's fiction inasmuch as it revolves about his central themes of the instinctive *vis-à-vis* both idealism and modern materialism. It also typifies his style with its "counterpoint" of "the lyrical phrase" and "language deliberately popular and brutal" aimed at revealing the primitive man. All these traits show up again as full-fledged naturalism and social criticism in Thériault's novels as they move over a wide range of subjects that vary from Indians and Eskimos to city alcoholics and the mountain farmers of Spain.

Thériault's work is studied at some length in G. Tougas' *History of French-Canadian Literature* (1967) and in another book with the same title, by G. Bessette, L. Geslin, and C. Parent (1968).

ANNE HÉBERT (1916–   )

Although Anne Hébert is a resident of both Montreal and Paris, she is no internationalist as a writer, for her work focuses on *la scéne québécoise vis-à-vis* the Parisien and European. That this should be true now seems to have been almost certain from the beginning. Miss Hébert spent her early years in the very heart of French Canada—at Sainte-Catherine de Fossambault, where she was born, and in Quebec City, where she studied in the city schools and, because of illness, sometimes at home under the watchful eyes of her cultured and talented parents. Moreover, Miss Hébert's work for the National Film Board (1953–1961) probably consolidated her interests in Canada. Not that she is provincial, for if she does concern herself with *l'âme québécoise,* she takes care finally to relate it to *l'âme de l'homme.*

Miss Hébert has published three volumes of poetry, three plays, a novel, and a book of short stories, *Le Torrent* (1950). Like Yves Thériault, Miss Hébert is a Fellow of the Royal Society of Canada (elected 1960) and has been the recipient of Canada Council Fellowships. She has also won several awards for her poetry.

"The House on the Esplanade" dates from the early years of Miss Hébert's career, but its delicacy of expression and sensitivity of feeling characterize all her fiction and poetry. The theme of the story is also common to much of her work, centering, even if with a lightness of touch here, on the search of the spirit for fulfillment in the face of loneliness and doubt.

There are several studies of Miss Hébert. Two are quite recent and detailed, one by P. Page (1965) and the other by R. Lacote (1969).

WILLIAM C. McCONNELL (1917–)

A youth with many different jobs in many different parts of Canada during the Depression, a private who rose to the rank of sergeant during the Second Great War, William McConnell is now settled comfortably in Vancouver, where he was born and educated and where he practices law and holds the position of Editor in the Klanak Press. McConnell began writing in 1939 and, for the most part, has drawn on the experiences of the Depression and war years for his fiction. As a writer who grew up during the 1930s and 1940s, he was much influenced by the authors of the time and has concentrated on presenting life realistically and sympathetically in terms of the social milieu —whether war, or poverty, or the frontier—that determines the lives of his characters.

McConnell was most productive as a writer in the late 1940s and early 1950s, when he published stories in several Canadian magazines, such as *Queen's Quarterly, Saturday Night,* and *The Canadian Forum.* At the time, too, he was actively engaged in radio work preparing scripts and occasionally contributing a story to Weaver's CBC weekly program "Canadian Short Stories." His stories have appeared in at least four anthologies. If anthologists have not neglected McConnell, critics and even compilers of literary handbooks unfortunately have, so that there is very little in secondary source material about his work.

BRIAN MOORE (1921–)

Moore is now a resident of California, where he writes film scripts as well as fiction, but for many years he has been associated with Canada and Canadian literature. He was born in Belfast and was educated there at St. Malochi's college (he left without a degree) and at the University of London as an extramural student. He came to Canada after a stint in the British armed forces during the Second World War. At first he did odd jobs, but finally became a reporter for *The Gazette* in Montreal. Shortly after getting this position he began working at fiction, and of his six novels (not counting thrillers published under a pseudonym) he wrote three during the years (1948–1959) he spent in Canada, as well as many of the short stories that have appeared in major magazines in Great Britain, the United States, and Canada. So far, however, he has not issued a collected edition of his stories. Of the three novels he produced in Canada, the first, *The Lonely Passion of Judith Hearne* (1956), won him the Great Britain Best First Novel Award, and the third, *The Luck of Ginger Coffey* (1960), his only novel with a Canadian setting, received the Governor General's Award for the best Canadian fiction of the year.

A Canadian citizen living in the United States writing largely about Ireland and the Irish, Moore seems to fit no national label any more than his fiction fits him into any literary group or trend. Although Moore admits his liking for Joyce, he is no mimic and, with a restrained directness, sets about giving his own vision of life. Centered in character, and usually the insignificant at that, it implies an awareness of all the frustrations, loneliness, and social injustice normally associated with grubby realism or even naturalism. Yet Moore assumes neither perspective, for his concern for his characters as human beings prevents his fiction from becoming a documentary on or illustration of social problems and theories. In a way, Moore's refusal to concern himself with the "larger issues" denies breadth to his novels and stories, but it gives them a kind of intimacy that adds to their effectiveness as studies of human personality.

There are many articles on Moore, and recently Hallvard Dahlie published *Brian Moore* (1969), a detailed study of him.

MAVIS GALLANT (1922–   )

Mrs. Gallant is a Canadian expatriate now living in France. She grew up in both Canada (in Montreal, her birthplace) and the United States and was educated in no fewer than seventeen schools, "public, private, French and English, American, Canadian, Protestant, convent, and even Quaker." After graduating from high school (in the United States) she began looking for a job, for, as she said long after the ordeal of her schooling had ended, "I wouldn't have gone to college if they'd paid me." Returning to Montreal, she worked at first for the National Film Board and then, as a feature writer, for the *Standard* (now *Weekend Magazine*). In 1950, however, after six years in this position, she resigned and left for Europe.

Mrs. Gallant had begun writing when she was nineteen and once free of her job with the newspaper she gave herself entirely to her work, producing over the years a sizable body of fiction—short stories for the most part (mainly for *The New Yorker* and frequently about Canada). Her first book, *The Other Paris* (1956), is a collection of short stories; her next, *Green Water*

Green Sky (1960), is a novel comprising four linked stories; and her latest, *My Heart is Broken* (1964; entitled in England, *The Unmarried Man's Summer and Other Stories*), is another collection that includes eight stories and a novella.

All Mrs. Gallant's work is marked by a graceful prose style and carefully selected and incisively described detail. Character is central, not narrative or situation. Mrs. Gallant normally takes a satiric view of her characters, largely middle class, dissecting their personalities with almost complete detachment, sometimes bordering on the pitiless. But she is always poised and never coarse or common-place. If the area she works in is limited, she is, within it, a most meticulous and subtle artist.

Surprisingly little work has been done in Canada on Mrs. Gallant's fiction, despite her achievements. Of late, however, she does seem to be attracting more attention here.

JACK LUDWIG (1922–   )

Jack Ludwig was born in Winnipeg and educated in the city schools and at the University of Manitoba, where he received a B.A. degree in 1944. He continued his studies at the University of California at Los Angeles and took his Ph.D. degree there. Ludwig has now lived in the United States for several years, having lectured at several different universities before becoming a Professor of English at the State University of New York on Long Island in 1961.

Ludwig has a firmly established reputation. He has long been associated with *The Noble Savage*, a semiannual periodical which he helped found and edit. He has written two novels, *Confusions* (1963) and *Above Ground* (1968), and a book of literary criticism, *Recent American Novelists* (1966). He has perhaps been most successful with his short stories, usually realistic, lively, and perspicacious studies of urban Jewish life. He has appeared in at least four anthologies (R. Weaver's, D. Pacey's, M. Foley's, and *The O. Henry Prize Stories*) and several major Canadian and American magazines, such as *The Tamarack Review* and *The Atlantic Monthly*. "Requiem for Bibul," published in *The Atlantic Monthly*, was given an Atlantic First Award.

Ludwig has received some attention in recent handbooks of Canadian literature, but as yet no particular study of his work has been made.

MARGARET LAURENCE (1926–   )

Of Scottish descent, Margaret (Wemyss) Laurence comes from one of the founding families of the little town of Neepawa, Manitoba, where she herself was born and lived until entering United College (now the University of Winnipeg) in Winnipeg in 1944. This, however, was only one of a series of moves that took her first (in 1950) to Africa with her husband, a civil engineer, for seven years, then to British Columbia for five more, and finally to England, where she now resides.

The years in Africa were important to Margaret Laurence's growth as a writer. Her experiences there stimulated her imagination, and she has drawn on them for four books—a translation of Somali literature, a memoir of her life in Somaliland, a novel about Ghana, and *The Tomorrow Tamer* (1963), a collection of ten stories about the people of the Gold Coast caught up in and often bewildered by the forces of rapid change. One of the ten, "A Gourdful of Glory," which appeared first in *Prism* (1961) and won the President's Medal at the University of Western Ontario the next year, typifies the high quality of these African stories very neatly. Mrs. Laurence's early home has been no less fruitful than Africa as a source of inspiration, however, and in recent years she has turned back to life on the prairies for two of her three most recently published novels—*The Stone Angel* (1964) and *A Jest of God* (1966), which received a Governor General's Award—and for all seven short stories (in a projected series of ten) that she has published recently.

The African stories center on the reactions of an "emergent" nation; yet they avoid any socially oriented theorizing. They reveal rather the attitudes, perspectives, and mores of their black protagonists as persons first. Yet beyond the individual, these stories catch something of the spirit of the local and the national, and above all something of the changeless change of behavior patterns and sets of values that characterizes all mankind. Mrs. Laurence sees her characters realistically and sympathetically as single human beings and as African natives, but she presents them ultimately as people in a broad, humanistic framework that encompasses both them and reader.

Clara Thomas's study of Margaret Laurence appeared in 1969 and Walter Swayze has one in preparation, due in late 1970.

HUGH HOOD (1928–)

Hugh Hood was born in Toronto and received all his education there, in city schools and at the University of Toronto, where he received his Ph.D. degree in 1955. Hood now lives in Montreal with his wife and family and teaches English at the University of Montreal. He spends his summers in southeastern Ontario at Athens, near Brockville. The fact that Hood knows both urban and rural life has had a marked bearing on his work, since he has made Montreal, Toronto, and rural Ontario the setting of almost all his stories and in this sense they are genuinely Canadian. They are Canadian, too, in that they catch a feeling for the nation, whether the city, as described in "Recollections of the Works Department," the rural world, as in "Getting to Williamsburg," or the small town, as in "Three Halves of a House." Hood does not, however, play city off against country like a romantic, nor is he trying for the effects of local color. He is no literary nationalist either, but simply a writer laying out a geography of experiences that have incited his imaginative responses, as is apparent in the description (in "Three Halves of a House") of Stoverville set as it is in all the spaciousness of the St. Lawrence River valley.

The contrast in the setting of small town and big country, of present small-town life and pioneer past and the timeless river flowing to the sea illustrates Hood's method of composition well —of the manner in which he makes facts significant. To begin with, his characters are individuals, and events are events, and so they remain. Yet if they are individuals and events first, they are also both studies in human personality and the elements of cohesive and vital statements about life. The themes grow from the facts, for Hood is very skillful in leaving the impression that he has not imposed a meaning on life, but has derived one from it. His subjects go beyond the particular. On one hand they reveal the inner life—attitudes, desires, memories, quirks, inhibitions, motives, reactions. On the other hand, they relate it to the external framework of society—family, profession, status —to the embracing constant of the past, to the search for meaning in existence, frequently as it relates to the inevitability of death. Hood is subtle in his implications, and if his stories read easily and interestingly as simple accounts of people and their experiences, the quality stems from his talent in hiding his art and from the flow and flexibility of his prose.

Hood's stories have appeared in *Esquire, Prism, Queen's Quarterly* and similar magazines, and in two recent anthologies. A collection of them, *Flying a Red Kite,* came out in 1962. Since then, Hood has written two novels, a book of sketches of personal experiences in Montreal, and a biography of Jean Béliveau as hockey star and folk hero.

Hood's work is discussed, briefly at least, in most recent handbooks and journals concerned with Canadian literature.

ALICE MUNRO (1931–   )

A native of Wingham, Ontario, Alice Munro attended school there and later went to the University of Western Ontario in

London. Since 1951, when she married, she has lived in British Columbia. There, aside from writing regularly, she looks after a family of three daughters and helps her husband run a bookshop in Victoria.

Mrs. Munro has so far published only short stories. They have appeared in such Canadian magazines as *The Montrealer, Châtelaine,* and *The Tamarack Review,* and some have been read over the CBC network. In 1968 her success with the genre received further recognition when Ryerson Press published a collection of fifteen of her best stories in *The Dance of the Happy Shades.* The story anthologized here appears in the book and typifies Mrs. Munro's fiction. It is simply, skillfully, and sensitively written. It is regional and descriptive of events in the day-to-day living of townspeople. Above all it illustrates Mrs. Munro's ability to give a sense of place to her narrative and to analyze and concomitantly to dramatize the complexities of human behavior and personality. If her objectivity sometimes seems to reduce the dramatic force of her stories, it does preclude them from becoming sentimental and slick.

"The Office" first appeared in *The Montrealer* (1964).

Canadian Literature (Winter 1969) contains an interesting commentary by Audrey Thomas on Mrs. Munro's book.

MORDECAI RICHLER (1931–)

A Montrealer by birth, a second-year dropout at Sir George Williams University (where in 1968, he held the position of Writer-in-Residence), and a former news editor for the CBC, Richler has been an expatriate for several years and now lives with his wife and four children in London, England. Since leaving Sir George Williams University in 1951, Richler has devoted his life to establishing himself as a man of letters both in Canada and abroad. During that time he has published six novels, two volumes of essays, and many short stories and has written successful TV plays and helped with film script for various movies, including *Room at the Top.*

Richler's first novel, *The Acrobats* (1954), and his third, *A Choice of Enemies* (1957), were set in Europe and were well received. It was his fiction about Canada, however—especially *Son of a Smaller Hero* (1955) and *The Apprenticeship of Duddy Kravitz* (1959)—that revealed his true stature, for Richler is at his best when writing of the impact of war, antisemitism, or poverty (or wealth) on the Jewish people of Montreal. Along with his knowledge and understanding of Jewish life he has a sardonic and frequently boisterous sense of the comic and a critical social awareness that frequently flashes through the facade of his fiction. Fiercely satirical as he may be at times, he always manages a serio-comic focus that may involve farce or merely the irony of situation, but that is effective, a fact that his latest novel, *Cocksure* (1968), clearly demonstrates, winning awards as fiction and as humor. Aside from these aspects of Richler's work, there is his skill in drawing characters quickly with a few strokes. They may be types, but they are nonetheless impressive.

Richler's stories have been published in leading journals in Canada, the United States, and England, and several have been anthologized. "Playing Ball on Hampstead Heath," for example, first appeared in *Gentleman's Quarterly* (1966) and has since then come out in N. Levine's *Canadian Winter's Tales* (1968). So far, however, no collection of Richler's stories has been published.

P. D. Scott, W. Tallman, and R. McKenzie have written articles on Richler. In addition, a study of him is in preparation for McClelland and Stewart's Canadian Writers series.

DAVE GODFREY (1938–)

Dave Godfrey is a native of Manitoba. He is married and now lives in Toronto, where he lectures at the University of Toronto on Welsh literature. In addition to this work, Godfrey writes regularly, edits a series of handbooks on Canadian writers for McClelland and Stewart, and runs the House of Anansi, a publishing firm that he helped found a few years ago. In the interval between leaving Manitoba and settling in Toronto, Godfrey did graduate work at the University of Iowa, toured South Africa as a trumpet player, and worked in lumber camps and at other jobs in Canada, thus packing away a wealth of experiences that have stood him in good stead in his writing.

Godfrey has contributed stories to *Saturday Night, The Tamarack Review,* and has appeared (as one of three authors) in *New Canadian Writing* (1968) and R. Weaver's *Canadian Short Stories* (1966). His recent *Death Goes Better with Coca-Cola* (1967), a collection of fourteen stories, reveals him as a provocative and imaginative young man with considerable breadth of knowledge. Godfrey frequently writes a simple, direct account of an event, but in such a way that it comments indirectly on its significance in some wider context. It might be (and usually is) a hunting trip, a fishing expedition, or a safari into some African bushland.

Godfrey never tries to deny fact by an escape into the imagined, even when he writes of far-off places and odd experiences. He suggests rather an area somewhere between the realistic and the romantic, a practice whereby he can produce a kind of story, exemplified at the extreme by "The Hard-Headed Collector," in which obvious symbols replace the more usual technique of letting overtones speak for meaning. Here, also, Godfrey organizes fact and fiction contrapuntally and examines rather than suggests the area between them, which, in broad terms, is revealed as myth and cultural mystique. (In a narrower sense, he is, of course, using past to comment on present and one culture to elucidate others.) Although Godfrey here accepts a special literary tradition and method, there is enough of the realistic in the story to demonstrate his ability to create living characters, even when only sketched in, and to describe events and setting vividly in succinct and unpretentious prose. Similarly Godfrey is here, as almost always, a social critic, for he never ceases to note the motives of men's actions in a world prone to violence or the encroachments of materialism on the natural, the aesthetic, or on the significance of life itself.

Godfrey has been written about briefly in recent issues of the magazine *Canadian Literature*.

JOHN METCALF (1938–)

Born in Carlisle, England, Metcalf came to Canada in 1961. He did his early schooling in Beckenham, near London, and then went to Bristol University, receiving a B.A. degree there in 1960. He now teaches at Loyola College in Montreal. He is married and has one daughter.

So far Metcalf has published some twenty short stories in such magazines as *Prism, West Coast Review,* and *The Tamarack Review,* and some have been broadcast over CBC. He won the President's Medal, University of Western Ontario, with "Estuary," and his work has appeared in two recent anthologies, *Modern Canadian Stories* (1966), in which he has two stories, and *New Canadian Writing 1969,* in which he has four. A collection of his work, *The Lady Who Sold Furniture,* has very recently appeared.

Metcalf is a young man of talent. He writes a deceptively simple prose and presents his scenes vividly through his ability to select and describe appropriate details and to create authentic atmosphere. He can also just as easily create living characters and seems especially good at depicting the child *vis-à-vis* the bungling adult, or the innocent faced with threatening experience. No matter what the theme or symbolic intent of his stories, however, Metcalf focuses first and throughout on the characters in them. They begin and remain people. The dialogue is right. The dramatic action of the narrative is right, admirably

paralleling that of the psychological. It ought not to go unnoticed, besides, that Metcalf knows how to tell a story.

CLARK BLAISE (1940–)

Born of Canadian parents in Fargo, North Dakota, Clark
Blaise grew up for the most part as a winter resident of the
United States, mainly in the Deep South, and as a summer
vacationist in Winnipeg, Canada. After graduating from Den-
ison University, Ohio, he attended the University of Iowa,
where he received his M.F.A. degree in 1964. He taught at the
University of Wisconsin for one year and then came to Canada, taking a position as a teacher of English at Sir George
Williams University in 1966. Mr. Blaise is married and has
two children.

For some years Mr. Blaise has been active as a writer, publishing reviews, poems, and essays. His chief interest, however, is fiction. He has published some twenty-odd short stories
in Canada. He won the President's Medal, University of Western Ontario, in 1967, and appeared as one of the three con-
tributors to *New Canadian Writing 1968*. Mr. Blaise is at
present working on a novel.

Blaise's long years in the United States are responsible for a
"negative Canadianism" in his work, according to Victor Hoar,
chairman of the Committee of Canadian-American Studies at
Michigan State University. He writes in *Canadian Literature*
(Autumn 1969, p. 89):

> There is in his work a density and atmosphere which is,
> without question, the product of that experience. What
> is more, all four of his stories employ narrators, while
> only one of the other seven is so constructed. This may
> be only coincidence, but the intense chatter of narrators
> in American fiction has long struck me as a characteristic
> tactic as well as a thematic feature. In any case, it is im-
> possible not to notice these elements of atmosphere, den-
> sity and structure; their presence in this volume of
> Canadian stories may assist those readers who are inter-
> ested in contrasting Canadian and American literary re-
> sources and traditions. Blaise is steeped in the values of
> American language and experience. And those values can
> be appraised not so much for their quality, although they
> will be, as for their historical and cultural relevance to
> the artist. While deploring the persistent complaint about
> Canadian identity, yet I would recommend Blaise's work
> for what it implies Canada is not.

RAY SMITH (1941–   )

A former Maritimer and a one-time resident of Toronto, Ray Smith now lives in Montreal. He was born in Mabou, Cape Breton, Nova Scotia, and received all his education in the public schools here and there in the province and at Dalhousie University, Halifax, where, in 1963, he obtained a B.A. degree. At Dalhousie, Smith tried his hand at poetry, but gave it up for fiction, and since 1964 has devoted himself entirely to prose. Smith received a Canada Council Award in 1968 and in 1969 published one of the best Canadian books of the year, *Cape Breton Is the Thought Control Centre of Canada,* an original, perplexing collection of "experimental" vignettes, sketches, and stories in which he has demonstrated a remarkable versatility in using different forms. Still, all are marked by Smith's wit (often satirical), his dexterity with language, and his predilection for weird characters and bizarre situations, after the fashion of the dramatists of the theatre of the absurd. Moreover, Smith's stories are "participatory." Organized by free association and fragmented as they seem, they require the reader to engage himself in patterning them, to take part in the creative process in a way different from (and in addition to) involvement in content or appreciation of form. Smith's work has appeared in *Tamarack Review* and *Prism* and in the anthology *The New Romans* (1968). Smith is at present working on a novel.